App

MW00613138

Doing Global Health Work:
Approaches that Really Make a Difference

Kirk Scirto, MD, MPH

Hesperian Health Guides
Oakland, California, USA

ISBN: 978-1-942919-62-9 paperback
ISBN: 978-1-942919-63-6 e-book

Front and back cover photos: Kirk Scirto

Cover and page design: Kathleen Tandy

This book was printed on recycled paper in the USA by Sheridan.

hesperian
health guides

Hesperian Health Guides
2860 Telegraph Ave.
Oakland, CA 94609
www.hesperian.org

Dedication

Dedicated to all the hardworking health workers in resource-limited nations, to my wife Vicki who joined me on many travels, and to my parents—Barb and Tony—who have supported me through these adventures.

About the Author

Kirk Scirto received his medical doctorate at the University of Buffalo and completed family medicine residency at the University of Rochester. He obtained a master's degree in global public health from the University of South Florida, HIV specialist certification from AAHIVM, and tropical medicine certification from ASTMH. His global health work has allowed him to contribute to and lead a variety of initiatives over 23 years in 11 resource-limited nations. He serves as a professor of global health in the United States and abroad, and currently works as the clinician serving the Tonawanda Seneca Nation.

Acknowledgements

This book would have been impossible to write without the committed work of those who dedicate their lives to the struggle for health equity around the world. I am particularly indebted to the writers among them who have contributed to the ever-expanding literature on global health: you are the skeleton upon which this book rests.

I'm especially thankful for the extremely helpful revision ideas of Todd Jailer, and for his extensive and thoughtful editing. I also appreciate Susan McCallister and Kathleen Tandy at Hesperian Health Guides, whose hard work in proofreading and graphic design contributed so much.

This book would not be nearly as relevant nor comprehensive were it not for the incisive reviews extended by Mercy Minde and Jyoti Puvvula, whose valuable and consistently constructive criticism reflect perspectives borne from their extensive work in other nations. I am greatly honored to host a *Foreword* by Abhay Shukla, given his critical work on community medicine around the world. I'm also indebted to Robin Young and Jessica Evert for sharing valuable insights on how this material can be used by trainees in the global health field.

I have learned much from the tireless and evidence-based public health work of my global health mentor, Doug Stockman. I have many other North American colleagues I would like to thank, but in keeping with the spirit of this book, I will instead draw attention to those I partnered with and was graciously hosted by, who taught me invaluable global health lessons in various nations around the world.

My heartfelt thanks to: John Paul, Dr. Laurent, Lumumba Mwita, Judith Gwimile, Ayoub Msalilwa, Salim Msonga, Gloria Frederick Mari, Mogomotsi Matshaba, Tonderai Farirai, Bathusi Mathuba, Abhilash Sathyamoorthi, Bonnie Kgathi, Mma Boitumelo Thuto, Edgardo Soto, Nelson de Jesus Ramos, Lydia Vera Méndez, Michael Baganizi, Nurse Jacklyn, Sam Kamanzi, Dr. Margaret, Dr. Mary, Ruby Blanc, Hahn Moe, Say Gay Shi, Nan San Kalan, Aung Si Thu, Zin Moon, Seng Ja, Eh San, Tu Aung, Cynthia Maung, Don Pedro Bautista, Apolinar López, Elia Hernández López, Carolina Sánchez, Doña Calixta Gámez, Phebian Abdulai, Margaret Sandi, Fodu Mami, Mohamed Sesay, Mariama Kondeh, Aminata Foday, Amara Sesay, Moses Kortu, CHO Christopher, Ramiro Laínez, Elvis Nataren, Leonel Rivas, Dr. Pérez, and many more. It was your innovative and sincere work from which I drew the inspiration to start typing!

Contents

Foreword

by Abhay Shukla, MD

Doing Global Health Work by Dr. Kirk Scirto is a deeply passionate, widely informative, very practical yet also intensely committed book; it is an excellent guide for engaging in health work beyond one's national borders. I have not yet met Kirk—perhaps not surprising since I work on the other side of the globe in India—but still, I connect with each of the messages in his book. It becomes obvious that the author is speaking from extensive and diverse experiences of global health work, articulated as a physician and public health activist who is deeply concerned about "making a real difference" by working for people's health.

I am struck with how Kirk's insightful perspective of international health work from the global North is similar and deeply complementary to my own view from the global South. This only confirms that the equity-oriented human values and partnership-based methods required to do *"global health work which really makes a difference"* remain fundamentally the same, from whichever corner of the globe we might approach such work.

While reading this book, I tried to compare Kirk's insightful observations with my "top down, as well as bottom up" notes on global health work. On one hand, I looked for parallels with my experiences as a postgraduate medical doctor, raised in urban settings in India and medically trained in a big city (New Delhi). Then, as a complete outsider (not even knowing the local language), I worked for several years in a completely different region of India: a remote, resource-deprived area, in communities of Indigenous people. We can call this my "view from above" of health work, which has many similarities with global health efforts. On the other hand, as a health activist who has spent over three decades doing community health work in the global South, I also have numerous experiences of collaborating with professionals from the global North (especially the U.S. and Europe), who have visited and worked in India in various settings. This can be considered my "view from below" of collaborative global health work.

I must admit that I started with some healthy scepticism about this book, written by a US-based author, to take such a comprehensive view to global health work. Yet I was pleasantly surprised to see how Kirk's approach effortlessly combines the "view from above" and the "view from below" to global health work in a seamless manner. For example, Chapter 2: Training Health Workers and Chapter 11: Community-Based Health Programs bring both views together and closely resonate with my own experiences of health worker training and community health work. More than 25 years ago, as a young doctor I stayed and worked in Dahanu, a forested and hilly tribal (Indigenous people's) area of Maharashtra state in western India. We were partnering with a mass organization of Indigenous people (Kashtakari Sanghatana), helping them to build a locally-sustained community health worker program:

> From day one, the people's organisation insisted that all health worker trainings must be organized in the tribal villages, completely through people's own limited resources. We were firmly told, "Bring your knowledge, not your money." The venue, accommodations, and simple food required for the training of local women volunteers were all arranged in their mud huts by the tribal villagers. They may have been poor in material resources, but they were generous in their collective effort to build a health program. The first training camp for non-literate women health workers was held in a remote hamlet, located on the banks of a dam backwater. It was the peak of the monsoon, with rain and mud everywhere! The only source of drinking water in that hamlet was untreated water from a nearby river. In our first training, one of the main topics covered was diarrhea. By the second day of the training, after drinking the raw river water, all the participants—trainers as well as trainees—came down with diarrhea!
>
> That first health worker training taught me two unforgettable lessons. First, when we health professionals share working and living conditions with our trainees, this might occasion consciously embracing certain discomforts and even risks. Although we could have brought in external funds and organized the training in a well-equipped, amenity-filled urban location, this would have totally alienated the health workers from their social roots; and being unsustainable, it would have been unacceptable to the people's organization. Although it meant inconvenience to us

*doctor-trainers used to comforts of the big city, organizing
the training with people's own resources in their mud huts
was the right thing to do. Second, we realized that, even if
the training was held in a remote tribal village, safe drinking
water must be ensured. In all further trainings we held in
rural areas, we always started by ensuring basic purification
of drinking water for everyone. Fortunately, we never had
another diarrhea outbreak during a health worker training!*

Since I often draw upon such stories, I thoroughly enjoyed the
personal anecdotes and snippets from Kirk's own wide experience;
they make the book lively, and keep the messages down-to-earth. The
author's stories often bring outsider health experts (including himself)
down a peg or two, making it clear that before teaching others, they
may need to learn quite a few things themselves. His self-critical
reflections on Suitcase Medicine among the seven approaches to global
health work, and the dissection of the diverse, noble as well as not-
purely-noble Agendas of various kinds of global health practitioners,
are refreshingly insightful.

Themes which came to my mind while reflecting on the approaches
detailed in this book include Communication, Collaboration, Capacity-
building, Counterparts, Community groundedness, and Co-production
of health. Each of these themes recurs in different forms throughout
the book. The last—Co-production of health—may not be mentioned
explicitly, but can be considered complementary to the book's overall
perspective. And underlying all of these, emanating from every page of
the book, is an underlying value of Compassion.

A highly appropriate emphasis of this book is the training of
overseas health workers and professionals. Perhaps all of us need to
be reminded that the word "Doctor" is originally derived from the
Latin word for "Teacher." The experience of training health workers
in a country and culture different from your own can be extremely
rewarding, sharpening our capacities for communication. Such skills
can keep us in good stead during diverse healthcare encounters
throughout our professional lives. Kirk repeatedly underlines the need
for such capacity-building to be developed on a bedrock of mutual
respect and equity between partners in the teaching process, reminding
me of Aristotle's counsel, "How can I teach, but to a friend?"

An important concern highlighted in several parts of the book,
especially in Chapter 5: Power to the People, is the need for local people
to lead, and outsiders to follow, during collaborative health work. This
includes the importance of outsiders respecting the priorities of local

communities regarding health work. While reading the section What they need most in Chapter 5, I was reminded of this experience from the late 1990s:

> *After our community health program in the tribal area was launched, the women health workers in various villages started regularly treating patients for various minor ailments. We would replenish their basic medicines during monthly meetings where we also discussed difficult or complex cases, and prevalent public health issues. After a few months, I was surprised to see that the anti-microbial co-trimoxazole was being used quite frequently by some health workers, even though the number of patients requiring it was not so large. In the next monthly meeting, I asked the women health workers about this. Somewhat sheepishly, they explained that they had also been successfully treating their chickens for minor infections, using smaller doses of co-trimoxazole! It had never struck us outsider health professionals that treating sick domestic animals—an essential source of livelihood and nutrition—was a priority for these village health workers, and needed to be addressed appropriately!*

Ensuring empowerment of people through health work is a bright running thread throughout the book, especially Chapter 5: Power to the People and Chapter 10: Participation to Empower. I could not agree more with Kirk's healthy emphasis on empowerment, which matches the evolution of our own community health work in various parts of Maharashtra state over the last two and a half decades. After developing community health worker programs in the late 1990s, our team has progressively shifted to catalyzing community empowerment processes, which support people to claim their health rights. This includes enabling rural communities to monitor local public health facilities and claim basic health services.

> *In most parts of India, primary health services in rural areas are supposed to be provided free of charge by the government. However, people face the not uncommon experience of being asked informally to pay some of the doctors and health staff who provide them services. During our health rights promotion, as communities became fully aware of their entitlement to free care, complaints of illegal charging started being commonly raised. In public hearings,*

patients described how they had been forced to pay hefty sums for treatment, which was supposed to be free. In several cases, the concerned doctor or employee was made to publicly refund the entire amount which had been extracted from the patient, witnessed by hundreds of people during the public hearing. These examples were hugely empowering for the participants.

In one tribal area Primary Health Centre, the medical officer had strategically placed a donation box in his consulting room, and asked each patient to deposit a donation after treatment–an illegitimate mode of extracting money from resource-poor tribal people. After community monitoring brought this practice to light, the issue was discussed in the local health committee. The involuntary donations were immediately stopped. Going a step further, the local activists converted the Donation Box into a Complaint Box, which now generates critical feedback on health center services!

Another theme which appears at various places in the book, especially in Chapter 1: Reversing the Brain Drain is the need for outsider health experts to re-learn various skills while doing global health work. As noted in the section Medical Tourists, health professionals from North America or Europe may be insufficiently equipped to work in the very different clinical and social settings which prevail in rural areas of many African, Latin American and Asian countries. From the very start, global health workers need to regularly ask themselves, "What do I need to learn myself, before I can properly help others?" This may involve learning new skills related to locally prevalent conditions, as well as unlearning high-tech medical protocols overly dependent on extensive and expensive tests available in developed-country settings. The latter may need to be replaced by a greater reliance on careful history-taking and physical examination, along with the basic tests which are locally available, all woven together with sound clinical sense. I would like to add that a useful approach to consider during global health work is "Right Care"—health care which is clinically competent and effective, but avoids excessive and unnecessary tests, medications and procedures.[1] Our Indian experience with commercial private medicine, ranging from large private hospitals in cities to rural clinics run by semi-qualified practitioners, shows that irrational use of medications and technologies linked with growing commercialization of medical care is both rampant and highly damaging.[2] Given such contexts, I feel that this Right Care approach is implicit throughout this book, especially in the section *Quality of Care* in *Appendix A* where the need to follow evidence-based guidelines and avoid inappropriate surgeries is emphasized. This Right Care approach is as relevant for practicing health care within the global North as it is in the global South, and can provide a useful framework for guiding global health work everywhere.

This brings me to my final reflections on this remarkable book, which I am sure you are anxious to begin reading now! The dilemmas and questions emerging from global health work are not just located "out there" in some less-developed country we might visit occasionally. The problems related to health care faced by people in North America or European countries are of course different from the health system issues faced by people in countries of the global South, but there are also significant parallels: growing commercialization of health care, inappropriate use of medical technology (both underuse and overuse), multiple stresses and constraints faced by health care workers, challenges faced by public health systems, and the significant barriers faced by most people in accessing quality, affordable healthcare. The COVID pandemic has further sharply revealed the fault lines in health systems everywhere. Hence I think it would be useful if, after reading this book, we become better equipped not just to work in other countries but also encouraged to reflect on the urgent changes needed to improve health systems within our own countries. Both kinds of health work are part of the same global movement for universal access to quality health care,[3] and each of us can contribute to this process in our own way, wherever we choose to work. As Kirk reminds us repeatedly, when we visit another country to do health work, we should not think of this as doing charity for someone else. Rather, we could view our endeavours as expressions of solidarity, continuation of the same efforts we carry out in our own national settings to ensure that everywhere those who need health care the most receive it with dignity and quality, in effective and just health systems. This can be summarised in the words of an outstanding global health activist of the mid-20th century, the Canadian surgeon Dr. Norman Bethune,[4] who insisted, *"Charity should be abolished, and be replaced by justice."* With such an approach to health work, globally and locally, each of us can realize our deepest human potentials, perhaps the most fulfilling goal to which any human being can aspire.

I end with the cautionary advice of Lilla Watson, an aboriginal activist and artist from Australia, who addressed outsiders who had come to "help." All of us global health practitioners can benefit from reflecting upon her words:

> *"If you have come here to help me you are wasting your time. But if you have come because your liberation is bound up with mine, then let us work together."*

Abhay Shukla, MD
Public health specialist and senior scientist, SATHI, India
National co-convenor, People's Health Movement – India

Endnotes

1 For explanation of the Right Care approach see https://rightcarealliance.org/about/what-is-right-care

2 See the book 'Dissenting Diagnosis' for testimonies by whistleblower doctors regarding the state of private medical care in India—www.penguin.co.in/book/dissenting-diagnosis

3 The People's Health Movement is one of the global networks involved in such efforts in around 70 countries across the globe, see www.phmovement.org

4 Dr. Norman Bethune was a surgeon who worked in Canada and US in the 1920s and 1930s, before launching into pioneering 'global health work' in Spain and then China. Bethune's life was as path-breaking as it was selfless and audacious, and provides lasting inspiration to anyone seeking to join the ranks of global health workers. His biography *The Scalpel, The Sword* (www.monthlyreview.org/product/scalpel_the_sword) is well worth reading for those who have not yet done so.

Partnering to Meet Needs

I'll never forget every detail of the trip that inspired me to study medicine. As a college sophomore, I joined a group of doctors and students visiting underserved rural areas of Jamaica. Our team showed up in a new village each day, greeted by hundreds of smiling faces as we set up a makeshift clinic. The free care was greatly appreciated, and we felt quite needed. Patient stories of poverty and lack of medical care touched us deeply. People were suffering from easily preventable and treatable diseases. A simple antibiotic like amoxicillin could save a life, and we felt like nobody would give it if we didn't. Every day echoed with meaning and inspiration. After seeing a few hundred patients, the sun would set and we'd hold our last few consults by flashlight. Finally, we ate and then staggered off to a deep and fulfilling sleep.

Nearly every health professional I've met has been profoundly inspired by volunteer work in resource-limited countries. Almost universally, they return from a volunteer trip with a spring in their step and an uplifting refrain, proclaiming:

This is exactly why I went into medicine! I was helping the neediest and loved every minute of it! I can't wait to go back there again!

I'm also part of this club, and I've lost count of how many times I've said this. Nearly every year of my adult life, I've volunteered in at least one resource-limited country (sometimes for the entire year). These trips have been among the most meaningful experiences of my life.

I feel like I'm on top of the world when I return from a volunteer trip abroad; I feel like I've really helped and I'm overcome with a rush of empowerment. Yet this book is not about the empowerment we get as medical volunteers from North America, Europe, and other high-income places; it's about how we can support the empowerment process of people living in resource-limited countries, since that is the ultimate goal that matters. People living in the deepest poverty throughout the world deserve to control their own health and health care; outside volunteers who keep this goal in mind and work towards it will make a much greater difference than those who simply, yet admirably, "just want to help."

After one of our clinics in Jamaica, we sat around a campfire reflecting on our work and the lessons of the day. A family medicine resident said something that I'll never forget:

"Well, it was a great day and I really enjoyed what we did. But I feel like it was more for us than for them. How did we really help in the long-term?"

At the time, I was too naive to understand how critical and insightful that question was. Yet on my second volunteer trip (to rural Mexico), I'd gotten past my global health "honeymoon period." In each village for only one day, we treated the people who showed up and then left. I started asking: Who would be there to give medical care the next day? Did we really do anything helpful, or was our work a superficial quick fix or even a health care "tease"? Why didn't we volunteer with the local medical providers? Why didn't we offer to further train people in topics they wanted to learn more about? Couldn't community providers do a better job caring for their own people, given their knowledge on local health conditions—knowledge that we lacked? Why didn't we offer to address the community's deeper public health needs? I vowed to make my next volunteer trip more meaningful. To prepare myself, I minored in public health, studied medical anthropology, and read global health books.

On my next two trips, both to rural Uganda, I was convinced our team was contributing in deeper ways. Community members requested that our team teach about HIV/AIDS, and we trained local people to be teachers themselves. They taught us about their clean water needs, and we organized the construction of wells. Only a small part of our program involved seeing patients, as local clinical needs were

In rural Uganda, we rode bikes from village to village training local people to become HIV educators.

clearly trumped by public health needs. However, our clean water programs were quite likely doomed because we had organized them rather than the Ugandans themselves. I had yet to learn the most important lesson in global health...

Local People Lead, Outsiders Follow

Medical education trains us through the study of problems so we can diagnose and treat them. We search for things that are wrong and we strive to solve them ourselves. While this may work in our own clinic or hospital, we must approach community health problems—at home but especially abroad—in an entirely different way. Community problems need to be identified and solved primarily by people of the community, or else the solutions just won't be appropriate and enduring. This is the only way for community members to achieve and retain power and control over their health and their society. It may be tempting, and our training may lead us to believe that we can solve problems for them, yet I believe that we must be humble and admit that we do not have the knowledge and ability to do this nearly as well as the community itself. In fact, we can easily cause more harm than good by implementing our own solutions in cultures that we know little about.

To keep communities in the driver's seat, only outside groups who are invited should jump on a plane. A genuine partnership is needed between foreigners and local community groups, health facilities, public health programs, Ministries of Health, and health care workers. Rather than providing foreigner-led health services, we should offer to integrate with existing health projects and health systems to assist in bolstering them in ways identified by the community. Keeping local people in charge involves seeking out community health efforts, talented leaders, and resources which are already in the community; these will be the bedrock for any enduring health improvements, not the fleeting presence of us people from faraway lands with honest intentions and strange accents.

During the civil war in El Salvador, an American health and human rights group was invited to form a long-term partnership there. When I applied to join them for six weeks, Salvadorans reviewed my application and invited me to integrate with and contribute to their preexisting health projects. Throughout the trip, I watched truly empowered local people organize their own groups and sustainable health programs. Our organization supported these efforts

A local handyperson builds a concrete latrine slab in the mountains of Honduras.

behind the scenes, while community members took the lead. We foreigners have contributed by supporting them in small ways while they organize their own programs in community-based health education, clinical care, and advanced training. These programs have thrived for decades due to the centrality of the hard-working Salvadoran protagonists to these efforts.

Next I joined a Global Health Track in Family Medicine Residency, through which we organized biannual health empowerment trips to a community in Honduras. We encouraged the community to determine its own health priorities; after doing so, it developed successful programs in community health worker training, medical care, clean water, sanitation, improved cook stoves, education, microfinance, and agriculture.

Empowering involves actively listening to a community as it identifies its health problems and further develops existing or potential solutions. Local people need to lead the process of improving their health, and outsiders can assist in this process but from the sidelines. It is the right of the community to decide what, when, and how health programs will emerge, and not surprisingly they often launch public health initiatives rather than the clinical programs in which outside health professionals may have more interest. Humble outsiders who follow such an approach are often said to be doing *health accompaniment*, where we extend solidarity to those with fewer resources in a locally-led and long-term partnership.

I refer to this generally as empowerment work since it consciously refrains from taking power away *from* community members and transferring it *to* foreigners. Outsiders do not design the health programs or carry out the care; rather, local people remain the central deciders and implementers. When appropriate and called on to do so, outsiders can go further by assisting communities in identifying and using their existing structures, programs, personnel, and other resources to improve health. In this setting, we can help to inspire or spark local people to use their community strengths to further improve their living conditions.

In these pages, I explore the ways in which global health **empowerment** approaches differ from the voluntarism and **charity** approaches that many foreigners have been used to following— including myself. While charity does things for others and gives things to others, because it is led by outsiders it cannot help but take power and control away from the people it is serving. I believe that empowerment approaches are especially important because poverty is not simply a lack of money, but rather a multilayered state of disempowerment. This is exactly what must be transformed.

Throughout the world, power derives from various factors including race and ethnicity, class and social status, gender, education, and nationality. Many of us simply have too much power compared to those who don't have enough power to meet basic needs such as housing, clean water, and health care access. Promoting social justice involves transferring power *from* those with an abundance of it *to* those with not enough of it to meet their basic needs. This lies at the core of what I believe global health work is about. Empowerment is central to health—especially in the poorest communities in the world.

I went on various visits to Sierra Leone, Uganda, Burma, Dominica, Honduras, Haiti, Botswana, and Tanzania, all with the goal of implementing the health empowerment approaches outlined in the next chapter. These "empowerment trips" were by far the most meaningful trips of my life, as I saw first-hand the incredible potential of communities to expand their health, without being dependent on outsiders. Over the course of 22 visits, I've spent over five full years living, working, and volunteering in these countries. Since my first trip abroad during college, I've spent every year organizing health partnerships with resource-limited countries—even when I'm not abroad. I'm a family practice doctor, tropical medicine specialist, and HIV specialist with a master's in global public health.

I've been a "global health nomad," working with various types of organizations while taking very different approaches to global health partnerships. I worked in settings of chronic poverty as well as disaster relief; I've done education, clinical, public health, and social justice work in these settings. Through each twist and turn, I've been on a personal journey of learning how to best partner with communities living in deep poverty as they work to improve their health. I'd like to take you with me on this journey through this book.

Doing Global Health Work is for health and public health professionals and students who've asked themselves or others how they can *really* make a difference in the health of a community. It's a guide to helpful global health approaches, methods, and activities as well as an explanation of why others may be less helpful. It explores ways we can facilitate the accomplishment of more and deeper results in the exercise of our time, energy, creativity, knowledge, and skills. All global health trips are not created equal, but they should be as helpful and meaningful as we can make them.

These pages will explore evidence-based approaches to improving people's health in meaningful and sustainable ways. Throughout I will reference best practices from the fields of global health, public health, sustainable development, disaster relief, facilitation, appreciative inquiry, engineering, social justice, human rights, and anthropology. In an effort to give examples and to make this book livelier, I'll jump back and forth between the literature and my own personal stories of health programs and adventures around the world.

I've refrained from using the names of organizations that I volunteered or worked with; this is because I aim to explore themes rather than to critique specific groups. Finally, the terms *outsiders* and *local people* are used throughout this book. *Outsiders* refers to people or groups from another society who visit a community living in deeper poverty, with the goal of assisting the *local people* who live there.

By reviewing the literature—and through my own experience— I've become convinced that helping the most we possibly can and empowering communities are actually one and the same goal. As local people take control of the process of improving health, they'll be far more likely to achieve long-term health improvements. There's much that adventurous and sincere outside health professionals can do to encourage the fruition of this critical goal.

Global Health Approaches

Health professionals have a variety of skills and training that combine with a wide range of personal motivations leading them to do global health work. People tend to think they can be most useful by doing what they are most used to doing, and in the past, this may have been a good way of thinking about how to make an individual contribution to global heath. The experience gained and research conducted over the past several decades have allowed us to evaluate the many accomplishments of global health volunteers as well as our shortcomings. Taking this evidence base into account allows us to categorize and discuss various approaches to doing global health work.

The seven most common, influential, and—in my view—important approaches to doing global health work will be explored here. I label the first two as traditional approaches since they have been done for a great many years and they are followed by most groups that do global health work:

1. Suitcase Medicine
2. Health Facility-Building

I'll explain more about what these are, but first would like to add five other approaches to global health work which have generated more impressive results. These other approaches have been developed over time, especially by larger and more professional global health groups. They aim to improve the health of local people while keeping them in control of the process, and I therefore label them as empowering approaches. They are:

3. Local Clinical Capacity-Building
4. Strengthening Local Health Systems
5. Professional Disaster Relief
6. Local Public Health Capacity-Building
7. Facilitating Community-Based Programs

I'll introduce them each here with a personal story, and then I'll delve much deeper in the chapters which follow.

Suitcase Medicine

We drove madly bumpy roads from the break of dawn trying not to lose our meager breakfast on the way. The line of 400 patients waiting gave me a quick, jolting hiccup as I looked back at our staff of three crammed between suitcases. Repeatedly brushing off cascades of sweat and

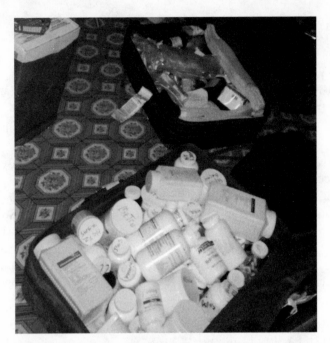

queues of mosquitos, I saw patient after patient with endless complaints as I kept referencing a short list of meds scribbled out under an array of thermometers and stethoscopes hastily being moved around the room. We skipped lunch and dinner, and were cutting open an abscess after dark with flashlights.

Another 80 remained lined up but we dared not turn them away since we somehow believed we were "their only hope." Since they showed superhuman patience, so would we. The spaces between my words lengthened and between patients I propped up my head with my hand. I thought to myself: "We could actually help much more by doing less work, but doing it much more deliberately."

What I call *suitcase medicine* describes what I did on my first global health trips in Jamaica and Mexico. Teams of foreign medical volunteers from wealthy lands travel for one to three weeks to a resource-limited nation and provide free patient care. Traditionally, participants carry medicines and supplies in suitcases, which become the supply cabinets from which they are distributed to patients. Makeshift clinics are set up in an empty building, church, school, or large tent, and the care offered is unrelated to the local health care system. Outsiders may stay at one health care site for a week or more, or they may spend only one or two days at each site, touring the country like compassionate travelling salespeople with bulging suitcases.

Suitcase medicine is by far the most common global health approach. Outsiders who do it demonstrate great concern and work extremely hard, treating hundreds or thousands of patients under difficult conditions before reboarding their planes. Unfortunately, volunteer teams typically lack needed awareness of local diseases, medical systems, language, and culture. Therefore, they may inadvertently give poor quality care and cannot offer patient follow-up. They also may unknowingly compete with local care providers and curtail the community economy. The fruits of their intense engagement typically last for only a few weeks, while much more sustainable benefits could be achieved by outsiders who work to further the training of local health workers in these communities.

Local Clinical Capacity-Building

Deep brown men waded in an equally dark river, expectantly panning for diamonds which might finally give them a shot at life beyond the mud of poverty. This is where I altered the typical suitcase medicine model to try to make a bigger difference.

Our team spent two days in each village, and I insisted that both days were heavily focused on health worker capacity-building. The first day involved learning about the village and its health workers and community groups; our team did a guided village walk and organized a focus group to learn about their health resources and problems. Of course, this was the tip of the iceberg, and additional days of learning and connecting with the community would have been far more helpful. Yet it allowed us to hear about some of the community's priorities which we could then act on by providing training on delivering babies using clean birth kits, as well as resuscitating babies that don't breathe. We boosted our limited awareness, expanded local health worker capacity, and started forging a clinical care partnership for the second day.

We arrived the next morning with a stack of med and supply suitcases, but I was determined to do things differently. We would only see patients at the local public clinic and only hand-in-hand with the health workers that normally run these clinics. I insisted that none of us would treat a patient without seeing them together with a local health worker. We used each patient visit as an opportunity to teach a local health worker, as well as to be taught by them.

At one clinic, my wife—a pediatrician—was paired with a local pharmacist and they dispensed meds together. She both taught and learned about how medicines are dispensed there. Meanwhile, the local health worker and I sat at the same desk and attended the same patients. When a patient presented with more classically "Western" issues such as diabetes and heart disease, I did more teaching than learning; when patients came with malaria and river blindness, he did more teaching than learning. We were clinical partners, and the training could make a much larger ripple than the patient care.

Training local health care workers can boost their ability to prevent, diagnose, and treat disease long after we outsiders have returned to our home countries. It can further the knowledge and skills of existing providers and be employed to train new ones, helping to reverse the critical shortage of health workers in many resource-limited nations. Capacity-building can be successful in both long-term and short-term trips abroad, and it generally makes a deeper difference than suitcase medicine's focus on individual patients.

Strengthening Local Health Systems

I volunteered in a rural African town with a struggling locally-run public hospital that was riddled with problems. The first outside medical group to approach the hospital found it so dysfunctional they decided to set up a completely independent HIV and TB care program. They gave up on working with the hospital, built their own clinic, and "did their own thing" in a way that was supposedly better. A second foreign medical group decided to construct their own clinic down the street, with minimal communication with the local hospital or the other foreign facility. They denigrated the bad care provided by the hospital and vowed they would do better. Patients could get the care they deserved from them instead of the hospital.

Then the Ebola Epidemic of 2014-15 arrived and deathly ill patients flooded the understaffed public hospital, with limited electricity and no running water! It could do little to support Ebola victims—and neither did the two outside organizations. Despite being unprepared, the public hospital served as the only facility accepting potential Ebola patients. After all, both foreign clinics were even less prepared.

*Finally, a third outside medical group came and formed a genuine **partnership** with the public hospital. Care given by community members took center stage in this partnership. Meanwhile, outsiders were asked to provide minor assistance to the hospital through staffing, supplies, and equipment. These cross-cultural partners also focused on Ebola preparedness and restored running water to the hospital. The outside nonprofit prioritized **system strengthening** over doing patient care themselves; it supported the hospital so that local health workers could do a better job with ongoing patient care. While the other two outside groups had recruited local staff away from the hospital to work at their clinics, the third group made a positive contribution toward addressing the understaffing crisis. They participated in improving the quality of the local health care system rather than constructing an alternative to it.*

Failing health care systems develop enormous gaps, and outside volunteers may rush in to provide care and attempt to fill this void. However, doing so doesn't fill the gap with quality and sustainable care. As outsiders, we could do more by partnering with local health care leaders to address the root problems of their health systems. Helping within such a system can be far more successful, empowering, and ultimately sustainable.

Health Facility-Building

An alternative to health systems strengthening would be the traditional approach of *health facility-building*. It is laudable that outsiders want to reach beyond their volunteer trips to create a longer-term health program in the form of a new clinic or hospital, as this is hard and expensive work. However, sustaining its services presents a major challenge, and for the minority of new facilities that endure, they also pull staff, patients, funds, and confidence from struggling local health systems.

Professional Disaster Relief

The compound consisted of one circus tent after another; you knew that you were entering a special place, but there was nothing fun or amusing inside. External fixators pierced a patient's leg from all directions, as he showed off what appeared to be a half-human and half-robot lower extremity. I was at the Haiti border in 2010, and the earthquake had crushed far too many houses, limbs, and senses of security. The main operating room table may have been hastily constructed from scrap wood, but many lives were saved on it. Before I arrived, surgeons were working without x-ray capacity, sometimes diagnosing fractures by cutting into the flesh and feeling with gloved fingers for cracks in the bone.

In this desperate situation, surgeons did challenging and incredible work. Primary care docs like me provided emergency and orthopedic care, as well as treatment for post-operative complications. As in my previous Dominica and Burma disaster relief experiences, I had no qualms about focusing on patient care here; local health services were overwhelmed and frantic. The need was high—and importantly, our professional relief groups were partnering with communities to address critical public health needs simultaneously.

Disasters almost always overwhelm the capacity of local people to respond; therefore, outside involvement can be critical to avoid unnecessary suffering and death. We outsiders can contribute by scaling up health and other services when affected communities are overwhelmed and request such assistance. Unlike in areas of chronic poverty, local people may ask outsiders to initially provide the majority of health services following a disaster or war; constructing a temporary health facility may also be helpful during such an acute crisis. Importantly, when disaster-affected communities make these decisions and lead response efforts, then they can remain empowered even as they accept outside help.

Local Public Health Capacity-Building

Tin roofs reflected the sun from so many scattered points; the scene blinded me in its simple beauty. Medical volunteers split up on paths hugging the volcanic slopes of Honduras. Teens passed us carrying live chickens and massive teetering stacks of firewood on their heads. One volunteer was assigned to a fish farm to assess how the project was functioning. Another passed a waterfall criss-crossed by yellow birds to check in with ongoing latrine projects. Still another visited the school to meet with teachers involved in a scholarship program for the kids from the lowest income families. One of us stayed in the center of town waving to school-going kids, as their parents stopped to discuss ongoing and proposed microfinance project ideas.

Public health projects were heavily structured into the daily routine of outside health volunteers; at any given time, only a few of us were seeing patients and we would rotate positions. Much more sustainable work was being done in tandem. Most volunteers spent their days addressing root causes of poor health in the mountains, part of our partnership led by the Lenca indigenous people. Disease was prevented through community-based public health work and the clinic would therefore expect to see fewer patients in the future. Some medical students would stay here six to twelve months, getting to know the community very well rather than quickly flying in and out.

Unmet basic public health needs almost always overshadow those of medical care in resource-limited countries. Medical volunteers can help in a deeper way by preparing themselves to address such needs in partnership, or else by inviting local and outside public health professionals to join and lead their teams. While providing clinical training serves as a very helpful and sustainable approach, public health capacity-building can make an even bigger difference.

Facilitating Community-Based Programs

Each community has its own unique location on the spectrum of developing and sustaining successful health programs. For those that have not yet identified their priority health problems and strategies for solutions, invited outsiders may be able to assist by facilitating community members to meet for this purpose. Community-based health programs can emerge from such discussions, and thousands of lives can potentially be improved or saved by local people as a result. Other times, the seeds of health projects may be sprouting or successful health programs may already have grown, yet they might encounter challenges for which a partnership with outsiders could be beneficial. There will often be some missing yet critical resources needed to achieve locally-identified goals. When requested, assistance from outsiders can be quite helpful in such scenarios.

Comparing Global Health Approaches

Table 1 compares these seven approaches to global health work in terms of their evidence-base and likely effect on local people; it summarizes data which will be presented in the chapters that follow.

Suitcase medicine and *health facility-building*—the traditional approaches—are based in sincere intentions and very hard work. Even so, they aren't rooted in an evidence-base, generally have the potential to be hurtful to resource-limited communities, and may not be helpful for such communities in the long-term. Further, these traditional approaches lead to duplicate and parallel health systems to those of local people; as such, they don't typically empower these communities or lead to sustainable health improvements. The other five approaches—the empowering ones—show much more promise.

Table 1: Approaches to Global Health Work: Evidence Base and Effects on Local People				
Approach	Evidence-Based	Potential Effect on Local People		
		Helpful	Empowering	Sustainable
Suitcase medicine				
Local clinical capacity-building	✓	✓	✓	✓
Strengthening local health systems	✓	✓	✓	✓
Health facility-building				
Professional disaster relief	✓	✓	✓	
Local public health capacity-building	✓	✓	✓	✓
Facilitating community-based programs	✓	✓	✓	✓

The Journey of This Book

This book will lead you through these different approaches to global health work, reviewing specific strategies and methods for maximizing benefits, minimizing harm, and keeping local people in control of their own health programs. This book focuses mostly on the empowering global health approaches which can make the biggest difference. Suitcase medicine and health facility-building will be mostly referenced in contrast, with more depth found in *Appendices A* and *B*.

Part I will explore the three clinical and educational empowerment approaches, and it will conclude by analyzing global health work one level deeper than the *approaches*—it will analyze the *agendas* influencing each approach. *Part II* will then review the two public health approaches, as well as related agendas. It will go on to explore the profound and determining influence on global health work of poverty and social injustice—and the struggle against them.

PART I

Health Care, Systems, and Training

The shortage of health care workers in Africa is among the most troubling public health challenges facing the world. For every 100,000 people, there were only three doctors in Somalia, two doctors in Tanzania, and eight in Zimbabwe in 2014.[1] Despite such shortages, African doctors emigrate to the United States and other resource-rich countries at alarming rates.[2] As of 2013, there were actually more doctors of Sub-Saharan African origin in the US than there were in 34 countries of Sub-Saharan Africa combined.[3] At the same time, African nurses are 70% more likely to emigrate than other health care workers.[4]

In 2013, the World Health Organization (WHO) estimated that Africa had a shortage of 4.2 million health workers which would be needed to meet its health care challenges; further, Africa is the only continent projected to have an even greater shortage of health care workers (6.1 million) in 2030.[5] Africa's health worker shortage represents a chronic crisis with no end in sight.

Many of the countries that expanded their health care and achieved Millennium Development Goal (MDG) targets did so by strengthening their health workforce.[6] The MDGs were regarded as the leading global development agenda from 1990-2015, and they've since been replaced by the Sustainable Development Goals (SDGs). SDG#3c aims to "substantially increase health financing, and the recruitment, development and training and retention of the health workforce in developing countries, especially in least developed countries and small island developing States."[7] A key WHO goal to achieve by 2030 involves countries "halving inequalities in access to a health worker… [and] halving their dependency on foreign-trained health professionals."[8]

In addition to development goals, key health care goals can only be reached with sufficient health workers. In 2005, Africa faced 25% of the global burden of disease, yet it counted with only 1.3% of the world's health care professionals to try to meet this challenge.[9] Unfortunately, disease burden and health worker statistics continue to register poorly a decade later.[10] Just as HIV prevalence has placed a large burden on African health care workers, the call to offer treatment to all people living with HIV has dramatically expanded their workloads.[11] Beyond HIV/AIDS, the burden of malaria, tuberculosis, pneumonia, and diarrhea has been staggering in Sub-Saharan Africa.[12] The 2014 Ebola epidemic in West Africa spread unabated, due in part to insufficient numbers of trained health workers.[13]

Health care worker shortages in Sub-Saharan Africa can often be traced to health worker and student desires to leave their home countries in search of improved working and living conditions.[14] Additionally, these shortages have resulted from workers deciding to go into fields other than medicine.[15] Still others leave medicine or leave their home country due to war or persecution.[16]

Recruitment agencies have also stirred the emigration of health workers away from Sub-Saharan Africa, often to the US and other wealthy nations.[17] There were over 13,000 doctors living in the US who were educated in Africa as of 2015, representing a 27% increase over the previous ten years.[18] Active and passive recruitment of health workers from Sub-Saharan Africa has been highly effective for wealthy nations, yet crippling for Africa.

Similar health worker shortages have been seen throughout resource-limited countries. Deep poverty, unemployment, and political instability have fueled a large and persistent exodus of nurses, midwives, and physicians to wealthy countries which face far less critical shortages. In addition to Africa's shortfall of 4.2 million health workers, South-East Asia is short by 6.9 million and the Western Pacific is short by 3.7 million.[19] Training more midwives could be a means of avoiding millions of deaths per year,[20] while physician shortages are also very acute throughout resource-limited countries.[21] In this context, nurses have also been especially difficult to recruit given a large brain drain of nurses migrating to North America, Europe, and Australia.[22]

As a result, health care workers simply aren't present in adequate numbers to meet demand in these environments.[23] More than half of all people on the planet lack access to essential health services, while health care access is especially limited for people living in resource-limited nations.[24] These same nations face much higher mortality rates[25] as well as lower life expectancies compared with high income countries.[26]

Reversing the Brain Drain

How can we reverse the brain drain of health workers from resource-limited countries to wealthier societies? Beyond this key goal, are there other ways we can address the critical shortage of health workers in these communities? How can we expand the provision of quality health care and improve the overall health status in these settings? There are many potential answers to these questions, and seven potential approaches will be reviewed in this book. Yet in this chapter, I'll center on two potential strategies to expand health care:

1. Fly in outsiders to expand medical care
2. Further the training and numbers of local health workers to expand care

The first approach is *suitcase medicine*, while the second one is *local clinical capacity-building*. I'll start with reviewing the first approach by sharing a story.

> *A man trudged over dirt roads and sweated up hills for 30 miles just to see me in the clinic. This was flattering. In his case, three weeks of pain and oozing of pus from his leg could be easily solved with one medicine bottle. Another patient kept buying acetaminophen for a fever and headache that just wouldn't resolve. There were no medical providers in her village and a quick prick of her finger let me do a malaria test. We both gazed over at a positive result, and I passed her antimalarial meds which may have saved her life. There were also complicated patients that I had no resources to help, but the majority of them were like these two: simple clinical solutions could ease their suffering. They appreciated it, and I felt good about the care I was giving.*
>
> *In many areas of the United States, a man wouldn't travel 30 miles to see me because he would pass by five other clinics on the way. My experience of giving medical care would feel altogether less important. This is a major draw of*

global health work. As healers, we want to help where we're needed more. Why not work where our knowledge, skills, and actions can make a much larger impact?

But what about the next time this man's leg is draining pus and he can't walk 30 miles to see if a foreigner might have visited to give care? If I had spent no time training a local person to do what I did, and if this scenario recurs for him or someone else, then the infection may spread throughout the body and lead to death. And what about the next time that this woman gets malaria? Who will help her? Have I done anything to promote the ability of people in her village to diagnose and treat her or someone else's malaria? Have I done anything to prevent skin infections or to prevent malaria in the first place?

I know I can recount many stories of how I helped individuals through suitcase medicine, or short-term medical service trips; yet this model provides very limited ability to help patients over time. Care provided by outsiders is far less sustainable than that provided by local health workers. Yet I believe that the main limitation of suitcase medicine involves our limited awareness compared to that of local providers. A second limitation is that open suitcases at makeshift clinics provide an *alternative* to local care systems, creating a parallel system that does not collaborate with the community's health care system. Because of our limited awareness, we outsiders have been called...

Medical Tourists

Many of us have had the classic tourist experience of showing up clueless in a new (to us) country. We don't know how to speak the language, how the culture works, what to see and do, how to stay safe, or even how to get around. This scenario not only applies to vacations, but often deeply affects our suitcase medicine. Regular tourists can stay uninformed if they want, but to do medical care we need to have good awareness of local health and social realities.

Even if we are experts in our field back home, we usually arrive in a new environment not knowing what to do and how to do it well.[1] We often don't know the common local health problems, social determinants of health, perceptions of disease, and resources available for treatment—especially on our first few trips. As outsiders, we usually travel from high income countries where tropical diseases such as blood flukes, river blindness, and Chagas disease are rare.

While local health workers are quite familiar with prevalent diseases in their community, visitors typically can't make the same claim.[2] For this reason, we're naturally less likely to make accurate diagnoses and treatment plans for patients in these contexts.

We have two other strikes against us. Outsiders don't understand local concepts of disease and health, and we're unfamiliar with the structure of the community health care system. For these reasons, local care providers are far more adept at knowing what care can be given, as well as where to refer patients for more specialized services. Such outsider knowledge deficiencies have been commonly noted by people living in resource-limited countries.[3]

Awareness and possession of skills relevant to local medical care are also very important yet commonly lacking for us outsiders.[4] In our home countries, we likely never mixed Oral Rehydration Solution for dehydrated patients or diagnosed tuberculosis without labs and x-rays. Working without electricity, bloodwork, imaging, and other resources serves as a major barrier to providing effective care when we are used to having these technologies.[5] Solely using signs and symptoms to diagnose disease is often an unfamiliar practice for us outsiders.[6] In contrast to our fresh faces, local medical providers also already know national and local health care protocols—which differ greatly from those of high income countries.[7]

Holding a chest x-ray up to a window in a village without electricity

Local providers have a unique claim to awareness of culture and language.[8] Not surprisingly, local people have complained about inadequate cultural preparation by outsiders.[9] Culture affects nearly every aspect of health care, such as behaviors, perceptions regarding disease, beliefs about when to seek care, use of alternative healers, and compliance with meds and other treatments. Language is an equally important aspect of awareness, yet it's rare for us outsiders to have a command of local languages.[10]

In *Appendix A*, I review various ways that we can make suitcase medicine more helpful. Briefly, outsider awareness can be expanded by improving our pre-trip preparation, screening potential volunteers to invite only the most qualified, and working with interpreters to help bridge the language and cultural gap. Yet even with stellar work in each of these areas, we will still never have the level of awareness of local health workers. For this reason, we're more likely to miss diagnoses and to give less than ideal treatment, follow-up, and referral plans. I think we should be humble and admit we're more likely to give sub-standard care and to unintentionally cause harm through patient care in an unfamiliar context.

What's more, perhaps our deepest limitation in awareness involves not knowing *whether* more health care is needed in a particular community, as well as what *type* of health care is most needed. Local health workers and communities understand what we don't, and they can also tell us *where, how*, and *when* we can best help. For all of these reasons, we simply won't accomplish very much without partnering closely with local health workers and facilities. We outsiders simply crash and burn when we operate with a...

Parallel Care System

They felt like brilliant improvisers in the jungle, making do with what they had and giving the best patient care possible in the middle of nowhere. Clinic volunteers in the bustling makeshift center took the burden of care onto their proud shoulders, but the foreigners couldn't help but notice that a second clinic had already been set up in the building next to them. It was a Ministry of Health outreach clinic and it was doing the same things they were! The Americans pretended they didn't see it and tried not to catch the eyes of the local doctors serving next door. Each clinic went on giving care as if the other was invisibly shrouded in the thick tropical vegetation.

When asked for feedback, local people throughout Sub-Saharan Africa have shared their frustration with outsiders' preference for creating duplicate and parallel health services.[11] Volunteers from nations with highly privatized, fragmented, and competitive health systems such as the US may unfortunately act under a similar model in resource-limited countries. Yet following a model of parallel and competing services doesn't lead to improved health outcomes.[12] Unfortunately, outsiders who might prefer to avoid parallel systems may still be forced to create them in order to access funding from donors that mandate this.

Rather than providing health care abroad in this way, we can help much more by partnering with local providers who can help us overcome many of our natural deficiencies; working at preexisting community health facilities is a major step in the right direction. This is a much-improved version of conventional suitcase medicine!

Beyond close partnership, there's the issue of what to do and how to best help out. Importantly, health workers and their communities could give us direction as to whether and how we could assist by providing health care and/or clinical training. So this next point in the decision tree involves whether we primarily treat patients or primarily train local health workers from within this partnership.

Treat or Train?

*Of the patients we **treated** on a week-long trip abroad, 5 of them had diabetes. After we flew home, another outsider team returned a year later to this community. Five diabetic consults in a year is quite a low number. Yet imagine if we didn't treat any ourselves but rather **trained** 5 health workers from different communities about caring for people with diabetes. If these 5 health workers each went on to see 5 cases of diabetes per week, then just imagine what they could achieve in the 52 weeks of a year:*

5 x 5 x 52=1,300 sessions for people with diabetes!

When outsiders train local health workers, we can assist exponentially more patients than we would by simply treating them ourselves on a brief trip.

Local training has been cited as a means to achieving more long-term benefits than transient medical care,[13] as well as being a means to making the presence of outsiders irrelevant in the future.[14] Local capacity-building has been advocated as a strategy for scaling up health programs abroad.[15] It also serves as a way to expand the quality of care and improve outcomes.[16]

When outsiders perform *needs assessments* abroad, they can be expected to highlight further local training as a deeper need than temporary health care.[17] However, surveys on short-term medical service trips have demonstrated that outsiders' and local people's central goals are at odds; while performing health care is the most commonly cited goal for us outsiders, local people mainly want an exchange of learning with outsiders if we are to visit.[18] Rather than hosting outsiders who will temporarily see patients, local people generally prefer to see patients themselves; yet they often would like assistance with furthering their training and with recruiting more local staff.[19] While outside professionals commonly train outside students or residents during their trips abroad, local people prefer to be trained *themselves* during such trips.[20]

Unfortunately, the first survey to evaluate the quality of short-term medical service trips ranked educating local people as achieving the lowest score.[21] According to one systematic review, only 48% of short-term medical trips performed some type of local education, while medical care almost universally ranked as their central goal.[22] Even so, many outsiders have highlighted the importance of promoting local capacity-building on such trips.[23]

There have been repeated calls for short-term trips to further build the capacity of local nurses,[24] midwives,[25] and physicians.[26] Many have also called on short-term surgery trips to do less patient care and more training of local staff,[27] often with the aim of helping local surgeons become able to independently perform quality procedures.[28] Some believe outsiders should do a combination of health care and education work,[29] while other groups have focused their trips entirely on clinical education.[30] I believe that local people should lead in deciding the type of work we do, although the singular focus on clinical education generally makes a larger difference.

Given the undeniable benefits of local capacity-building[31], there is a general consensus around its recommendation as a best-practice standard for suitcase medicine trips[32] and short-term medical service organizations.[33] The strength of the evidence[34] has made the training of new and existing local health workers a central feature of a proposed non-governmental organization *code of conduct* aimed at assisting community members in a deeper way.[35]

In the Honduran mountains, the government built a clinic which remained empty; this was inviting for a short-term medical group like ours! Although we'd treated some patients there, this was an important but small component of the program. We'd helped much more by funding proactive community members to go to school for training as community health workers. They filled this clinic with patients and hope, rather than us—as it should be.

We sat with them and practiced placing stitches, using a sock as if it were skin; we reviewed the treatment of rashes and sexually transmitted infections, and then answered other clinical questions. These local women were the stars of the clinic, and we were just assisting from the sidelines. The community health workers never asked us to stay through the year to see patients. They were perfectly happy to treat patients themselves, and that was the objective.

Small Wrench, Big Nut

It's clear that our clinical trips can generally make a bigger difference by training rather than treating in resource-limited nations. There are further compelling reasons, as we turn back to the daunting task of reversing the brain drain and the overall health worker shortage in these settings. Just as a small wrench can't fit and turn a big nut, there exists a fundamental mismatch between the limited availability of outsiders to perform health care on the one hand and the massive scale of the global health worker shortage on the other.

The number of volunteers assisting with short-term medical service trips been steadily increasing since 2009; hundreds of thousands of volunteers from the US alone join these teams in resource-limited countries annually.[36] Over 500 organizations are involved in short-term medical trips, some coordinating up to 20 trips annually.[37] Yet these impressive efforts are limited by the fact that most trips are under two weeks long;[38] as in wealthy countries, resource-limited nations need health care access throughout the year.

The potential supply of willing outsiders is extensive, yet it pales in comparison to the overwhelming need: a health worker shortage of 4.2 million in Africa, 6.9 million in South-East Asia, and 3.7 million in the Western Pacific.[39] When over 50% of all humans can't access essential health care,[40] we clearly have a gap that 2-week health care trips can barely touch. Residents of resource-limited countries have pointed to the irony of how rich countries recruit away their health workers and then send only a small number of temporary outside volunteers in exchange.[41]

Even if outside volunteers could fill this gap, it would be far from ideal to do so. It would create dependency rather than the more practical, empowering, and sustainable solution of advancing the training and number of local health workers.

I picked coffee beans, dried them on the tin roof, crushed them, and added them to cold water as my morning pick-me-up. Then I shaved with a razor while staring at a broken shard of mirror; I visited the ever-stinky latrine and took a cold shower by bucket—sometimes with curling worms at the bottom. This was the morning routine of Ugandan village life that I loved, and by night, there was always a candlelight dinner since the electric grid didn't reach that far.

But one night, a screeching, jarring sound jolted my hand and my noodles fell to the concrete floor. A large flatbed truck crammed with 40 people in its open back was pretending to drag race through the night and flipped over on its side. For an obvious fracture, we used a dish tray as a splint and tied it in place with my shirt. A local health worker was attending the most serious case from

*the accident: A woman lay unconscious on the ground
and he raised her legs up while fanning her. Yet she wasn't
breathing and I couldn't find a pulse! My friend and I started
CPR, found public transport, and we took her to the nearest
hospital. On the way there, I sighed in cold sweat relief when
she started breathing spontaneously!*

*But then I noticed that we hadn't invited the local health
worker to join us. We happened to be at the right place at
the right time and we'd saved her life, but we'd missed a
golden teaching opportunity. We could have taught him how
to potentially save similar lives in the future. We left the
country without teaching him about resuscitation, airway,
breathing, and circulation. The work of outsiders just isn't
impressive unless it goes towards boosting the capacity of
local people and reversing the health worker shortage that
cripples resource-limited nations.*

If you're reading this on a flight and you'll start doing medical
care abroad tomorrow morning, then I'd recommend you flip now to
Appendix A: Improving Suitcase Medicine. It reviews ways to address
other shortcomings of this approach, and ways to expand the impact
of our work through it. I'd also recommend starting there if I haven't
convinced you that we outsiders can help more through capacity-
building than medical care. Otherwise, please join me in the next
chapter as I explore especially helpful training methods and activities.

Training Health Workers

This chapter reviews practical ways in which outsiders can work to alleviate health workforce challenges by furthering the training of *existing* local health workers as well as by training *new* health workers. Increasing the number and expanding the training of health workers is a proven way of lowering mortality rates in resource-limited countries.[1]

Before reviewing training methods, I want to emphasize that this must not be conceived of as a one-way process. Although most short-term teams that perform education only teach local health workers,[2] it's more equitable, effective, and rewarding to both teach *and be taught by* them. Medical anthropologists point out that *bidirectional learning* fosters cross-cultural understanding and trust.[3]

In a true and equitable partnership, local people and outsiders will both share their clinical strengths and weaknesses—each helping the other to expand knowledge and skills. Bidirectional learning helps to equalize the power imbalance inherent in outsiders from rich countries working in resource-limited settings. When outsiders always take on the role of teachers while local people are always students, then learning becomes a top-down process of disempowerment disconnected from the local context. Among the lessons transmitted is the superiority of foreign knowledge and the inadequacy of local skills and understandings.

Local health workers are intelligent, experienced, and have valuable things to teach. We can take advantage of their experience by asking these health workers medical questions, even if we think we know how we would answer the question. Their knowledgeable participation can assist us outsiders to overcome the large gap in our awareness of local health, medical care, society, and culture. We need to be open to new cultural expressions, information, and health methodologies. If our aim is to empower local providers, then we shouldn't assume we know the best way to give medical care. This is true even if our preferred methods have been proven by large randomized, double-blind, placebo-controlled studies.

Appropriate training empowers local health workers to make major sustainable improvements to community health. There are many effective ways to expand local health worker capacity, some of which I'll review here.

Training for Hope

Continuing Medical Education involves ongoing training workshops for health workers throughout their careers in an effort to maintain and expand their knowledge and skills. Such workshops are unfortunately quite rare in resource-limited nations,[4] yet they are often quite suitable to being conducted by outsiders on short trips.[5] Local health workers should decide on needed training topic—for example, prenatal care, palliative care, and HIV stigma-reduction—while we outsiders can match requested topics to our areas of expertise and prepare teaching sessions before arriving. Community health workers, nurses, midwives, physicians, and other health workers can be trained with continuing medical education sessions best carried out in a *bidirectional* manner; that is, coordinating with and making space for the local health workers to share their knowledge and demonstrate their techniques alongside our presentations.

In addition to arranging continuing medical education sessions directly between outside and local health workers, ministries of health can be contacted by outsiders so that we can contribute to ongoing health worker capacity-building efforts. For example, there may be an ongoing program to train health workers in malaria diagnosis and treatment; we could offer to assist them in meeting their training goals by using the locally developed curriculum and methodology as part of our work.

The Integrated Management of Childhood Illness (IMCI) offers another example of a common health worker training program which is organized by health authorities in resource-limited countries. IMCI is an 11-day training program on the use of evidence-based simplified algorithms for the diagnosis and treatment of child illness.[6] IMCI training has been implemented in over 100 nations; it results in improved diagnostic and treatment skills, as well as increased education of caregivers on how to care for their children when they're sick.[7] Districts in Tanzania that implemented IMCI training experienced 13% lower child mortality rates compared with those that did no training.[8]

Outside medical volunteers can familiarize themselves with IMCI protocols, developed by WHO to diagnose pediatric disease based on signs and symptoms alone.[9] Such training can better prepare outsiders for giving effective care without access to testing or to electricity in resource-limited settings, while also preparing us to assist in extending this training to local health workers. IMCI approaches empower local health care workers to make effective decisions without advanced labs, imaging, and equipment; they can also empower parents and caregivers to provide lifesaving care for health problems, such as rehydrating children who have diarrhea.

> *By doing IMCI training, I had the opportunity to discard many of the less practical and less clinically-relevant lessons I'd internalized from med school. It was bare-bones, condensed, and applicable to the everyday child breathing too fast due to pneumonia. Without the guidance of the IMCI text, it would be difficult for me to teach this nurse how to work more like a doctor by diagnosing and treating patients in rural areas.*

Further training of birth attendants and midwives in resource-limited nations can effectively prevent many maternal and newborn deaths; 80% of stillbirths and 90% of maternal deaths occur in 58 nations largely due to a lack of skilled birth attendants.[10] All too often, babies aren't able to breathe properly without support immediately following birth. Training on newborn resuscitation expands birth attendant skills and knowledge, and reduces neonatal death rates; refresher trainings on these techniques help make these lifesaving skills and their benefits permanent.[11]

Helping Babies Breathe is one such program through which outsiders can share low-tech and low-cost neonatal resuscitation techniques with midwives, birth attendants, and community health workers to effectively reduce death rates.[12] This program promotes newborn breathing through drying, stimulating, and the use of suction bulbs and bag-and-mask ventilation. These techniques don't require electricity, employing a plastic bag and mask which can be disassembled, boiled, and reused.

> *It would have taken several hours to walk to the nearest hospital, yet this woman was in labor and couldn't even stand. The sun left a beautiful pastel trail in the sky contrasting with the painful moaning emanating from a modest dwelling. The wrinkled Lencan features of the traditional birth attendant testified to the many deliveries she had attended along these spiderweb mountain paths.*

A baby boy was pushed out after some painful hours, yet he simply didn't start breathing. An entire life rested in the birth attendant's careful hands as she resuscitated him to begin breathing on his own.

My wife met with these birth attendants in Honduras to review the Helping Babies Breathe techniques in "Train-the-Trainer" sessions so they could pass these skills on. We did the same in Sierra Leone, along with clean birth kit demonstrations and trainings on delivery complications such as hemorrhage.

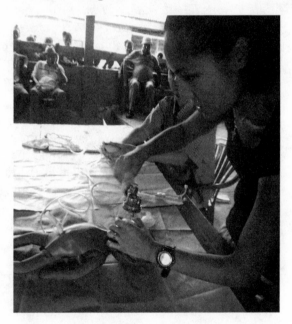

My wife Vicki uses a bag and mask on a plastic doll during a Train-the-Trainer session on Helping Babies Breathe.

The provision of low-tech clean birth kits for deliveries can also provide another way for outsiders to promote education among birth attendants. These kits commonly include soap, gloves, gowns, clean drapes, pieces of string for tying the umbilical cord in two places, and single-use razors for cutting the cord between these two strings. Newborn deaths from infection can be reduced by using clean birth kits.[13] Outside medical teams can demonstrate their use and learn with local providers how to assemble them using materials available in the community.

Train-the-Trainer sessions can be organized to pass on many other evidence-based and locally-appropriate medical skills and concepts. Beyond simply teaching individual or groups of health workers, Train-the-Trainer sessions prepare people to serve as teachers themselves. Short-term medical teams can organize these sessions over a limited period of time[14] and leave the country knowing that the perpetuation of knowledge and skill in each of these areas can continue indefinitely. Future outsider visits can then focus on *refresher trainings* on IMCI, Helping Babies Breathe, clean birth kits, hypertension, and other topics—as well as expanding such knowledge to other health workers.

We rode our bikes from village to village through the Ugandan bush, carrying light posters but heavy news about HIV. We arrived and the Ugandan teens were ready to show off their latest dramatic skit on HIV transmission; it was fun but hit hard and its message amplified with the frantic xylophones in the background. Forming a circle, we placed labels around the neck of each participant: body, antibody, HIV, and germ. The antibodies locked arms and formed a protective ring around the "body." The germ couldn't break through the ring to get to the "body;" yet when HIV was present, the antibodies all sat down and the germ easily reached the body.

These demos were quite visual and participatory; the messages stuck with the teens. We left the props behind, since the teaching on transmission and prevention had only begun; teens used the posters, skits, and antibody demo in village after village. We'd prepared them with Train-the-Trainer sessions and now there was no need for us to do the teaching ourselves.

Pairing each outside health worker with a local one is another effective capacity-building approach for short-term teams. Pairing is a partnership of mutual education and skill-building sustained over time and over multiple trips. Continuing medical education requests can be made through pairing; for example, a local doctor may teach an outsider about vitamin deficiency rashes, while an outsider doctor may return the favor by teaching about ankle sprains. Local providers can learn different approaches to history-taking, physical exams, and the use of labs, diagnosis, and treatment. Ideally, local providers will take away new knowledge, skills, and inspiration which they can use to serve their community long after outsider teams have come and gone. Such pairing also allows us outsiders new ways to understand problems we thought we had already mastered. By becoming a kind of medical anthropologist, we can learn about local disease perception and treatment, prescribing practices, referral resources, social determinants of health, and much more that we can relate to our practices at home. Medical anthropologists refer to such immersed learning as *participant observation*.[15]

Further medical education sessions can be provided to the same local clinician each time that a visiting physician returns.[16] Long-term pairing of providers also allows for quality improvement over time through cross-cultural *second opinions*. Partnerships for mentoring over many years can be created through pairing of groups and individuals.[17]

> *The laughing doves rose out of the desert, finding the massive bright flowering trees that made this town an oasis. In such places throughout Botswana, one in every five people is living with HIV. Overwhelmed with patient care, local clinicians in the villages were paired with us as they saw their most challenging cases. These were the children and teens with the most advanced HIV disease, drug resistance, opportunistic infections, high HIV "viral load" labs, and seemingly insurmountable social barriers to care.*

> *The job of local clinicians was to provide these unfortunate souls with primary care, while my job was to try to advise providers on how to care for them even more effectively. I was also paired with a Botswanan nurse prescriber who consulted on these challenging patients once monthly; in turn, she and I were paired with the village clinician who cared for these patients on a daily basis. We all put our heads together to plan the best care we could, and we taught each other—and emotionally supported each other—much in the process.*

In Table 1 of the *Global Health Approaches* chapter, I labeled local clinical capacity-building as being evidence-based, helpful, empowering, and sustainable. I've already reviewed its evidence-base in providing sustainable health benefits, and I'll add a word here about avoiding potential harm and promoting empowerment. The training methods outlined here force us outsiders to collaborate and partner with local health workers and systems, which in turn prevents the development of potentially harmful parallel health systems. As outsiders link with local health workers, we're also less likely to cause harm through our limited awareness. When learning is engaging and bidirectional, local people can be empowered to improve the health of their communities rather than serving as passive recipients of medical care, knowledge, or skills.

Teaching by Seeing Patients Together

Although we outsiders can help more through training than treating in resource-limited countries, patient care can be used *for purposes of education* when requested by local health workers. Nursing and medical students are often trained by watching or directly providing hands-on patient care with their instructors present. We can also use this experiential form of teaching abroad within established local health facilities.

> *In the granite-strewn hills of Tanzania, I knew that each outsider-led patient visit was a missed teaching opportunity. Thousands of doctors from around the countryside came in small groups scheduled throughout the year for advanced training in HIV, TB, and malnutrition care. They each spent two weeks with us, and after some lecture- and discussion-based learning, the rest of the training program involved hands-on patient care. A Tanzanian doc would see all patients together with me; I would point out additional insights on HIV and TB care, while s/he would direct me as to how care works in Tanzanian society.*
>
> *Rather than use my broken Swahili to "guide" patient visits, these local doctors would do the talking, and then interpret information into English for me when needed. Yet they served as so much more than interpreters! They gathered the patient history, formed a treatment plan, and carried out patient education. In other words, they gave the medical care while I was simply an advisor temporarily embedded into their daily patient care routine.*
>
> *Local docs were better qualified than I to do such care, and they were less likely to make cross-cultural and medical mistakes. Rather than local people being dependent on the knowledge, skills, and goodwill of outsiders, I found myself nearly helpless without their knowledge and skills regarding their society, medical system, and language; this situation inherently empowers local providers—as it should.*

By contrast, an outsider-led clinical care model just pairs foreigners with interpreters; yet we can go much further to train and empower local health workers. If outsiders are to see patients in the community, then I believe we should aim to do so with at least one local health professional—whether it be a community health worker, nurse, midwife, traditional healer, doctor, pharmacist, or other provider. In this way, each patient encounter can serve as an important training experience for the local provider; the same is true for the outsider, even though this isn't the main aim. Seeing patients together can stimulate much conversation, questioning, and learning; training can then continue in greater depth after patients have left.

Large families were tucked behind narrow bamboo-pole walls in the camp for the internally-displaced. My wife and I only saw patients together with local Burmese nurses and doctors. Every patient visit was a potential training and learning opportunity. A patient's spleen spanned across his entire abdomen like a football; we gave him treatment for probable complications from recurrent malaria, but only after a long discussion with local health workers regarding possible diagnoses and treatment courses.

As community members watch their local provider training a foreigner in malaria diagnosis, they see how capable that community provider is; local patients will tend to have more confidence in their services as a result. Patients can also watch an outsider gently teaching a local provider about ways to diagnose the cause of their headache.

This can serve to instill greater confidence in the patient's mind, as they may think:

> *Now I have two people caring for me, and the outsider isn't keeping his medical secrets to himself. He's sharing those secrets with my health worker—who can use them to help me with headaches in the future.*

Finally, *guidance* for local health workers can be provided by visiting ones. Rather than attend patients themselves, outside medical volunteers can visit a facility where local health workers are treating patients; we outsiders can essentially *stand by* while patient care proceeds, making ourselves available for any cases in which local health workers would like feedback, direction, training, or perhaps a second opinion. With such a *guidance model*, community members importantly take the center stage while outsiders maintain a background role of education and empowerment. Alternatively, and perhaps most usefully in high demand situations, this could be flipped into a *supervision model* through which local providers could supervise and train outsiders as we perform the patient care. While less than ideal, this would appropriately put community members in charge and also demonstrate the competence and capabilities of local providers to their patients.

Filling Whole Clinics, Not Just Waiting Rooms

New health workers can also be trained to address severe workforce shortages. Outside medical organizations can offer to train local health care students, as long as it's done in partnership with community schools. Other outside organizations can assist by extending new medical specialties[18] or new residency programs to resource-limited nations. When outsider teams can commit to longer stays abroad, then we can make a more significant impact on local health worker training in these and other ways.

Even so, offering training for only a few weeks can make important contributions. Outsiders could serve as guest lecturers for topics beyond the comfort level of local health professors. In addition to direct teaching, we could offer to partner with local nursing, midwifery, and medical schools to provide feedback and further improve their training programs.[19] We can also provide scholarships so that more community members can attend in-country health professional training programs.[20]

Physician training is often prolonged and expensive, yet alternative health provider training programs may exist. A WHO meta-analysis showed that nurses and midwives, compared with physicians, can provide at least equally effective care for HIV, high blood pressure, diabetes, and routine pregnancy care.[21] Non-physician clinicians, such as nurse practitioners and medical officers, have been trained successfully in Sub-Saharan Africa to perform the diagnosis and treatment duties that physicians normally perform,[22] leading to a reduction in maternal and child mortality rates.[23] An alternative to obstetrical or nurse-midwife training involves further training for traditional birth attendants, which has led to improved health outcomes.[24]

While nurses often require additional training to guide diagnosis and treatment plans, community health workers (CHWs) can be trained specifically for this task; in this way, they serve as another option for improving health outcomes in resource-limited settings.[25] CHWs serve their communities, often being selected by and paid by the community.[26] They can be trained in the diagnosis and treatment of various conditions, making them a key resource in closing the health care access gap worldwide.[27] They commonly promote healthy individual behaviors along with collective public health solutions, provide pregnancy care and family planning, and refer complex cases to medical providers with more training. The many potential roles of CHWs often overlap with those of physicians, nurses, midwives, social workers, teachers, and public health professionals.

Community health worker training is one of the key strategies proposed by WHO to meet critical health workforce shortages in resource-limited nations.[28] Although CHWs can't fill the functions of all health care professionals, their contributions to care are undeniable. CHW care in some communities has led to a reduction in child deaths by 40% from malaria, by 24% from pneumonia, and by 33% from overwhelming bacterial infections (sepsis).[29]

Training of new CHWs is best done by those who share the same language and culture, although outsider assistance can often be helpful.[30] Short-term medical service organizations can assist resource-limited countries by funding the training programs of CHWs where needed. Many remote communities don't have any health care professionals to start with, nor do they have nearby CHW training programs. In this scenario, outsiders may be called upon to start and sustain a CHW training program in partnership with local community and health authorities. Until we are replaced, outsiders should make the commitment to return on a regular basis to provide CHW support, supervision, evaluation, and program improvement.[31]

The toughest cases came rushing in by motorcycle from the most remote villages between the craters of Western Uganda. The nonprofit that my wife and I assisted had trained and graduated classes of village-based community health workers; they were the ones seeking out those without access to care and connecting them to this public hospital. Without their insightful vision and long-established trust, these patients with lymphoma, TB, and meningitis would almost certainly have died in the same houses in which they were born, never having received care. With their help, many walked out of the hospital looking like entirely different people.

Outside medical providers can do much by connecting with CHWs on our trips abroad, offering to answer questions, troubleshooting complex patients, boosting their confidence, and providing further training when needed. CHW training programs that begin with outside teachers are best replaced with local ones when available.[32] Additionally, we should be careful to use and adapt national CHW training curricula, rather than teaching knowledge and skills more applicable to our home countries. Finally, we should familiarize ourselves with the national plan for utilizing the services of CHWs before we offer to contribute to such programs.

Patient Teaching and Empowerment

Empowering patients also serves as an important goal. When outsiders see patients jointly with local providers, we should model *patient empowerment* by informing patients about their disease and its treatment options and prevention. If local providers aren't already doing patient education in an empowering way, then we outsiders can encourage them to set a higher bar.

The limited number of health workers in many countries, along with the cost of accessing care, often leads patients to self-diagnose and self-treat many diseases, such as rashes and ear infections. Until affected communities have access to more health care workers and more comprehensive services, providing quality health worker training simply won't be enough. Patients also need to be empowered to best prevent, diagnose, and treat diseases themselves.

In communities with limited medical care access, each patient encounter can be viewed as having a potential short-term and long-term impact. Treating back pain has a short-term impact, while teaching the person what caused it and what can be done to prevent it has long-term impact. Treating pink eye may help short-term; yet a deeper contribution comes from teaching the four main causes of pink eye, as well as prevention and treatment for each cause. It may enable patients to treat their next case of pink eye when they don't have access to a local or outside health worker.

Community members who lack access to medical care can themselves be trained to care for common health problems, rather than depending on health care providers who are often nonexistent or inaccessible in remote areas. This boldly empowering approach was first promoted in the influential book *Where There Is No Doctor*, which both instructs how community members can care for their neighbors as well as highlighting when additional medical help is needed.[33] This work has been joined by several other key medical empowerment books.[34] *Chapter 10: Participation to Empower* will review some practical methods for empowering patients, such as the approaches of patient-centered care, self-management of chronic disease, and motivational interviewing.

Training local health workers and patients provides much hope for health improvement, as does partnering with communities to strengthen their health systems. I turn to this promising approach in the next chapter.

Strengthening Health Systems

Physically and emotionally exhausted, we stumbled
out of the Ugandan District Hospital and gazed back at it
in dismay. Too many had died there and we had a sinking
feeling that more would join them before the sun tapped our
shoulder, nudged us out of bed, and pushed us back into this
mess. The town had a few lights on, so there was some hope
for electricity. Although the hospital windows still glowed,
we suspected that soon light would be lost: both for the ward
and for those struggling to breathe on oxygen concentrator
machines.

Why join a crumbing public health care system?

So that it doesn't crumble, or so that it crumbles less.

Our international financial order permits wealthy nations to exploit the people and resources of poorer ones (see chapters *Exotic Diseases & Social Justice* and *Poverty & Empowerment*). While it is difficult for health professionals to act on that global level to change the course of ill health, we can have an effect more easily at the level of the health system. Further, the failure of health care systems throughout resource-limited countries is responsible for much of the poor health outcomes seen in these settings.[1] Systems-level interventions are needed in many such contexts,[2] and they form the centerpiece of enabling *sustainable* health improvements to occur.[3]

While a common approach is to focus on a single disease like TB or a single demographic group like pregnant women, efforts to strengthen community health systems have proven to generate better outcomes across multiple diseases and demographic groups.[4] For example, the expansion of available resources to diagnose and treat HIV globally was desperately needed and beneficial up to a certain point; but after that initial expansion, the general weakness of care systems prevented further improvements in HIV outcomes.[5]

The strengthening of these systems also makes health care more equitable and efficient. One general indicator of health system equity (whether needed care extends to the poorest members of the society) and efficiency (whether care reaches people enough to improve health outcomes) is the infant mortality rate, and nations with the weakest health systems have double the infant mortality rates of other countries.[6] Finally, consensus has emerged that the main barrier which prevented resource-limited nations from achieving the Millennium Development Goals was the continued weakness of their health systems.[7]

In order to strengthen local systems, we outsiders first have to learn about them, partner with them, and integrate our efforts with theirs. This could involve visiting and collaborating with Ministry of Health offices, public facilities, or community programs such as health home-visits. Outpatient primary care services can be strengthened as a very cost-effective means to improving local health status.[8] Alternatively, district hospitals can be approached on a systems-level to improve the quality of care.[9]

The priorities of local people should serve as the origin for all systems strengthening efforts.[10] Outsiders and community members can best work in collaboration in order to achieve it.[11] Although we can aid individual patients or health workers, we can also aim for a deeper impact by teaming up to fortify the general health system in one or more ways.

Boosting Up the System

The first and arguably most important component of stronger health systems requires the presence of health workers in sufficient numbers and with sufficient training. In this way, local health worker capacity-building is a critical element of strengthening health systems. Yet strengthening the health system extends far beyond that. WHO has identified five other key components of a strong health system: service delivery, medical products, vaccines and other technologies, leadership and governance, and financing.[12] Others have expanded this list to include socioeconomic factors, access to and the state of health facilities, and disease prevention.[13] The WHO category of *service delivery* has been broken down by others to include quality improvement, care access, case management, staff supervision, referrals, and monitoring and evaluation.[14]

Approaches to health systems strengthening can focus on one of these components or they can address multiple areas at once to achieve broader results. For example, maternal health programs have registered better outcomes when multiple evidence-based interventions are integrated and provided at the same time; such success has occurred after increasing clinician numbers, providing emergency obstetrics training, improving facilities, and expanding access to meds, supplies, and equipment.[15] The evidence-based, beneficial, and sustainable work of strengthening health systems can also empower health providers and the community (the four variables in Table 1 of the chapter *Global Health Approaches*). In this chapter, I'll briefly review several options on a quite extensive list of possible systems-strengthening activities.

Doing System Strengthening

I worked with an impressive outsider nonprofit which promoted the formation of locally-led pediatric HIV care organizations in resource-limited nations. Each of the local nonprofits that it helped create was closely partnered with their respective Ministries of Health and public hospitals. This nonprofit took a sustainable approach which has proven effective for decades. Staffing for new pediatric HIV centers wasn't initially available in sufficient numbers, and so outsiders comprised a significant portion of the staffing. From the beginning, they progressively worked themselves out of their jobs by training local clinicians in HIV care, as well as community leaders to run the clinics. Each year, the number of foreign staff dwindled until it became 100% locally-staffed at some sites and required less than 5% of foreign staffing at other sites.

Effective community leadership is a critical component of a well-functioning health system. Rather than leading health initiatives ourselves, we outsiders could potentially assist local people in their efforts to lead them well. Ministries of Health often provide such *centralized* leadership in resource-limited countries, and their own skills can be boosted through administrative training initiatives of outsiders who have significant experience in this area.[16] Conversely, leadership skills can be *decentralized* by training and empowering District Health Managers to more effectively lead health programs in the communities that they serve.[17] Leadership training can be extended to those managing local hospitals and clinics.[18] Effective health program leadership can also be promoted through training on the specific themes of each program, such as palliative care or the treatment of mental illness.

Quality improvement (QI) serves as another major area in which we can support the strengthening of local systems. Training in QI can benefit local health teams,[19] who can go on to identify QI projects of interest to them. Their projects can improve health outcomes in a locally-led, culturally appropriate, and cost-effective way.[20] We outsiders can offer to facilitate the creation of local QI teams, as well as to assist in the development of standards for improved patient care.

Disease management protocols are locally-specific guides for diagnosing and treating common diseases based on the resources available.[21] Quality of care can be improved by assisting in developing these protocols, and then through their promotion as benchmarks. In Sierra Leone, for example, our local-outsider team partnered in adapting evidence-based national and WHO guidelines to develop clinic protocols for handling infectious diseases, diabetes, hypertension, and prenatal care.

Health outcomes research can be used to develop better systems of care, and this can be facilitated through brief studies on short-term outsider trips.[22] QI can also be achieved through better systems for health worker supervision[23] and accreditation, as well as those for health program monitoring and evaluation.[24] When invited by local health authorities, outsiders can assist by jointly brainstorming and evaluating potential improvements for local health initiatives.[25] Sharing experience in starting or improving case management services for complex patients offers another means to improving quality and building stronger systems.[26]

> *The perpetual Tanzanian rains weighed down the roof and the drips became a full gushing stream. It was loud and our shoes were soon wet, but it didn't deter the busy staff. After all, the hectic hands of this nonprofit stretched far beyond primary care services and into a great many systems issues. It advises national working groups on HIV, TB, and pediatric care; it aids in developing the national care guidelines and disease management protocols in each of these areas. The team identifies and works to fix barriers to care locally and throughout the country. They manage their own QI projects, while training health facility staff throughout the country to start QI teams at each facility.*

Expanded access to health care is also critical for robust health systems. We outsiders can partner with local health services that aim to expand their reach and enroll more patients in care. WHO has acknowledged that universal coverage of medical services globally can only be achieved through health systems strengthening.[27] Yet few health programs in resource-limited nations (much less in wealthy nations!) have succeeded in achieving universal coverage; the scaling up of practical and effective delivery mechanisms are among the efforts needed to expand access to health care.[28] Outsiders could also be asked to assist local health authorities in improving medical referral systems as well as positioning health facilities within appropriate reach of communities.[29] Finally, refurbishing health facilities can expand their effective use by more community members.[30]

Volcanos rose steeply from behind the hospital, leaving behind the clouds as if their height was nothing significant worth noting. Inside, a child was inconsolable with a temp of 103 and a neck as rigid as a steel pipe. The antibiotic ceftriaxone was the quick and easy tool which could save his life. But where could I find it? The hospital pharmacy ran like an auction site, and it always emptied faster than shipments came in. I ventured into town to buy the meds that the hospital lacked, as I had the day before and the day before that. "Are you the hospital pharmacy stockperson?" the town pharmacists could have asked when they saw me. If they had, I would have answered, "No, I work in a struggling, disorganized district hospital where many come to suffer and die while some are lucky enough to leave in a healthier

state." Yet rather than shuffling around looking for meds on a daily basis, I should have been working with local staff to improve the medicine supply distribution system.

Strong health systems need access to adequate and appropriate medications, supplies, and equipment. Rather than blindly donating these items on short-term service trips, we can assist more by arriving empty-handed until we have a good understanding of what items are used locally and which are needed and requested. By pairing outside clinicians with local ones, we can receive direction as to what donations are appropriate and needed. Then we could best pass these donations on to local health workers.[31]

Per WHO, medicines should only be donated when they are on the nationally-approved list and have a shelf-life beyond one year; they also need to meet quality, transport, and storage standards through their delivery.[32] Similarly, medical equipment donations should be of good quality and *locally-appropriate* in that they're simple to use and maintain, standardized with other local equipment, and have minimal energy-requirements and accessories; they also should be accompanied by manuals, spare parts, and training on operation and maintenance.[33] However, following WHO protocols offers no guarantee that donations can be sustained over time. In fact, sustaining them over time may be a recipe for creating dependency. We outsiders can often assist more on a systems-level by improving the efficiency of local supply chains, as well as helping develop maintenance and repair protocols and skills.[34]

> *Her African palms were almost as white as my skin, so I knew that IV malaria medicine wouldn't be enough to keep her alive. Convincing the hospital powers-that-be to give her a blood transfusion would be a highly political act of acrobatics and it would take the better part of four hours to accomplish. Listening to her breathing, I wondered if she had four hours. Also, could we find the tubing to run the transfusion?*
>
> *Meanwhile, the keeper of the hospital oxygen tank key clenched it closely as if he had the crown jewels. Two tanks could be partitioned at times, but today all departments and clinicians were competing for a single unused tank. It was the centerpiece of strife and jealousy, and actually, of life itself in that tiny place for the desperate, sick, and the dying.*

Technology provided by outsiders—including lab equipment, vehicles, and health information systems—should follow similar standards of being locally requested and locally appropriate. Adding additional diagnostic equipment may expand the capacity of a community health system, yet it should only be provided for locally-relevant diseases and if its use can be sustained with local supply channels. Health information systems are needed for strong overall systems.[35] These can include paper or electronic records used for diagnosis and treatment documentation, disease surveillance systems, Ministry of Health data collection, and health indicator monitoring. Outsiders can partner with local facilities to develop or improve such systems, as well as to analyze and interpret their data to improve health services and outcomes. Transport technology such as ambulances can potentially strengthen local systems too.

> *Funds were raised by outsiders for an ambulance to be used to help the US-funded medical groups in town. The local hospital wasn't invited to use it, nor was anyone in the public health care system. The local hospital had no ambulance of its own, so it was left incapable of adequately responding to emergencies, including the Ebola cases that began spreading in the town. This private ambulance served as another key missed opportunity to fortify the network of community health systems.*

Vaccines are among the most beneficial, evidence-based, and cost-effective global health interventions.[36] Outsiders who partner in improving vaccine delivery systems are therefore able to help far more than those who go abroad to deliver brief patient care.[37] Effective local-outsider partnerships can go far to improve the functioning of vaccine systems, including adequate vaccine supply and cold-chain, introducing new vaccines into a community, and assuring access to and safe disposal of vaccination supplies.

In addition to vaccines, many other disease prevention efforts can strengthen health systems. These include nutrition monitoring and counseling, breastfeeding promotion, water and sanitation improvements, and use of improved cook stoves (see the chapter *Global Health is Public Health*). Each of these interventions lowers the burden placed on health care systems through disease prevention, thus strengthening systems indirectly while improving health.

> *The vaccine coverage rates for measles were impressive, yet it still spread unabated through the mud-walled towns. One of the Ministry of Health presentations clued me in to why: half of the vaccines given locally weren't kept properly*

> *cold; they were essentially placebo shots. A deep systems*
> *issue stared us in the face. If we helped to fix this problem,*
> *far more lives could be saved than by treating measles*
> *ourselves or even training local providers to treat it.*

Finally, health systems need adequate financing, policy, and political support in order to endure.[38] While a nation's health budget and policy are internal issues, outsiders from wealthy nations play an indirect role in them as well. Aid from resource-rich nations is largely devoted to international non-governmental organizations (INGOs) which tend to be led and staffed by us outsiders; national governments and Ministries of Health would need a much larger share of aid in order to strengthen their health services.[39] Following Haiti's 2010 earthquake, for example, only 1% of initial international aid funding was provided to the Haitian government and only 0.4% was provided to Haitian NGOs; INGOs received nearly all of the foreign aid funding.[40]

New approaches to health care aid delivery should actively weaken the influence of outsiders and strengthen the capacities of affected communities and governments.[41] As outsiders, we can advocate for these essential changes. Additionally, we can partner with local authorities in developing sustainable health systems financing and risk-pooling methods.[42] One of the roles of my last job was to help organize local fundraisers in Tanzania, as well as to apply for international grants; new funding was then applied to outpatient system-strengthening efforts. Outsiders can also partner on income-generating projects to support local health care.

A Marathon, Not a Sprint

Regardless of which component of strengthening is selected, outsiders contribute much more to such efforts by moving from short- to long-term initiatives and partnerships. The strengthening of health systems is a complex and multifaceted process that can't be achieved quickly; it's therefore not an appropriate activity for a single short medical service trip. To work effectively towards this end, outsider organizations have fostered long-term partnerships with local health workers and groups,[43] including local Ministries of Health.[44] At the same time, *short-term* service organizations can also form *long-term* partnerships with communities and groups in resource-limited nations. This allows long-term outsider commitments and organizational structures to support multiple short visits to the same community.[45]

This *hybrid short-term/long-term model* for outsider intervention has been recommended by local communities[46] and has appropriately been treated as a best practice standard for short-term medical service teams.[47] This model has also been embraced by some short-term surgery groups.[48] Such an approach led various outsider groups to create a long-term presence abroad in an effort to do sustainable development work—and not simply short-term patient care.[49] In the chapter *Global Health Approaches*, I shared the example of how 2-week biannual trips to the same Honduran community over many years promoted the sustainability of various health programs (including community health worker training, fish farms, improved cookstoves, clean water interventions, latrines, school scholarships, and small business loans).

Outsider clinicians who've done systems strengthening work in their own country are better poised to find success with such work abroad; alternatively, public health professionals generally have more training and experience with systems strengthening. For all outsiders, it is critical to embrace cultural differences as well as to acknowledge difference—perhaps severe limitations—in accessing health resources.

> One of the department leaders of a Tanzania District Hospital mentioned on my first day: "I'm very glad that you're here to help, but while you're here, please try not to complain about all the things that we don't have in our hospital. Previous volunteers from your country spent so much time reacting to all of the things they usually have in their hospitals but that they didn't have here. We know we have little and I hope you can work with what we have and don't complain much about it."

Finally, this brings me to an important challenge with long-term systems strengthening work. A tough but critical adaptive technique involves coming to see many of the systems challenges without immediately and fiercely reacting to them. This doesn't mean that we should ignore the lack of spinal needles or functioning sinks, for example, but we can simply add these shortcomings to a growing *to do list* that we can offer to partner in addressing over time. We can gradually come to understand how a particular health system functions and what its longer-term challenges are. We can foster closer and more trusting partnerships with local people and then slowly compare our own *to do list* with their more important one. After finding common concerns, we can work together on addressing them.

Slowing the Brain Drain

Our participation in short-term service trips or longer-term outsider interventions can either further burden or further strengthen a health system.[50] Just managing outsider medical groups creates extra work for host health systems, and pursuing our own desired projects can further fragment local health services. Instead, our projects should be planned together with the Ministry of Health so they best fit into their broader goals and ongoing health interventions.[51]

Outsiders have hired local health workers for our own initiatives by pulling them away from the public system with offers of better salaries and benefits.[52] Our identification and attraction of talented people can easily weaken the public health care system and lead to remaining health workers being overworked, burning out, and quitting.[53] When hiring community staff, offering salaries comparable to those of other local health care positions may avoid pulling staff from the public system.[54]

There were only two doctors to run the whole district hospital and the foreigners lured one of them away for part-time work at their facility. Some nurses were also drawn away to get their hands on higher salaries for full-time work. The foreigners' clinic got increasingly busy since it helped to make the local facility less functional.

Outsiders should not only hold back on causing such an *internal* brain drain, but we can work to help reverse it! In resource-limited nations, health workers commonly move from public to private work and from rural to urban areas in search of better salaries and working conditions. Systems strengthening efforts can reverse this trend by creating larger incentives to work in rural areas, as well as prohibiting public employees from doing private health care work at the same time.[55]

I've worked with two professional outsider groups that have "topped up" the salaries of local docs so that they wouldn't run from the challenges of the public hospitals. Too many were falling into the arms of the ever more comfortable private sector. These groups also assisted with recruiting outsider clinicians to temporarily fill areas where there was a local staffing shortage. In Western Uganda, when foreigners were no longer needed at one hospital, the outsider program was appropriately deemed a success and they stopped sending volunteers there. They effectively worked themselves out of a "job!" After "graduating" from the assistance of one district hospital, this nonprofit proceeded to reach out to other Ugandan hospitals and, after discussions, found another that was amenable to forming a systems strengthening partnership.

Outsiders can also help to reverse the *external* brain drain to other nations by promoting the retention of local health workers. This can be achieved by improving their work environment as well as providing incentives;[56] topping up inadequate salaries offers one example. Those of us doing systems strengthening can partner in upgrading local health facilities and improving their stock of medicines, supplies, and equipment. Enabling better working conditions in an improved environment can entice many professionals to stay. Health workers can also be retained by improving government efficiency and oversight.[57] Half of all doctors in the US who were educated in Africa came from the same six schools; a partnership with key medical schools may help better address medical education itself in an effort to reduce migration.[58]

Working on a systems level, outsiders can provide incentives to health workers who have already migrated to contribute to health development in their home nations. Scores of doctors who fled Liberia during the civil war have been seen as a potential solution to its current health worker shortage; these doctors could be recruited to return to Liberia and train the next generation of health care providers.[59]

Further, many of the doctors from Sub-Saharan Africa currently living in the US first emigrated here to attend medical school.[60] Outsider medical volunteers in the US and elsewhere have a unique opportunity to encourage these doctors to return to their home countries (assuming it's safe to do so); they can even travel together, using a volunteer trip abroad as the first phase of an inspiring proposal to serve their home country once again. Incentivizing the return of health workers to their home countries can curb the workforce shortage, and international organizations can play a key role in training and funding them to do so.[61]

Additionally, we outsiders could advocate for tougher legislation at home and internationally to prevent the recruitment of health workers from resource-limited nations. The WHO Code of Practice on the International Recruitment of Health Personnel was adopted by 193 nations in 2010 to stem the unethical recruitment of health workers away from countries experiencing critical shortages.[62] Yet this code is voluntary and has had a minimal effect globally.[63] Strong and binding health worker migration agreements with substantial fines for recruiters are desperately needed on both international and national levels. These and other efforts to prevent and reverse the brain drain are required to strengthen health systems in resource-limited nations.

Where to Put Our Efforts

In this chapter, I've shared some hopeful stories as well as some concerning ones about the tragic lack of medicines, supplies, transfusions, oxygen, and vaccines abroad. On the one hand, health systems could really use help in resource-limited nations. Yet on the other hand, they can be dysfunctional and hard to work with. The temptation to bail is natural, and this creates a major branch on the global health decision tree. You may ask:

Can I really contribute to quality health care under these challenging conditions?

Should I jump into this highly flawed community health system?

Or should I build a better—and parallel—one in this same town?

Each of these shortcomings demonstrates exactly why the strengthening of local health systems is needed in the first place. These weaknesses lead to unnecessary suffering and death. It's hard to join an existing and flawed system in an effort to improve it, yet it's a requisite for strengthening such a system.

Not surprisingly, many outsiders have chosen to build their own health facilities and systems in resource-limited countries rather than doing uncomfortable and difficult systems strengthening work. For more on the health facility-building approach, please see *Appendix B: Building Clinics… Or Confidence?* I review more challenges with this approach, as well as appropriate times to build health facilities and helpful ways to pass on the control of them to local people. If you're already convinced of the need to work *within* local health systems, then I'd encourage you to go on to the next chapter on disaster relief.

4

Disaster Strikes: Outsiders Arrive

Hurricane Maria widely destroyed Dominica's trees and buildings.

Cars were sweeping by him at 30 miles per hour—yet no one was inside any of them! The river swelled and nearly the entire capital city of Roseau was afloat with cars and people drifting out to sea. The storm surge took out houses by the water, sweeping out entire families in a one-way grab. Some 95% of all buildings on the island were damaged or completely destroyed; it was rare to find a house with an intact roof anymore. Looking down from the ridge of the volcano, towns looked like a patchwork of blue tarps which covered some of the lost roofs. The Caribbean island-nation of Dominica had never seen a hurricane of this size, and we all stood in awe of its force and destruction.

Many resource-limited countries—or communities within them—are facing earthquakes, hurricanes, landslides, wars, ethnic violence, and other disasters. These cause a sudden decline in living conditions, including lack of food, water, shelter, security, and medical care. In other resource-limited countries, settings of chronic poverty leave people to suffer from unmet medical and public health needs—problems which have persisted for a long time, not due to a sudden deterioration caused by a catastrophic event.

So there are disaster-affected communities on the one hand and those facing chronic poverty on the other; professional disaster relief work targets the former, while all other approaches to global health work and development work target the latter. At times, unprepared and unprofessional outsider groups rush in to simply treat as many patients as possible following a disaster; I consider this to be suitcase medicine. By contrast, professional disaster relief work follows evidence-based global standards which generally provides a very helpful approach.

In this chapter, I'll describe professional disaster relief in an unconventional way, by applying it over several variables to compare and contrast it with both:

1. **Empowering approaches** to global health work in settings of chronic poverty
   (local clinical capacity-building, strengthening local health systems, local public health capacity-building, and facilitating community-based programs), and
2. **Traditional approaches** to global health work in settings of chronic poverty
   (suitcase medicine and health facility-building)

Through these comparisons, I'll explore the differences between professional outsider health interventions in settings of disaster and those of chronic poverty; within settings of chronic poverty, I'll also explore differences between empowering and traditional global health approaches.

In the first part of the chapter, I'll review similarities between 1) disaster relief and 2) traditional approaches to global health work in chronic poverty settings. Table 2 compares these two categories over several variables, as well as empowering approaches to chronic poverty work. Table 2 (and Table 3 which follows) display generalizations, rather than cleanly depicting characteristics of all groups that follow a given approach.

	DISASTERS	CHRONIC POVERTY	
Table 2: Medical Care Differences: Comparing Disasters and Chronic Poverty, part 1			
	Disaster Relief	Traditional Approaches*	Empowering Approaches**
Disease priorities	Acute	Acute	Acute and chronic
Type of care	Emergency	Emergency	Primary
Who primarily gives care	Outsiders	Outsiders	Local people
Parallel systems	Created	Created	Not created
Health facilities	Built	Built	Not built
Care organization	Top-down	Top-down	Bottom-up
Empowerment focus	Minor at first	Minor or none	Major
Capacity-building focus	Minor at first	Minor or none	Major
Local service improvement	Minor at first	Minor or none	Major
Sustainability	Not desired	Not desired	Desired

* Traditional Approaches: Suitcase Medicine and Health Facility-building
** Empowering Approaches: Clinical & Public Health Capacity-building, Strengthening Systems, & Community-based Programs

In Table 2, the columns *Disaster Relief* and *Traditional Approaches* are remarkably similar. Yet it makes little sense to apply a disaster relief approach where no disaster exists. Even so, across several variables, traditional global health approaches resemble *disaster relief which has been applied to settings of chronic poverty*. The last two columns represent settings of chronic poverty, and in these environments, the column of *Traditional Approaches* should actually resemble the column of *Empowering Approaches*. In order to demonstrate these troubling conclusions, I'll go on to briefly apply each variable in the first column to these three types of strategies for assisting others abroad.

Disease Priorities

In resource-limited countries, disaster settings and areas of chronic poverty usually have differing disease priorities. In refugee camps, the majority of deaths are attributed to measles, acute respiratory infections, diarrhea, malaria, and malnutrition.[1] While chronic diseases also play a role in the health of refugees and other displaced people, they're given lower priority since they generally have less effect on immediate mortality.[2] Resources such as staff, meds, supplies, and funding are minimal during disasters and they must be directed towards high-priority conditions like measles during the initial emergency phase of disaster relief.

In settings of chronic poverty, by contrast, chronic diseases are expected to surpass infectious diseases by 2030 in terms of their effect on disability-adjusted life years (DALYS).[3] DALYS serve as a measure of the overall burden of disease. Disaster relief appropriately targets acute infectious diseases, while empowering approaches to care in chronic poverty appropriately address both acute and chronic disease. Suitcase medicine primarily focuses on acute diseases, while short medical trips are poorly suited to providing chronic disease care.

Type of Health Care

Emergency care is generally provided immediately following a disaster, while *primary health care* is the preferred approach in areas of chronic poverty. For those affected by wars and natural disasters, emergency care isn't limited to the typical bounds of the medical specialty of emergency medicine but rather encompasses all immediate health concerns following a disaster. These can include setting up treatment programs for severe acute malnutrition and malaria, as well as vaccinations.[4]

Disaster medicine has emerged as a medical specialty combining disaster management and emergency medicine in an effort to better address the unique health concerns of people affected by disasters.[5] Following the 2010 earthquake in Haiti, those with disaster training made *triage* a priority, such that the sickest patients who could be helped were treated first.[6] Although triage is also utilized in primary care, it is central to the process of disaster medicine because it quickly sorts out planned treatments for those who are sickest but can't be helped, those who are the sickest and can be immediately assisted, as well as others with less acute problems.[7] Additionally, a community level of triage separates and encourages people with less acute problems to visit outpatient facilities rather than overwhelming hospitals with all cases.[8]

While disaster relief groups don't aim to offer primary care services[9], professional groups serving areas of chronic poverty offer it as their central care strategy.[10] Primary health care may utilize *medical homes* where patients can regularly access acute care, chronic disease management, and preventive measures such as cancer screening. Empowering approaches address local primary care systems strengthening, while the suitcase medicine approach focuses on emergency care instead. When we build and also sustain a new health facility in an area of chronic poverty, then primary health care may be given as well.

Who Primarily Gives Care

Disasters typically surpass the ability of local people and institutions to respond, so the contribution of outsiders to disaster response can limit the disaster's damage and deaths.[11] While local people typically constitute the majority of first responders,[12] outsiders can do much to expand medical and public health services for the overwhelmed communities.[13] In contrast to settings of chronic poverty, the majority of medical care providers following many disasters are outsiders working for United Nations (UN) groups or NGOs.

When this is the case, every effort should be made to expand the involvement of local people following a disaster. Professional relief agencies should seek out and offer employment to refugees within camps,especially those trained previously as community health workers, nurses, and doctors. Some health services are often best and *only* provided by the refugees themselves, such as traditional birth attendants and home visitors.[14]

Additionally, local staff can be recruited from within the host country of the refugee camp as long as this doesn't detract from local health services; professional disaster relief agencies avoid this practice if higher salaries are luring local people away from public systems where they're also needed.[15] Finally, refugees from within camps can be trained to serve as health workers. In areas of chronic poverty, empowering approaches include local capacity-building and health systems strengthening. By contrast, traditional approaches involve outsiders being the main stars of medical care.

At least this refugee camp had no tents, but the narrow bamboo buildings sat like unimaginably dull and crammed shipping containers. Some of these refugees had been wealthy before their villages were bombed by the Burmese military. Here there were Burmese health workers treating Burmese people in the camps, with two of us foreigners for a little staff support.

Parallel Systems and Health Facilities

Outside disaster response often calls for the creation of parallel health systems and new health facilities, even though they're intended to be temporary. This is because local health services are not able to handle the increased number of patients with their available staff, space, medicines, and supplies. Refugees sometimes outnumber the host community, obviously overwhelming available health services and resources.

Although often necessary, professional disaster relief groups don't automatically set up parallel systems. When feasible, these relief groups aim to work within locally-run health facilities; they prefer to reinforce existing local hospitals with extra meds, supplies, staff, funding, and perhaps tents to expand the space available for patient care.[16] When needed and agreed upon by local authorities, relief groups will sometimes take over the operations of local health facilities in order to multiply and improve their services.

Professional relief groups create a parallel system only as a matter of *last resort* when health needs exceed the local capacity to respond.[17] Additionally, they may be necessary when disasters destroy local health facilities[18] or if a warring government deliberately excludes an ethnic or political group from using its health facilities.[19] Relief organizations may negotiate on behalf of such a group to ensure that they're not excluded, yet this isn't always possible.[20]

Health facilities within combat zones often can't be used safely, unless relief groups are able to work out a medical neutrality policy whereby health facilities are excluded from violence. (It should be noted that, while guaranteed by international law, this protection is routinely violated.) While refugees leave their home country, internally displaced persons (IDPs) are forced to flee their homes and migrate within their own nation. IDPs in a disaster zone may not find sufficient local health workers available to care for them given that many have been injured, killed, or displaced themselves. Inability to pay for local health care serves as another reason why outside financial or health services support is often needed.[21]

As in settings of chronic poverty, health facilities should only be built in or donated to disaster-affected communities when requested by local health authorities and when integrated into the public care system.[22] Empowering approaches in chronic poverty settings appropriately minimize the creation of parallel systems and health facility construction; meanwhile, traditional approaches do the opposite, although facility construction isn't a common feature of suitcase medicine.

Care Organization and Empowerment

Other key differences between medical care following disasters and in areas of chronic poverty involve the method of organization of services and goals of empowerment. Initially, disaster relief tends to be organized in a largely *top-down* fashion by both local and outside emergency response teams. The involvement and empowerment of refugees in initial stages of emergency services are not stressed given the conditions and the time-sensitive priorities at hand. Immediately following a disaster, mortality tends to be extreme and preventable; highly organized and targeted health services must be provided immediately to save lives. Maximum effectiveness is achieved by quickly organizing and deploying medical care and vaccination.

During the *post-emergency phase* of disasters, mortality rates drop and refugee camps tend to be more stable. This is when the empowerment of refugees becomes an increasingly important aim of professional relief groups.[23] *Rehabilitation* of local service systems is also organized in order to restore them to a functional status. This may involve repairing damaged local health centers, water supply systems, etc.; once achieved, local people should be encouraged and empowered to sustain these systems.[24]

Camp health services are more closely aligned with national ones during the post-emergency phase as well; local health care and social service groups are encouraged to start taking over programs using their own resources.[25] Government and individual responsibility for health and other services is promoted, as relief groups work to phase out their operations.[26] When conditions stabilize, refugees are encouraged to construct peer leadership committees to meet regularly with relief groups; the formation of refugee social groups is also encouraged.[27]

Professional disaster relief generally has a minor focus on empowerment at first, and this should exponentially expand over time. Even so, these partnerships with disaster-affected communities are primarily empowering from the very beginning in that professional outsider groups only come when hand-picked and invited by local authorities. Further, these medical and other aid groups do not lead but follow locally-driven response efforts. Whenever possible, local Ministries of Health should lead and coordinate the health response of outside and local NGOs and UN groups from the very start of a disaster response.[28] The code of conduct of the International Committee of the Red Cross stresses the importance of including "local capacities" throughout disaster response; this also includes employing local people and buying relief supplies from them.[29]

Empowerment is also being encouraged by a new approach to housing and community design which uses feedback from refugees and the host community in setting up the more permanent features of camps. This approach aids the better integration of refugee communities into the communities which surround them. As some camps persist for many years, gradual transition to such bottom-up organizing is becoming more common.[30] Host communities and refugees are encouraged to visit each other and share resources and infrastructure such as health services, energy, water supply, schools, and markets.[31] While not negating the desire and right of refugees to return to their communities of origin, this approach both improves conditions for and lessens tensions between refugee and host populations. Empowering approaches to chronic poverty actively engage local people and encourage the bottom-up organizing of health services. However, traditional approaches in chronic poverty settings organize care in a top-down and disempowering way.

Capacity-Building

The training of additional health workers from within refugee camps is an important activity in bridging the gap in needed health care.[32] Refugee community health workers train by apprenticeship, as they learn key skills in the prevention, diagnosis, and treatment of common camp diseases.[33] During the post-emergency phase, the role of outside medical staff increasingly shifts from providing care to further training local staff, supporting them, and facilitating health program management.[34] Capacity-building receives some attention in disaster work, while it serves as a major focus in empowering approaches to chronic poverty. Unfortunately, it's minimized or avoided under traditional approaches.

Local Service Improvement

As WHO health teams respond to emergencies, they aim to integrate with and improve the existing health system. Many other disaster relief groups do the same, and strengthening of such systems may occur as a result; even so, such strengthening may not persist long-term given that the presence of relief groups and additional funding is fleeting. Dedicated attempts to improve the quality of health services usually aren't undertaken until the post-emergency phase of disasters.[35] By contrast, health systems strengthening is a major component of empowering approaches to care in chronic poverty settings; yet traditional approaches tend to avoid this work.

Sustainability

Disaster relief organizations don't aim to provide sustainable and indefinite health services following a disaster.[36] In fact, doing so would be equivalent to fostering complete and long-term dependency on these groups. Health services for refugees are phased out once it is safe for them to return voluntarily to their home country (*repatriation*), integrate into the host community, or else settle in another safe country.[37] Professional relief groups view their role as offering services *until* local services and/or development groups can replace them.

While refugee camps should be temporary centers of housing, medical, and other services, chronically poor communities tend to be permanent and their health care should therefore be sustainable.

Rather than providing sustainable outsider health services, empowering approaches bolster the ability of local health systems to provide quality, sustainable services. However, suitcase medicine makes no attempt at providing or encouraging sustainable health services; health facility-building unfortunately attempts to provide sustainable outsider-led services, rather than locally-led ones.

Up to this point in the chapter, I explored how traditional approaches to chronic poverty are applied like disaster relief to non-disaster settings. We outsiders may find a quiet and poor village in which to set up shop for a week or two. Yet we would then oddly treat it like an earthquake zone by focusing on acute disease and emergency medical care. When there's no life-threatening disaster at hand, I think it's harder to make excuses for minimizing the training of local people, their empowerment, and the improvement of their health systems. While disasters make compelling exceptions, it's harder to see the need to build outsider clinics when a village is experiencing the same old long-term poverty; likewise, it's harder to justify organizing top-down outsider-based care with parallel systems.

I'll go on now to explore ways in which there are fundamental differences between traditional chronic poverty approaches and *both* 1) disaster relief and 2) empowering chronic poverty approaches. Table 3 summarizes general comparisons over five additional variables; again, I'll briefly address each of them.

Table 3: Medical Care Differences: Comparing Disasters and Chronic Poverty, part 2			
	DISASTERS	CHRONIC POVERTY	
	Disaster Relief	Traditional Approaches*	Empowering Approaches**
Follow standards of care	+	-	+
Address public health needs	+	-	+
Needs assessments, focused (+) or comprehensive (++)	+	-	++
Impact studies, focused (+) or comprehensive (++)	+	-	++
Comprehensive pre-departure prep	+	-	+
* Traditional Approaches: Suitcase Medicine and Health Facility-building ** Empowering Approaches: Clinical and Public Health Capacity-building, Strengthening Systems, and Community-based Programs			

Standards of Care

Disaster relief organizations have increasingly followed evidence-based standards.[38] The Sphere Project created minimum standards to which all humanitarian aid groups are asked to adhere, for example, reducing crude mortality rates and those for under-fives to less than twice the pre-disaster rates. Another standard involves making at least one basic health unit, one midwife, and 22 health workers available to serve every 10,000 refugees.[39] *Professional* relief organizations use Sphere standards as benchmarks, while small and improvisational medical groups unfortunately may not even be aware of their existence.[40] The Inter-Agency Standing Committee (IASC) has also promoted best practices in relief work by coordinating UN and NGO relief groups, and discouraging gaps or duplications in services.[41]

The Humanitarian Accountability Partnership (HAP) was created to set standards for relief group accountability to disaster survivors, and it also monitors and independently audits these groups.[42] HAP monitors whether local people were empowered to contribute to disaster needs assessments and project design and evaluation; it also monitors whether relief workers possess needed skills, knowledge, and cultural sensitivity, and whether they have fulfilled their commitments.[43]

As in settings of chronic poverty, disaster relief has also seen a troubling history of unsolicited and inappropriate medicine and supply donations from outsiders;[44] yet much has been done to rectify this. Professional relief groups use the WHO *Model List of Essential Drugs*—a list of basic, safe, and inexpensive medicines available and used worldwide for common and significant conditions.[45] WHO has also created *Emergency Health Kits*, which include a list of standardized and commonly needed supplies in resource-limited settings.[46]

Areas of chronic poverty are subject to more rigorous and comprehensive standards of care as developed by WHO and respective Ministries of Health. Although sometimes adapted in disaster settings, national health care guidelines are followed by both professional disaster relief teams[47] and professional groups serving chronically poor areas;[48] traditional approaches, however, tend to neglect them.[49] Standardized disease treatment protocols and the use of *essential medicines* are followed by disaster relief and empowering chronic poverty approaches, but not usually by traditional ones.[50]

Public Health Needs

When people are forced to flee their homes and find refuge in shelters or camps, the United Nations High Commissioner for Refugees

(UNHCR) may provide housing and protection, while the World Food Programme (WFP) may provide food.[51] Other groups provide access to clean water and sanitation. Without speedy interventions to cover such basic public health needs, death rates are much higher immediately following a war or natural disaster.[52] Public health needs in such settings exceed the clinical health needs of affected people.[53] The top ten priorities recognized by Doctors Without Borders (Médicins Sans Frontières) following a disaster are largely public health interventions: "1) Initial assessment, 2) Measles immunization, 3) Water and sanitation, 4) Food and nutrition, 5) Shelter and site planning, 6) Health care in the emergency phase, 7) Control of communicable diseases and epidemics, 8) Public health surveillance, 9) Human resources and training, and 10) Coordination."[54]

> *The needs were desperate, with expectant faces both stern and hungry for more. The health care nonprofit patiently listened to tortured stories, worked out diagnoses, and gave out needed medicine for free. The water nonprofit provided wells and water filters, so people could worry less about having enough safe drinking water. Meanwhile, the education nonprofit gave the kids promises of a better future. The three nonprofits were led by outsiders and the community was pleased to be the centerpiece of their combined attention.*

> *Yet this wasn't a disaster zone! Outsider health, water, and education services can be desperately needed during a war, but this was just another day in this "dependency village" of passive aid recipients. Nonprofits flocked to this village and treated it like a helpless refugee camp; in response, it started to act like one.*

Areas of chronic poverty within resource-limited countries have large public health needs, although they're rarely as dire as those experienced during disasters. Housing may be inadequate but still present; agriculture may be at a subsistence level, yet basic food is typically available. Water access may be insufficient and of poor quality, yet is generally present. Professional groups responding to disasters and those assisting in settings of chronic poverty *both* take primarily public health approaches; meanwhile, clinical care has a lesser but still important role in both settings.[55] However, traditional approaches to chronic poverty tend to neglect public health challenges as well as the measures to address them.[56]

Needs Assessments

Disaster relief organizations routinely and quickly perform an *initial needs assessment* before assisting an affected community. These assessments examine conditions regarding shelter, water, sanitation, nutrition, and health; such needs are compared to the resources and services available in the host community to establish whether outsider involvement is needed in the first place.[57] Professional disaster relief groups ask disaster-affected people what their medical problems are and then design health programs to address those needs.[58]

Initial assessments in areas of chronic poverty ask the same key questions and gather similar data; yet without the urgency of disaster, they can be more comprehensive. Another important difference involves data being mainly evaluated and acted on *by outsiders* during disasters. By contrast, health needs assessments are primarily done and acted on *by local people* with empowering approaches in settings of chronic poverty;[59] traditional approaches usually neglect to do them.[60]

Impact Studies

Health impact studies haven't been used extensively by disaster relief groups, yet such evidence-based research has become increasingly common since 2000. As the Sphere standards and IASC coordination became widely implemented by disaster relief groups, important evidence-based benchmarks have illuminated this field.[61] Disaster groups frequently monitor rates of crude and under-five mortality, severe and moderate acute malnutrition, and infectious disease attack rates.

Similar data to that of disaster relief groups is also collected and followed by surveillance systems in areas of chronic poverty. Yet health indicators are generally more broad in these settings; they include access to health care, objective and perceived health status measures, and socioeconomic, behavioral, environmental, and health systems determinants of health.[62] These health indicators usually aren't measured or followed with traditional approaches.[63]

Pre-Departure Prep

Outsider training programs can effectively promote professional disaster health responses and the provision of appropriate health care.[64] Trainings often include public health, Sphere standards, initial health assessment techniques, disaster epidemiology, malnutrition management, and many other topics. Professional relief groups maintain an international roster of outsiders with disaster training and experience, so the best prepared can be deployed when needed.

WHO also maintains a register of those aware of and willing to follow evidence-based standards in the event of a disaster. They initiated this roster after the 2010 flooding in Pakistan and the earthquake in Haiti, upon realizing that various responding teams were not aware of disaster relief standards and did not coordinate their services well with others.[65] The important role of outsider pre-departure training has also been stressed by empowering approaches to chronic poverty, yet traditional approaches again often neglect them.[66]

Professional disaster relief is designed to help communities through a temporary rough patch—it's not intended to be sustainable. While I noted this in Table 1 of the chapter *Global Health Approaches*, I also labelled it as being evidence-based and generally helpful and empowering for communities affected by disaster. While health needs may be universal, different scenarios call for different approaches to meeting them. I'm impressed by professional disaster relief as well as professional health approaches in chronic poverty settings. While they share some similarities, they both stand in stark contrast to suitcase medicine and health facility-building.

5

Power to the People

*The hearty scents woke up my stomach but I passed the ladle away from myself each time the assembly line of people stepped towards me. I organized food pantries like this during college, as well as nursing home social visits and construction and painting teams. I stayed in a community service dorm and I later became its volunteer work director. I felt satisfaction from doing charity service and I enjoyed the planning and organizing. I became indoctrinated as a guy with good intentions who did things to and for others without involving them in the planning and execution of it. I became a **volunteer** and not a guy who **empowers** others to find their own sustainable solutions to challenges.*

My medical friends who volunteered abroad were a lot like me: they did charity work in the US and they naturally extended this approach in their work abroad. What wasn't intuitive to us was encouraging people living in poverty to help themselves as we supported their empowerment to do so. As a "recovering charity-giver," I understand the appeal of this mindset. It took me a good deal of time and experience to find fulfillment from doing empowerment work instead.

Charity involves giving things or services for free or at low cost. If we have extra resources, funding, or time to give services, then it appears natural and kind to offer them to those in need. It also gives us a warm feeling to be a giver. Yet while charity—or volunteer work— can help on the surface, it can also reduce the self-confidence of those receiving it. Giving in a *top-down* way rarely brings sustainable benefit, and if it's done repeatedly, then it may generate dependence.

By contrast, we can help in a deeper way through **empowerment** because it provides the needy with tools to become less needy themselves. It allows the disadvantaged to take more control over their lives and their health in a *bottom-up*, or community-led way.

Empowerment generates power and control among the disadvantaged so solutions can be found internally rather than creating dependence on outsiders and our resources, funding, or services. Compared to charity, it can be counterintuitive, can take longer, and doesn't always give us the same easy warm feeling. Empowerment is beautiful on paper but complicated in real life; for a bleeding heart volunteer, holding back on giving things or doing things for others runs contrary to our very blood.

So how does one *do* empowerment work? This chapter will address this question more broadly than prior chapters which described specific activities that can empower local people. I'll start by discussing how charity work and empowerment work are far from disconnected; there's an important give and take here:

1. Charity causes disempowerment, while
2. Empowerment lessens the need for and interest in charity

Charity Disempowers

What did you do on your volunteer trips?

We built a clinic there and we set up care protocols for it. We brought meds and supplies and we took lots of volunteers over to fill it up with staff. We handed out mosquito nets and we gave people water filters and we provided school funding. We even set up a pregnancy care and delivery program. We organized a surgery program too and we brought our surgeons to run it.

If the "we" refers to local people, then it sounds like a very impressive, successful, and sustainable health program!

Yet the "we" here typically refers to outsiders, and this would mean local people have all the problems and outsiders have all the solutions. This would be a perfect set-up for disempowerment. Charity usually arises out of power imbalances, such as the rich helping those with less income or the "able" helping the "disabled." Yet it also serves to reinforce these power imbalances, since it gets things done in a way that bypasses the agency of the people served.

Muhammad Yunus, the founder of Grameen Bank's innovative microloan program, notes that "charity only perpetuates poverty by taking the initiative away from the poor. Charity allows us to go ahead with our own lives without worrying about the lives of the poor. Charity appeases our consciences."[1] People on the receiving end are passively given things rather than gaining them through their own effort. Worse yet, people living in poverty may end up being dependent upon the goods and services of the rich.[2] When communities in resource-limited nations are empowered enough to care for themselves, then they won't have to give a hoot about offers of foreign charity. They become less vulnerable and more independent. I believe that these communities deserve to have the *power* to access and give quality health care, to prevent disease, and to live successful and fulfilling lives that they're in control of. This is why empowerment is a deeper goal than simply giving things or services from the outside. Health programs in resource-limited countries can be more than charity work; they could be deep, long-lasting, locally-led successes.

However, outsider suitcase medicine trips and health facility-building can easily disempower local people because they are charity-based. Although good intentions, knowledge, skills, funding, supplies, and a well thought out plan can seem we have everything needed to really help out abroad, without an empowerment agenda these remain the starting conditions for charity work.

Few short-term medical trips seek to empower either local health care providers or patients.[3] I wonder if this has as much or more to do with the familiar charity-based model as it does with the intentions of their organizers. When medical services are provided by outsiders in a top-down manner, it reduces local people's drive to care for themselves and to organize their own health programs.[4] Further, seeing patients on our own without involving local health workers often serves to reduce the confidence the community has in its own health system.[5] This is charity work that disempowers; I think we can do better on our short-term and long-term trips abroad. While encouraging community members to have control isn't natural or easy, it always starts with...

Preexisting Embers

The kindling lit right up and warmed our faces. Later in the night, the bonfire flame dimed down and only glowing hot embers remained. These preexisting embers were the perfect conditions for re-lighting an impressive fire—just as soon as a little wood was placed on top of them.

I consider *preexisting embers* to be anything and everything that could contribute to health program success which already exist before outsiders show up. We outsiders often have a temptation to create new initiatives in resource-limited countries. We respond to seeing dire living conditions as *doers* that find excitement and fulfillment in designing solutions. Yet by starting new health programs ourselves, we tend to ignore and bypass existing community strengths.

A more empowering alternative involves seeking out, valuing, utilizing, and working to expand on *what's already existing locally*. For example, I've reviewed three global health approaches so far which all hone in on preexisting local health workers and health systems in an effort to empower:

A. Local clinical capacity-building
B. Strengthening local health systems, and
C. Professional disaster relief (to a lesser extent)

Preexisting embers for empowerment also include local health groups, other community groups, individual talent and experience, programs, ideas, dreams, and plans; they even extend to existing medical resources such as medicines, supplies, and equipment, as well as public health resources like vaccines and safe water. Not only is it more empowering to start with preexisting embers, but it's also more sustainable. After all, these plans, tools, materials, and people are found in the community rather than somehow needing to be imported on a long-term basis.

Rice fields spread out like infinite tablecloths. There is no beginning or end, except for one break in pattern which is a narrow dirt path leading to the few houses that comprise

this "village." There are no health facilities, community
health workers, nurses, doctors, lay midwives, pharmacists,
traditional healers or other medical staff. The neighboring
villages also lack health workers and there are no visitors
from the Ministry of Health or other medical teams. Tall rice
stalks sway as if waving in outsiders to contribute to this
remote corner of the world which has been left on its own. Is
it lacking any health worker "preexisting embers"? No! The
people living there can build on their traditional notions of
health to become active community health workers.

Communities are truly empowered when they can prove one thing
to themselves: that they can solve problems using their own ideas,
resources, and people. The final three chapters will explore approaches
of focusing on a community's preexisting embers to improve its
living conditions; these include *appreciative inquiry* and *asset-based
community development*.

Volunteering vs. Facilitating

Volunteering typically describes charity work, while *facilitating* is the
active promotion of empowerment. Facilitating involves inspiring
or stimulating positive internal change in others rather than doing
the work directly ourselves.[6] Facilitators, or catalysts, search for
preexisting embers and help local people to light a sustainable fire.
They aim to inspire and support local thinking, planning, and action—
ultimately increasing the odds of success for community action.[7]
Facilitators can be local people or outsiders, yet I'll focus my discussion
here on outsiders; I will discuss the importance of local facilitators in
the *Community-Based Health Programs* chapter.

In order to be successful facilitators, outsiders would best hold back
on defining local problems and identifying and enacting solutions;
instead, we could stimulate community members to do the same. It can
be hard to bite our tongues and hold our hands behind our backs, but
being a facilitator means smiling as a friend in the background while
the community does the work of deciding about its future.

An open mind is essential for successful facilitation. It's important
not to steer, control, or micromanage community work, and it is best
to refrain from judging people and their ideas and plans. Facilitation
promotes freedom as community members determine what needs to
change and how, while facilitators just guide them through the search.[8]
When facilitators are asked for advice on a problem, we can turn this

question back to its source by asking how local people can use their resources and skills to address this problem.[9] Facilitator Dr. Christine Hogan points out that "development workers and facilitators should build on assumptions that they do not know the problems, answers and what to do. But they do know processes to build on the resources of and within people."[10]

Like health systems strengthening, empowerment can feel painfully slow for the *type A* outsider expecting to quickly achieve deliverables. Often it would be so much easier for us to *do* the work ourselves, but we would best fight this urge. When ideas come from local people, then they'll more likely take ownership of the problems and potential means to solve them; if an outsider points out a problem, then it becomes our problem to solve. When an outsider blurts out a solution, then hope unfortunately centers on foreigners rather than communities.

Outsiders cause the demise of most of our health initiatives abroad by working to create our own solutions rather than facilitating local people to develop theirs.[11] Successful health initiatives tend to spring from the ground up; community members pave the way, yet outsiders can play an important part by facilitating the process. To achieve this, it is helpful to undergo the paradigm shift from volunteering to facilitating *before* we arrive at the resource-limited site. Outsiders would benefit from mandatory trainings on facilitation methods prior to doing overseas work.

A second paradigm shift from volunteering to facilitating is needed within the minds of community members. Outsiders functioning as facilitators will find success only when local people accept us in this role. If they expect and want us to serve as volunteers, then community members may aim to sit back and watch us do the health work. The importance of local people expecting to plan and lead the work themselves is reviewed in the concluding chapter, *Doing Global Health Work to Really Make a Difference*.

What They Need Most

Although rarely asked by us outsiders, local people have understandably claimed that they could organize their health programs better than we have.[12] Unfortunately, outsider health programs are typically driven by our own preferences regarding *what* is done as well as *where* and *when* it is done.[13] As I mentioned in the introduction, the most critical lesson in global health involves local people leading and outsiders following.

*White people sat around a table deciding which health
programs would run in Africa. Their thoughts and whims
would determine a poor community's health or lack thereof.
It was an entirely inappropriate meeting, and it happened
once a month; the outsiders would plot the course for the
local people with minimal feedback and direction from
them. In a just world, however, it would be a room full of
Africans deciding on their own health programs. If one or
two outsiders were there, it would be by invitation only and
they'd be there on the terms of the Africans. Outsiders would
be invited to the table only if they followed rather than led.*

Individuals or groups of outsiders often go abroad with a single
area of burning passion, or with one major *pet project* that we want
to accomplish. This may represent an area of academic interest or
curiosity; it could also be an area of research experience or interest.
However, upon arrival, we may quickly learn that it doesn't reflect a key
local need. Other times, we learn the project may be needed but that
there are other far more pressing needs and community desires.

Pet project plans can also be developed by outsiders *after* arriving
abroad. After taking note of a skyrocketing prevalence of malaria and
diarrheal disease, for example, we could quickly react by organizing
programs for malaria treatment and latrine building. Yet our limited
awareness stymies our success in so many ways (as was reviewed in the
chapter *Reversing the Brain Drain*). We may not realize these villages
have the resources to tackle such problems themselves; further, they
might have community groups already doing so.

Despite the importance of doing so, outside medical volunteers
rarely ask about and seek to understand local needs.[14] Rather than
performing a needs assessment, our groups often assume that a great
need is present in the health area that we aim to work in.[15] Skipping
the needs assessment and springing into action can be an easy way to
do more harm than good.[16]

Before rolling up our sleeves and pitching in, we would best find
out what's already being done, what's desired, and what could be most
helpful; our groups should therefore start by doing a thorough *assets
and needs assessment* with local people (if we're invited to do so). In
the previous chapter, I reviewed how this is a mainstay of professional
disaster relief as well as professional groups serving areas of chronic
poverty; in *Part II* of this book, I'll discuss how outsiders can do this
general assessment in partnership with communities. Importantly,
this assessment may have already been done by community members

or other outside groups; if so, there's no need to reinvent the wheel by repeating a full assessment.

Briefly, an asset and needs assessment process combines a search for preexisting embers with the empowering methods of facilitation. Through participatory assessments, facilitators can ask community members to brainstorm their *assets* (or preexisting embers) as well as their health and other *problems* simultaneously. By identifying local resources as well as challenges in the same process, the exploration focuses on the positives as well as community problems. It is therefore more likely lead to an empowering analysis of locally-led solutions: how the community can use its own resources to solve its problems. Before brainstorming potential solutions, an activity of ranking and prioritizing can empower community members to identify their biggest medical and public health needs, choose which ones they'd like to work on, and figure out how they'll do so. Respectful outsiders will listen and contribute if and when local people conclude that we could be part of the solutions they envision.

My advice to outsiders is to leave our ideas, plans, and pet projects back home. By listening to the voice of the community, we can help in a deeper, more appropriate, and more empowering way. I believe that outside organizations which don't aim to empower local people simply aren't worthwhile to work with. I'll end this chapter with a very personal example.

> *I felt like a dead-beat Dad, living a life apart but parallel to that of my estranged child: a small health nonprofit partnership with rural Uganda. I founded it in a burst of idealism and enthusiasm; throughout medical school, I somehow squeezed out an average of four hours per day to organize it. Yet I left it three years later with pangs of anger, sorrow, and dizzied confusion, and with the taste of betrayal in my mouth.*

> *"Let It Be" was the last recording released before the Beatles broke up, and it's about leaving our problems behind and forging on. It was also the title of my email to the group announcing that I was leaving the nonprofit. I left because I had become a minority voice in calling for Ugandans themselves to develop and lead the health initiatives that we'd partnered on. I insisted on us foreigners serving merely as facilitators of an empowerment process. Almost all of the other group leaders wanted to bring in foreign "experts" who would design and implement programs in Uganda, leaving*

local people as the passive recipients of aid. I was exhausted from unsuccessfully trying to sway the group over several months.

It was clear that I would either need to leave, to compromise my core values and beliefs, or to dive into conflict and play a power-grabbing game in which I had no interest. Plans developed behind my back and I had a sinking feeling in my stomach regarding an impending coup. I walked into what I knew would be my last meeting with the team; then I aimlessly strolled the sidewalks of New York City with my head down, as after a funeral. In a challenging but important decision, I left my nonprofit baby to work with more professional and empowering groups.

6

Agendas We All Have

The alarm clock reached between my eyelids and reluctantly propped them open. Then the reflection of palm trees swaying in the bright blueness of the morning pushed me to my feet. I reached past my machete, guitar, and maps, grabbed my doctor bag, and drove across the mountain from this mango-dotted fishing village.

Upon arrival at the primary care clinic, I would do physicals, diagnose dengue, treat hypertension, and work to improve my Spanish. I would teach doctors and patients, while learning about culture and health. My daily activities would satisfy my own needs and help to meet some of the needs of others; in each of these activities, I had self-serving agendas as well as altruistic ones.

There's no such thing as a trip abroad without an agenda. A traveler without an agenda does nothing more than sit in the airport until their return flight. This chapter explores common agendas in global health work and then balances the benefits for outsiders against the benefits for local people within each agenda.

So far, this book has explored approaches to health care, systems, and training in global health work; in this final section of *Part I*, I will analyze these *approaches* through the lenses of the *agendas* which drive them. I've identified seven common agendas in global health work and volunteering. I call these *Work Agendas*:

1) Tourism Agenda

Seeing different places, people, and cultures can be a major driving force to visit resource-limited settings. Tourism was cited as a reason for volunteering by 9% of those interviewed in one study.[1] Participating in single-day clinics in various areas of a remote nation serves as an interesting way to travel around, and this can consciously or unconsciously motivate such nomadic work.

*The first medical volunteer team I joined abroad started
in a mansion, visited gorgeous waterfalls midway through
the trip, and ended at a world-famous beach with pristine
sands. At one point, I was ordering a beer at a beach bar
when I gazed off in the distance wondering whether I was
vacationing or volunteering.*

Volunteers may choose to serve in a beautiful and interesting
place with the intention of doing sight-seeing in addition to medical
care. Local people are often aware of this and have complained about
some volunteers being little more than tourists.[2] The central altruistic
purpose of the trip can become clouded and morally compromised by
self-serving plans for leisurely travel and vacation.[3]

2) Education of Outsiders Agenda

Learning is a natural and inseparable aspect of all trips abroad, unless
we spend the entire trip with our eyes closed or our fingers dancing on
a smartphone. Even so, some trips focus on outsider education much
more than others. University and health professional school trips tend
to focus on educating outsider students.[4] There's typically one or more
outsider *preceptors,* or fully-trained health professionals, who teach
other outsiders. Students or residents may see long lines of patients
and then present their cases to the teaching preceptor. Outsiders teach
outsiders about global health, medicine, and the local culture and
context in which we're working.

A variation of these outsider education trips involves those focused
on education from the community. Rather than learning from fellow
outsiders, the education on such trips is provided directly by local
people. A health professional student may shadow or assist a local
health worker while learning from them. Such trips can include
training on tropical diseases, care in underserved settings, language,
and/or culture.[5] Finally, research is commonly done on global health
trips. Depending on how it is organized and carried out, it may advance
the knowledge of outsiders and/or that of local people (see the next
section).

3) Education of Local People Agenda

Some global health trips focus more on educating local people, rather
than oneself or other outsiders. These trips may further the general
training of local health professionals, such as community health
workers, nurses, doctors, or physical therapists; alternatively, they may

target the local students in these fields (see the chapters *Reversing the Brain Drain* and *Training Health Workers*). International training program partnerships also promote the learning of outsiders, yet local people are usually the main intended beneficiaries.

4) Charity Service Agenda

Charity and empowerment were compared and contrasted in the previous chapter. While charity can describe a way of working abroad, it can also label two types of agendas behind such work: charity service and charity construction (#6 below). The former occurs when we outsiders aim to primarily perform a service such as medical care. Providing direct patient care has been the most frequently cited reason for doing medical volunteer work abroad.[6] As a charity service, it's performed for free or at low cost by outsiders and for local people.

5) Local Service Improvement Agenda

In contrast to charity services, this agenda seeks to partner with an existing service through which local people help local people. Examples include a locally-led clinic, hospital, or home care service. An improvement in the quality of care is often sought, as this is one of the key agendas driving *health systems strengthening* work.

6) Charity Construction Agenda

In contrast to service, other outsider projects focus on building clinics, hospitals, schools, or other health or education facilities. Such construction services are performed for free or at low cost by outsiders and for local people. They usually aim to make new facilities which will be staffed and/or run by outsiders.

7) Empowerment Agenda

Charity service and charity construction agendas involve outsiders doing things for local people. By contrast, outsiders with an empowerment agenda aim to inspire and stimulate local people to better help themselves. As mentioned in the *Introduction*, I consider the concept of *health accompaniment* to be synonymous with empowerment; accompanying a community in a resource-limited nation involves developing and maintaining a locally-led and long-term partnership in which outsiders engage in solidarity with community members who identify and work toward their own health goals.

This list of global health *Work Agendas* isn't exhaustive, but it does represent common agendas driving international work and volunteering. Further, there are many areas of overlap among agendas. For example, *charity services* such as patient care are commonly used as ways to simultaneously *educate outsiders*—including students of the health professions. An *empowerment agenda* overlaps substantially with one to *educate local people,* since education can itself serve as a powerful form of empowerment. Further, *local service improvement* functions as another specific way to drive local *empowerment.*

Global health work is complex, as are the groups involved in carrying it out. I have yet to see a single group which acts on only one work agenda. Just as we all have a complex mix of ever-changing agendas, so too do global health groups. A single group may have simultaneous agendas for charity service, education of outsiders, and education of local people. Their approach may change over time as they evolve to enact an empowerment agenda. The suitcase medicine approach, for example, typically follows the agendas of tourism, education of outsiders, and charity service.

Are all agendas created equal? Absolutely not! The tourism agenda is appropriate for enjoying vacations but certainly not for promoting the health of community members in resource-limited settings. While I'm not aware of any outsider medical group with a purely tourist agenda, it does factor into the activities of many of our global health groups to a lesser or greater extent. A tourism agenda can't be expected to have much of a positive effect on the health of local people, nor would it empower them or lead to sustainable health improvements. Naturally, it doesn't lend itself to evidence-based health interventions in resource-limited settings.

All seven work agendas are evaluated in reference to their evidence base and the same three variables in Table 4. Under the *tourism agenda,* for example, the table illustrates the lack of an evidence base and the lack of positive results for these variables. If this table looks familiar, it's because Table 1 in the chapter *Global Health Approaches* makes use of these same variables, applying them to global health *approaches* rather than the *agendas* behind them.

Table 4: Global Health Work Agendas: Evidence Base and Effects on Local People				
Work Agenda	Evidence-based	Potential Effect on Local People		
		Helpful	Empowering	Sustainable
Tourism				
Education of outsiders	✓			✓
Charity service				
Charity construction				
Education of local people	✓	✓	✓	✓
Local service improvement	✓	✓	✓	✓
Empowerment	✓	✓	✓	✓

Now, let's compare the two agendas for *educating outsiders* and *educating local people* through global health work. Only the agenda to *educate local people* can be expected to help and empower community members. Like the tourism agenda, educating outsiders mainly serves us rather than local people.

Obviously, global health practitioners need to be trained first in order to be successful later at assisting people in resource-limited countries. So an argument could be made that the education of outsiders as a global health agenda can potentially be a sustainable and evidence-based intervention that can eventually promote other agendas which benefit local people. This wouldn't be the case, however, if a resident did one medical volunteer trip and never made a further contribution to global health. In prior chapters, I've reviewed how the education of local people is helpful, empowering, sustainable, and evidence-based.

Next, I'll compare *charity service* with *local service improvement* as agendas to assist local people. The previous chapter explored the shortcomings of charity service in depth: it can have harmful effects for local people, doesn't empower them, isn't sustainable, and isn't evidence-based. Local service improvement functions as the exact opposite in each of these ways (see the chapter *Strengthening Health Systems*).

Finally, the agendas of *charity construction* and *empowerment* contrast sharply, even though they're not direct opposites. In terms of these four variables, charity construction has an entirely negative track record (see *Appendix B: Building Clinics... Or Confidence?*). The empowerment agenda responds positively to all four variables, and stands in stark contrast to both charity construction and charity service. All three approaches are typically rooted in good intentions and hard work, yet their effects differ significantly.

Based on the analysis of these four variables, Tables 4 and 5 have listed four of the work agendas discussed above as being primarily negative. Meanwhile, the other three agendas serve as positive agendas for the promotion of local people's health in resource-limited countries.

Table 5: Global Health Work Agendas: Who They Serve			
Agenda	Group served		
	Outsiders	Neither	Local People
Tourism	✓		
Education of outsiders	✓		
Charity service		✓	
Charity construction		✓	
Education of local people			✓
Local service improvement			✓
Empowerment			✓

Table 5 classifies agendas in terms of whether they're self-serving for us outsiders (*tourism* and *education of outsiders*), or whether they primarily serve local people (*education of local people, local service improvement*, and *empowerment*). Meanwhile, *charity service* and *charity construction* fit into a third category in which neither group is typically benefitted. Although outsiders intend such agendas to serve local people, they don't generally benefit communities as planned. Professional disaster relief efforts, addressed later, are exceptions to this generalization.

Personal and Group Agendas

Beyond these agendas in global health work, I encourage the reader to analyze your own current agendas, think about how they fit into this list, and whether you'd like to continue with or change these agendas. The same process of reflection holds for *approaches* to global health work: which are you following, and which do you want to follow? Truly assisting local people the most we can has everything to with agendas and approaches, and they are closely linked.

Identifying agendas is also helpful in our efforts to select the best outsider global health group with which to work. Where should I apply and why? Learn about the agendas of groups you're considering working with and then compare them to your own agendas. If they roughly match, then the odds of you feeling satisfied working with this group are increased; additionally, such a group would be more likely to appreciate your work and keep you on board. Finally, your work is more likely to be successful if there's a concordance between your agendas and the group you're working with.

On more than one occasion, I felt very restricted in my attempts to support local people because I joined an outsider group with discordant agendas from my own. I had an agenda for the education of local people, yet the group was determined to do charity service. Education was always put in second place as they scrambled to treat the largest number of patients possible. In another group, I had an empowerment agenda while the rest of the team had a charity construction agenda. I quickly settled with a more helpful group.

The agendas selected should also depend on local context. If there are many highly-trained local health professionals, for example, then an agenda to train new local clinicians would make little sense. The more important factor, however, involves *what local people want*. There is no need for paternalistic outsiders to analyze local needs and determine which agenda is best for community members when they can be encouraged to determine and present their own priorities.

Local People's Agendas

All of the agendas outlined here can apply to local people as well as outsiders. For example, local people may have an agenda to expand their skill set (education of local people agenda) or to be recipients of a newly-built hospital (charity construction agenda). If and when the agendas of outsiders and local people roughly match, a functional partnership is more likely to form.

What happens when, for example, community members have an agenda to further educate their own people while outsiders have a charity service agenda with little desire to teach? With discordant agendas, this pairing of outsider and local groups isn't likely to work well. Yet while matching agendas is an important condition for partner compatibility, it isn't everything. Global health work isn't a *speed dating service* that simply matches potentially compatible partners! Alternatively, this outsider group could act on its commitment to this community by responding to local feedback and changing their

Table 6: Comparing Global Health Work Approaches with Work Agendas

Global Health Work Approaches	Tourism	Education of Outsiders	Charity Service	Charity Construction	Education of Local People	Local Service Improvement	Empowerment
Suitcase medicine	Negative	Negative	Negative				
Local clinical capacity-building					Positive	Positive	Positive
Strengthening local health systems					Positive	Positive	Positive
Health facility-building				Negative			
Professional disaster relief			Negative	Negative	Positive	Positive	Positive
Local public health capacity-building					Positive	Positive	Positive
Facilitating community-based programs					Positive	Positive	Positive

approach from providing clinical care to doing clinical training.

Although local preferences should weigh more heavily than our own, they aren't the only important considerations; like approaches to global health work, there's more to agendas than simply selecting favorites off of a menu. For example, chicken simply has more protein than fried plantains; that's an objective fact beyond preferences. Similarly, it's an objective fact that agendas such as the education of local people tend to help more than charity service.

A community may insist on and even beg for such a charity service—perhaps one month of free, outsider-driven clinical care. Yet we have a responsibility to do more than endure a bad meal with a polite smile. Charity service isn't an adequate meal, and pretending that it tastes good is not helpful to our host community. Our work is to partner with communities to develop more helpful agendas which will drive more helpful approaches.

Table 6 compares the seven work *agendas* with the seven *approaches* to global health work. Each approach (column 1) is annotated as to whether it follows previously identified negative or positive global health agendas.

Not surprisingly, Table 6 shows that the traditional global health approaches align more closely with the negative agendas. However, professional disaster relief serves as a special case. It utilizes all three positive work agendas but also uses two traditionally negative ones: charity service and charity construction. Crises often call for different agendas and approaches. As I reviewed in the chapter *Disaster Strikes: Outsiders Arrive*, needless suffering and loss of life can be prevented in disaster zones by doing both charity service and charity construction if and when there's no other option.

A final point I'd like to raise here involves progressing from negative work agendas to increasingly positive ones. I'll return to the story of my introduction to global health, viewed through the lens of agendas.

On my first medical volunteer trip to Jamaica, I was a college sophomore and it was my first time wearing scrubs, learning to check blood pressure, and memorizing pneumonia symptoms. I contributed little but took a lot away—most notably my inspiration to pursue a career in global health. My trip was spiced with the negative work agendas of tourism, education of outsiders, and charity service—as was my next trip to rural Mexico. As I became aware that we were only scratching the surface of what was needed and what could be accomplished, I became critical

> *of these three agendas. I started med school and founded*
> *a small nonprofit serving Uganda, driven by agendas to*
> *empower and further the education of local people. My*
> *global health trips since then have focused almost entirely*
> *on the three positive work agendas.*

I have seen many others similarly progress through negative agendas to increasingly positive ones. As I touched on earlier, *education of outsiders* on global health often needs to precede our ability to effectively facillitate *education of local people* as an agenda. Yet much of this global health education and preparation can be done from within our home countries as well as training courses in resource-limited settings. We need not *practice on* local people until we can both effectively diagnose and treat tropical diseases *and* participate in empowering health partnerships.

I don't believe that everyone needs to try out the traditional approaches in order to see their shortcomings and then progress to more beneficial ones. We can learn from our *collective* mistakes so each of us need not make the same mistakes on a personal level. It's not fair to outsiders who want to spend their time as effectively as possible; it's especially not fair to local people, since they deserve evidence-based interventions which will improve their health in an empowering and sustainable way. It's my hope that readers of this book will experience this *progression of agendas*, and not learn the hard way through troubling and perhaps harmful experiences.

The first part of this book has explored health care, systems, and training—as well as global health approaches and agendas within these areas. The second part of the book will do the same in the critical realms of social justice and public health.

Social Justice and Public Health

The previous chapter reviewed seven global health *Work Agendas*: tourism, education of outsiders, education of local people, charity service, local service improvement, charity construction, and empowerment. These describe the *type* of global health work which is done. It's also helpful to acknowledge two other layers of agendas which don't fit so neatly into tables: *Organizational Agendas* and *Sweeping Health Agendas*. These have special relevance to social justice and public health abroad.

Organizational Agendas

Organizational agendas differ according to the type of outsider group, given that each has its own set of values, organizational culture, and sources of funding.

A. Religious Agenda

While religious beliefs often *motivate* outsiders to do global health work, only sometimes do those beliefs shape the *type* of global health work done or *how* it's done.[1] Following or promoting one's religion often does determine, either consciously or unconsciously, the approach to global health work which is taken.

> *A Christian outsider group built a clinic in a primarily Muslim resource-limited community. A pastor visited the waiting room every day, preaching to those who wished to be patients of the clinic. As a result of this agenda, many members of the community avoided this clinic and had to forego needed medical care. Local evidence-based care protocols weren't given much attention there, as clinical care was primarily used to expose more local people to Christianity.*

For many programs, medical care is a means to the end of spreading religion;[2] yet host communities largely prefer outsiders to keep religious agendas separate from patient care.[3] Outsider volunteers may be motivated by the desire to put their religious principles into practice or perhaps to convince others to convert. Still others have an agenda to connect the religious groups of outsiders to those of local congregations, or to provide care as charity based on religious tenets or the wishes of their religious community back home. The ethical issues raised by medical care given in this context are both serious and obvious. Interventions with this *organizational agenda* often have a *work agenda* of charity construction, charity service, and/or the (religious) education of outsiders or local people.

B. Government/Military Agenda

Global health work is often funded—and may also be carried out—by an instrument of the government of an outsider nation. The military may also be involved in global health work, especially in settings of disaster relief during conflicts. Health work with government funding typically mandates that government priorities and procedures are followed; the aim may be political, such as improving the image of the outsider nation or offering a health service to reciprocate for some other resource, service, or policy.[4]

Such global health programs are crafted out of self-interest, as opposed to being designed to maximally benefit local people. For example, outsider governments may offer health program assistance only to prevent disease from spreading to their own borders.[5] Militaries classically follow a security agenda, offering health services as a supplement to or in order to achieve broader security goals.

C. Corporate Agenda

Corporations or their foundations may offer or fund global health interventions only to promote their image or their market base.[6] They may also produce drugs, medical equipment, or supplies which are required to be used should they be involved in a global health initiative. The next two chapters will review some unfortunate examples of corporate agendas in global health work.

D. Donor-driven Agendas

While religious organizations, governments, militaries, and corporations serve as common donors to global health programs, other small and large donors may also be involved, each carrying their own agenda. They may have interest in or experience with only a certain type of health intervention, which may be selected without regard to its effectiveness or the local burden of disease.[7] They often dictate the terms of interventions, which may fit far more closely with donor preferences than with the desires and needs of local people.[8] Donors restrict the autonomy of non-governmental organizations (NGOs)[9], and they generally prefer to fund top-down *vertical programs* rather than those which would best empower local people.[10]

The World Bank and other large funders of global health programs have required major local economic changes, such as *structural adjustment,* as a condition for extending aid to health programs.[11] Such meddling in economies has demanded major cuts in health systems and privatization schemes which have proved to be very counterproductive.[12] *Sector-wide approaches* are a new model of health development assistance under which the national government supposedly leads a partnership with donors and the community; yet in practice, donors still usually lead the agenda.[13] Following the 2010 earthquake in Haiti, for example, international NGOs largely followed their own agenda and that of their donors rather than seeking out and following the direction of the Haitian people and their government. Outsiders decided where money was spent, how much, and when it would stop.[14]

> *Sweat perpetually dotted his forehead, even when it wasn't hot. It was a burden that he carried since the day he was first asked to come to these remote mountains and serve those living in poverty. His donor group gathered slowly and deliberately around a table drinking tea; between muffins and cakes, they scribbled notes about what the mountain community needed. They planned every detail and left no potential stone unturned. Now it was his burden to follow the dictates of the donor on every level. He was always in a rush and barely stayed around for conversations with local people; he'd like to be here for them, but he felt like a chess piece played by white hands in a far-away tea room.*

The *organizational agendas* of religion, government/military, corporations, and other donors determine which global health *work agendas* are used, largely ignoring any self-expressed priorities and needs of local people. Set by outsiders, they reflect our preferred activities and interventions. They limit, sometimes explicitly and by design, the amount of local empowerment that can be achieved, and serve as a hurdle for the sustainability of locally-led programs. Although the global health activities of each of these organizations are both potentially hurtful and potentially helpful for local people, these benefits are lessened or even incidental due to the primacy of their organizational agendas. There is no evidence-base that adding this additional layer of complexity to outsider intervention improves local health.

Sweeping Health Agendas

Global health groups also differ in terms of the general type of health work that they do, whether it be primarily clinical, public health, or social justice work. Such *sweeping health agendas* serve as a third layer of global health agendas.

1. Clinical Agenda

Outsider global health programs tend to focus on clinical care, other clinically-related services, health facility construction, or clinical education.

2. Public Health Agenda

Alternatively, many global health groups focus on public health issues such as potable water, sanitation, immunization, nutrition and agriculture, income-generation, and improving indoor air quality.

3. Social Justice Agenda

Still other groups aim to partner with local people as they work to achieve more social justice within their own nations and communities. This work strives to increase access to the social determinants of health, such as housing, education, and health care.

Which *sweeping health agendas* are positive and negative? For local people, which are helpful, empowering, and sustainable? Which are evidenced-based? These agendas can go either way. They don't inform a specific way to do global health work or an organizational culture and style; they're descriptive and they simply label the general type of health-related work which is done. Outside clinicians naturally focus on clinical care, yet this is usually the tip of the iceberg regarding local people's health. Labelling sweeping agendas is helpful insofar as it may encourage us medical people to plunge in deeper and beyond our comfort zones. *Part I* dealt with clinical issues, while *Part II* will now move on to those of public health and social justice.

To briefly summarize the three layers of global health agendas:

1. Sweeping agendas: clinical, public health, and/or social justice
2. Organizational agendas: religious, government/military, corporate, and/or donor-driven
3. Work agendas: tourism, education of outsiders, education of local people, charity service, local service improvement, charity construction, and/or empowerment

These three layers can apply to a single outsider group simultaneously. For example, there can be a group with clinical and public health *sweeping agendas*, a corporate *organizational agenda*, and *work agendas* involving charity construction and local service improvement. Just as there can be a *progression of agendas* from negative work agendas to increasingly positive ones, the same also applies to removing, minimizing, or transforming *organizational agendas*. Finally, a positive progression of agendas for most medical professionals involves expanding beyond the clinical health *sweeping agenda* and embracing public health and social justice work. It is worth reminding ourselves that this can only be done successfully in partnership with communities, and we must be invited to do so. Let's now delve into those other two sweeping health *agendas*, as well as the final two *approaches* to global health work which involve public health:

- Local public health capacity-building, and
- Facilitating community-based programs

7

Exotic Diseases and Social Injustice

Her hairline was decorated with a headband of flat warts congealing into each other while her neck was pale and flakey with barely recognizable "skin." Her tongue was white as snow and the fungus extended into her throat, making every swallow add to her pain. Her headache had been building slowly over the weeks, and fever trailed it like an unwelcome shadow.

She'd been hiding her cough for 3 weeks, but it was no longer possible; it would erupt from her mouth before the end of every sentence. I held the chest x-ray up to the window where there was enough light for the TB cavitary lesion to stare back at me like an unblinking eye. Her father had given HIV to her mother, who passed it to her before moving to the other side of Botswana, leaving her with this illness as well as many childcare duties. While it was amazing that she survived without treatment, her body had become a distorted and unfair playground for candida, HPV, cryptococcus, TB, and perhaps other infections as well.

Another patient, this time in Uganda. Her lips pealed like an orange and her skin was sliding off of her body in large sections that fell weightlessly onto her hospital bed. All she had done was to lightly rub her arm. Like a porcelain doll, she waited as we sorted out which life-saving medicine we would have to stop since the side effects may have caused her fragile state. HIV

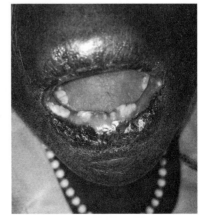

*medicines are successfully treating HIV and preventing
transmission throughout the world, yet they do not lack
challenges and burdens.*

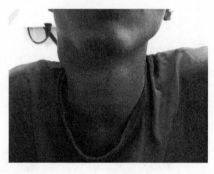

*Looking for a better life
in the north of Botswana, his
neck slowly became distorted
and lumpy—especially on its
right side. A nagging cough
awoke him even more than
the sensation that he was
sleeping in a bathtub, due to
his sweat. But what finally
brought him to our clinic was
being unable to breathe when he was lying down. Sleep was
a luxury of the past and this 20-year-old acted more like an
ancient 90-year-old. His heart sounded distant and looked
like a boot on the x-ray. TB wasn't satisfied with filling his
lungs, neck, and abdominal glands; it moved on to surround
his heart with a massive airbag of fluid which took his
independence, breath, and nearly his life.*

Diseases of Poverty

HIV and TB hang like deep, eerie clouds over every ward and clinic I've
visited in resource-limited settings. Within every country, those with
the lowest incomes are especially burdened with them. Academics call
them *tropical diseases*, an unfortunate term with origins in concerns
over the health of colonists as they invaded tropical lands. Imperial
powers labelled the prominent diseases of the tropics in this way,
assuming that less "developed" societies would remain plagued by these
diseases.

A more appropriate term is *diseases of poverty*. Although they are
infectious diseases that occur more in the tropics, those who suffer
and die from them are primarily determined by their place in the social
order, not by the pathogens themselves or their geographical latitude.
Just as poverty is preventable, unfair, and socially-created, so too are
these diseases which so predictably create devastation in poverty's
wake. Clinicians who treat only the diseases of poverty are merely
scratching the surface; those who treat poverty and injustice can truly
assist in curing patients and their society in a deeper way.

The young children all looked nine months pregnant, with their distended bellies stuck out far in front of them. At times, they couldn't see the soccer ball at their feet because of their abdominal swelling. The health worker soccer spectators wondered if they were "pregnant" with ascaris worms, or if it was malnutrition, or massive spleens from chronic malaria infections. Diseases of poverty overtook and ran the town; they were uninvited guests inside all community members. It was as if the people here were run-down hotels with eternal vacancies, the doors to their rooms perpetually open to the germs around them.

These children were really cute, but they looked at me as if gazing past me or through me. I threw them the ball and they tried to catch it in slow motion, then sadly watched it roll away from them. This was what their lives were doing too. They couldn't concentrate in school and some did so poorly that they were asked not to continue. When they shat, they left large piles of worms which looked like spaghetti for two; yet the worms' effect on their intelligence and development was the really tragic part.

Adults everywhere were grabbing their bellies and I saw that typhoid had a grip over the whole place. Others were scratching fiercely everywhere and were being led through the town by small children; the disease of "river blindness" unfairly wrenched away the possibilities in their lives. A young miner had massively swollen ankles and fluid in his abdomen and lungs; he became crazy with "hepatic encephalopathy" as his liver failed, even though he had no hepatitis infections and had never tasted alcohol in his life. Like many other miners and rice farmers who stood for hours in water, blood flukes claimed his life just after he turned 30. Another couldn't speak, but I'm sure he wanted to complain that his muscles hurt everywhere. His clenched jaws, arched back, and rising temperature warned us that he'd soon die of an infection that a simple vaccine available nearly everywhere would have prevented: tetanus.

Shoeless kids were killing cobras by stomping on them; they were perpetually covered in flies and wore the same clothes every day. Yet they still frolicked around, passing empty containers as would-be toys. They danced between

> *concrete above-ground graves with sweeping smiles on their*
> *faces, which struck me as surreal and literally unbelievable.*
> *These children were just too young and innocent to*
> *understand the suffering and disease around them. It was a*
> *simple mosquito bite that filled most of the cemetery where*
> *they played: Falciparum malaria was the strongest, most*
> *enduring, and most unwelcome town "guest."*

There's nothing natural, inevitable, or fair about having any of these diseases of poverty. Their presence is the flashing lights and blaring sirens of social injustice. This chapter and the next will address the *sweeping health agenda* of social justice. While up to now I've largely explored the clinical agenda, and most outsider medical teams are also clinically-focused, agendas of public health require an examination of social justice.

Social Justice and Health

If there was no social injustice, then every nation would likely provide exemplary health care to its residents and there would be no need for global health work. Yet this just isn't the case. The implications of global health empowerment work on social justice, health, and poverty will be explored here, as well as the close relationship among them.

Poverty isn't born out of laziness but rather the abuse of power; we outsiders need to understand this reality in order to assist people living in poverty in a way that's more than superficial. Some argue that poverty and social justice are political issues outside the purview of medicine. Yet the evidence shows they are transformed into physical issues requiring health and medical care. Casting poverty and social injustice aside is like diagnosing and treating a patient while ignoring their vital signs and physical exam.

> *The peaceful clicking of thousands of bamboo poles*
> *echoed through the forest like a symphony. Western*
> *Uganda hosts fertile fields with explosive crop growth yet*
> *the hospital next to some of these fields is filled with cases*
> *of malnutrition. The potential for local development is*
> *impressive, yet family income is abysmal and community*
> *members are dying from preventable illnesses before*
> *reaching adulthood.*

Why are Ugandans so starved and unhealthy in this land of plenty? Their resources were stolen for decades through colonialism, as Uganda's development was artificially stunted. When England handed over political power, it also passed along a legacy of corruption which continues to thrive among Uganda's current leadership. The Ugandan government shamelessly stole millions from the Global Fund to Fight AIDS, Tuberculosis and Malaria as well as the Global Alliance for Vaccines and Immunization.[1] Health care remains neglected and underfunded; this is an injustice that people living in poverty should not have to endure.

Social justice is critical for health. WHO identifies it as one of the main priorities for health, claiming "health equity depends vitally on the empowerment of individuals to challenge and change the unfair and steeply graded distribution of social resources to which everyone has equal claims and rights".[2] As illustrated in Figure 1, the economic status of high-income countries has been steadily increasing while that of low- and middle-income countries has been chronically stagnant, as measured in Gross Domestic Product (GDP) per person.

Figure 1[3]

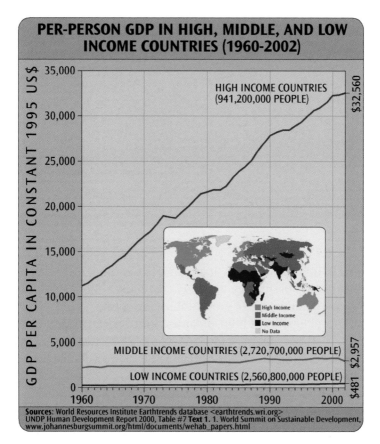

Sources: World Resources Institute Earthtrends database <earthtrends.wri.org>
UNDP Human Development Report 2000, Table #7 Text 1. 1. World Summit on Sustainable Development, www.johannesburgsummit.org/html/documents/wehab_papers.html

Figure 2 illustrates the Human Development Index (HDI), which is a general development measure combining life expectancy, education level, and standard of living. A lower number/ white colored HDI indicates more development, generally seen in countries which weren't recently colonized; "less-developed" countries—depicted by increasingly dark shades of grey are typically areas which were recently colonized. The strong link between colonialism and underdevelopment is far from coincidental, as outlined in Walter Rodney's classic *How Europe Underdeveloped Africa*.[4]

Figure 2. Human Development Index (HDI) and Recent Colonial Control[5]

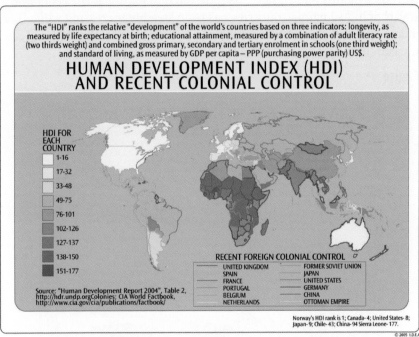

It's critical to understand that "inequality is the fundamental cause of poor health and premature death. Global inequality has produced a world where millions die of preventable causes every year."[6] Much of the wealth (and health) of high-income countries can clearly be traced back to the theft of resources, food, and people which occurred under colonization and the slave trade.[7] Stealing so many valuable human beings, their possessions, and their resources leveled many preexisting civilizations. Rich colonizers made little attempt to contribute to the health and education of these lands, which were quickly transformed into the most impoverished nations on earth.[8] Following "independence," rule by white-skinned outsiders was often replaced by local dictatorships that were equally oppressive and continued to feed the greed of the former colonial powers.

Such an *unhealthy history* has a major effect on the health and social conditions of the formerly colonized countries today. Figure 3 presents three *social* maps of the world; they depict continents and countries which have been re-sized based on the variable being compared, while Map 1 serves as a reference (with no re-sizing).

The countries and continents with more people living in absolute poverty (e.g., Africa and the Indian subcontinent) appear larger in Map 2, while places with less poverty appear smaller (e.g., the Americas, Europe, and Australia). Absolute poverty is currently defined as earning less than US$2 per day. Global maps of water access and infant deaths follow this map and demonstrate a very troubling pattern.

Figure 3. Global Injustice Maps[9]

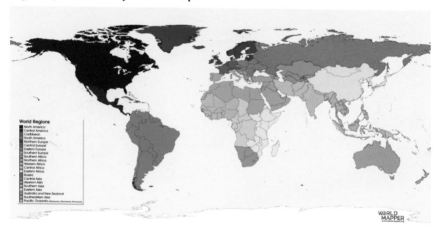

1. Reference World Map

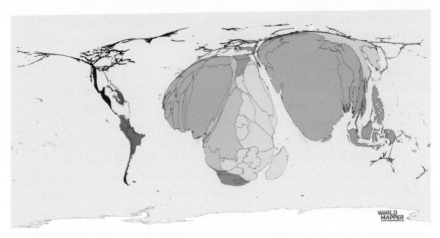

2. Absolute Poverty

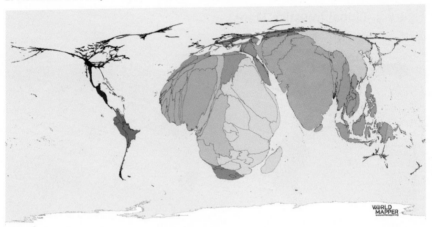

3. No Water Access

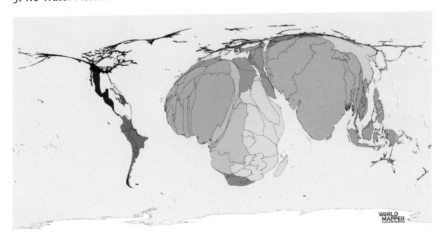

4. Infant Deaths

A comparison of these eerily similar *injustice maps* shows our system's complete disregard for human life and health in the formerly colonized countries, especially in Africa, where people suffer the daily effects of inequalities in income, education, water and sanitation access, and health. Those living in poverty throughout the world lose far more infants to preventable causes of death; they also suffer far more deaths from epidemic diseases and malaria, as well as serving as home to far more people living—and dying—with HIV. Paul Farmer has appropriately labelled HIV, malaria, and similar infectious diseases as a "biological expression of social inequalities."[10]

Social Determinants of Health

There is overwhelming evidence that poverty and general socioeconomic status—rather disease—are the main determinants of how healthy people are.[11] The lower one's income level, the worse one's health is throughout the world.[12] Because poverty causes poor health, and poor health further deepens poverty, we have set up the conditions for a downward spiral in much of the world. However, the opposite is also true: good health reduces poverty.[13]

Communities with deeper poverty have higher death rates, as do ethnic groups subject to discrimination.[14] A brief comparison of lower and higher income countries reveals dramatic health inequalities, including a life expectancy 48 years longer in Japan compared with Sierra Leone.[15] These health inequities are caused by the *social determinants of health*, or "the conditions in which people are born, grow, work, live, and age, and the wider set of forces and systems shaping the conditions of daily life."[16]

Unequal access to education, work, income, voting rights, government participation, and societal power causes unequal health status in a socially engineered manner. Each of these variables serves as a social determinant of health, as well as gender equity, health care access, social security, and finance, market, and other social policy;[17] race, ethnicity, culture, and societal values can be added to this critical list as well.[18] While this is mainly what makes us healthy or unhealthy, it is rarely discussed in medical school!

The WHO Commission on the Social Determinants of Health identifies 75% of the health inequalities in the world as being avoidable.[19] When social determinants of health are changed, then health outcomes change as well because they are directly related.[20] Not surprisingly, empowerment serves as a central strategy for improving health by influencing its social determinants.[21]

A malnourished child slept on his right side all night. He woke and stared at me with groggy eyes. The right side of his face was swollen like a boxer's the morning after a big fight. Meanwhile, in a dimly lit closet-sized office, a man quietly mixed his powders as if putting together a magic potion. He made a therapeutic formula for children to drink, and he was the Ugandan Nutritionist who would save their lives with it. The kids' weight and energy would steadily increase until they could leave the Malnutrition Ward. Yet they returned to homes with empty shelves, so the same kids were admitted again and again with severe acute malnutrition. The problem—and its solutions—were fundamentally societal.

Even a superficial look at the data reveals that world hunger and malnutrition aren't primarily related to overpopulation or underproduction of food.[22] For farmers living in poverty throughout the world, "powerlessness lies at the very root of hunger… [it] isn't a scarcity of food, but rather a scarcity of democracy."[23] Those living in the deepest poverty also typically find the least access to education, safe housing, safe water, and freedom from violence. So how could they possibly be expected to be as healthy as the rest of the world? Poor health is but a nasty reflection in the mirror of an unjust world.

An Unhealthy History, Part 2

As colonies, slaves, and kings have gradually gone out of favor, the upper hand of rich countries has been maintained through their dominance of world markets, corporate poaching of natural resources, and foreign aid. Further, massive debts were thrust upon the shoulders of resource-limited countries that had supposedly cut off the colonial chains. A few ongoing abuses will be touched on here.

1. Unfair Loans and Debt: Many resource-limited countries spend far more yearly on interest payments on their "debt" to rich nations than they can spend on health and education combined.[24] As required conditions for loans, the International Monetary Fund (IMF) and World Bank force resource-limited nations to further cut health care and other social services. Such *structural adjustment* conditions have had a hugely negative impact on poverty, health care access, malnutrition, and HIV/AIDS prevalence in these countries.[25]

2. Foreign Aid: While some economists believe foreign aid from rich countries needs to be expanded[26], others point to how it

often worsens conditions through failed top-down planning by outsiders.[27] Foreign aid commonly prioritizes the concerns of outsiders and creates dependency in resource-limited nations.

3. *Free* Trade, Not *Fair* Trade: Free trade inherently favors high-income countries and the large corporations based within them; meanwhile, *economic globalization* has deepened inequalities and poverty in most resource-limited countries.[28] Social services and public goods and rights have been devastated by exponential corporate growth and Western-dominated trade. Even the privatization of water has been pushed by the World Bank and large foreign corporations which stand to profit from denial of the right to water and reduced local water access.[29]

4. Corporate Abuse of Health: Critical HIV medicines were developed and produced by pharmaceutical companies which then dramatically elevated their prices, keeping them beyond the reach of the majority of people in resource-limited countries who desperately needed them.[30] Insurance companies not only curtail the provision of health care services to impoverished Americans; they've extended their reach and infiltrated resource-limited nations to increase their profits by minimizing health care access overseas.[31] Taking advantage of globalized markets, large corporations flood these same countries with cigarettes, guns, junk food, and infant formula (as they campaign against healthy breastfeeding). Some transnational corporations even play a leading role in violent coups overthrowing democratically-elected leaders in resource-limited countries.[32]

Outsiders have quite a legacy of abuse, fostering dependence, and maintaining the *status quo* in resource-limited countries. As outsider medical professionals, will we join them? Or will we go against the grain by working to support the empowerment of local people so they might control their own destinies?

By now it should be clear that diseases of poverty are only the tip of the iceberg. Much larger threats to life and health are posed by historical abuses of power (colonization, slave trade, world trade patterns, etc.) and modern abuses of power (international financial institutions, self-serving aid, environmental destruction, corporate abuses, etc.). Together they have created a socially unjust and unequal world: a world of needlessly wealthy people and countries as well as the tragedy of needlessly impoverished ones. This is not just an ethical problem, but a direct challenge to health workers: *abuses of power cause the poverty and social injustice which result in poor health.* Global health has everything to do with those who abuse power and those who have been driven away from power. This is the main reason why we should work toward the empowerment of communities in resource-limited countries.

8

Poverty and Empowerment

The last chapter explored the relationship among the abuse of power, social injustice, poverty, and poor health. However, there are ways in which we outsiders can *promote* health and social justice among those living in poverty. Let's begin with a fresh look at poverty as being a *state of disempowerment*, rather than simply a lack of money. Beyond gifts or even the redistribution of money and material things, I propose that the central need of those living in poverty is to be in control of their lives and their health.

> *If a well-educated white man with a stable job and good social support comes home to find his house burned down, then he becomes "poor" overnight according to the strict economic definition. Yet he may easily find family or friends to stay with, and he can save up money from his job to quickly rise out of material poverty. Now imagine a lonely, unemployed African-American woman with few material resources, mental health challenges, and an education that didn't include completing high school. If her inner-city apartment burns down, she may easily become long-term homeless and struggle to meet even basic needs. The poverty she has been subjected to runs much deeper than economic deprivation, and rising out of poverty will not be achieved by a simple gift of money.*

Poverty typically has a one-dimensional definition of being a state of economic deprivation. By contrast, John Friedmann proposed that "poverty is a condition of systematic disempowerment whereby implied *structural conditions* keep the poor poor and confine their access to social power to the level of day-to-day survival."[1] Economist Amartya Sen similarly proposes that "poverty must be seen as the deprivation of basic capability rather than merely as lowness of incomes."[2] In resource-limited nations, Narayanasamy points out that local people often define poverty in terms of the presence or lack of land, property, food, and dependents.[3]

In the above example, a man and woman both face house fires but with very different challenges. The conventional *income definition* of poverty fails to characterize their fundamentally different social scenarios. However, the deeper and more holistic poverty definitions of Friedmann, Sen, and Narayanasamy can account for the consequences of extreme poverty for the woman compared to the recovery for the man. Understanding poverty as disempowerment allows us to see its multiple possible dimensions:

- Lack of money, land, property, and/or safe housing
- Lack of support from family, friends, and/or society
- Exclusion from opportunities based on race, ethnicity, gender, disability, age, sexual orientation, caste, religion, and/or other social characteristics
- Exclusion from education and/or employment
- Lack of a productive environment (e.g. living in ecological devastation, a refugee camp, an urban slum, etc.)
- Lack of physical safety from violence due to war, policing, gender inequalities and/or other social strife
- Lack of food and/or safe water
- Lack of health based on disease, access to medicines, and/or access to health care
- Lack of physical, social, and/or political freedoms

Many of the same variables discussed as *social determinants of health* also feature in the expanded definition of poverty proposed here. Further, "because poverty is multidimensional… solutions that focus solely on income are not likely to entirely break the vicious cycle of poverty."[4] A caring adoption or a quality education could clearly help an orphan rise out of poverty more than just getting a stack of cash, for example. If poverty is defined as disempowerment in one or more of the ways listed here, then empowerment would naturally be key to finding a path out of poverty.

Empowerment can be good or bad, depending on who gets more power and what they do with it. Power isn't just the precious currency of a ruthless CEO who systematically steals the wages of his hard-working employees; it's not just the territory that a strong army or government hungers over. Power is also the glorious aim of someone starving who is driven to acquire needed meals for themselves and their family. Power is also the critical goal of slaves organizing to end their bondage and gain an equality of resources with their former owners. Power should be shared in a just way so that all can meet their basic needs and have equal access to opportunities.

Power is neither created nor destroyed, just transferred among people and groups. Social justice is a way of transferring power that meets needs and promotes equity. All have a right to the power required to meet their basic needs. Abusing power involves transferring it unjustly away from meeting the needs of some to disproportionately serving the wants of others. This is of concern to health workers because large-scale human suffering and ill health can nearly always be traced to abuses of and inequalities in power.[5]

If those living in poverty need more empowerment, then rich people often need much less. Empowerment can be life-saving to those lacking any of the basic needs, including safe housing, food, and health. Meanwhile, overly-empowered people take much more than they need, in terms of resources, wealth, and social and political power. This is unjust, and it demands a transfer of power from the rich to the poor. After all, "poverty…is created by the structures of society and the policies pursued by society. Change the structure…and you will see that the poor change their own lives."[6]

Who to Empower?

So how can outsider medical professionals help? Should we poke our noses in local people's affairs and make revolution, reverse genocide, or eject corrupt corporations? As addressed throughout this book, butting in with our solutions to local people's problems is no business of outsiders. Yet because empowerment is a prerequisite for local people taking control of their own health, this is an end to which we outsiders can and should contribute. Local people must be empowered to confront the injustice that features all too prominently in their lives.

Those living in the deepest poverty typically suffer the deepest injustice, live the unhealthiest lives, and have the most to gain from empowerment. Outsider medical teams often seek to serve those living in poverty abroad; this is exactly what we should do, provided that we've been invited and form empowering partnerships. We can also go a step deeper by partnering with local people to explore *why* injustice occurs and support them in seeking solutions to it. As with other global health work, local people should lead this process while we outsiders play a supplementary role.

It was my first day settling into this passionate Salvadoran village, and the town tour included visiting a mural of US planes dropping bombs. Next, we visited the school, where an old bomb shell was set up as a monument.

*Painted in white on the shell were the names of the many
students killed when the bomb was dropped on their school.
Although riddled with post-traumatic stress disorder, this
inspiring town of returned (repatriated) refugees was awake
to the social injustice affecting their society. They organized
both a radio show and journal on human rights abuse,
and they planned how to send village students to college
for the first time. Those accessing higher education would
become the next generation of village advocates and leaders.
Responding to their requests, our nonprofit helped with each
of these projects.*

*Then a Canadian company started mining nearby
without asking for community permission as required by
international law. Local people raised awareness and spoke
out against this intervention. They were on the front lines of
changing their society, and our nonprofit supported them in
the background.*

*Outsiders intervened in two opposing ways in this
community. The company took their resources and made
a handsome profit while contaminating their drinking
water; our "health and human rights" nonprofit supported
empowered community members who worked to control
their village, water supply, health, and future.*

In order to help out the neediest and least healthy, outsiders should
work to empower those living in poverty; we should also seek out the
most isolated and excluded, as well as those throughout the world who
have survived serious human rights abuses. Some examples follow:

A. **Persecuted Minorities:** Outsider health professionals can seek
partnerships with groups that have been ostracized and/or
persecuted. We could look for those with less education, those
with worse housing, and those with less medical care. The most
underserved may be of a certain ethnic, racial, caste, or religious
group. For example, Indigenous peoples are often chronically
mistreated and therefore face large health disparities throughout
the world.[7]

B. **Oppressed Women:** Outsiders can seek to empower women who
have experienced oppression, such as survivors of rape, physical
abuse, and sex trafficking. Meeting local women's groups or
encouraging their formation can be especially empowering long-
term.

*Two curious eyes peered out from a cloth wrapped around
her back. She also had a load on her head which matched
her size and seemingly her weight. But the burden on her
shoulders surpassed even that upon her blistered bare feet
which roamed the countryside to fetch water again and
again. She kept her families' lives afloat with full plates and
cups but her mind and spirit were kept thirsty by decades
of exclusion from education and opportunity, subjugation,
beatings, mistreatment, humiliation, and rape. Women are
the strength which lifts impoverished communities out of the
mud, yet they often must extricate themselves from the mud
to lead that process.*

C. **Homeless or Landless:** People who are homeless or landless in
resource-limited countries have acute income and health needs.
We outsiders can help to inspire and support them in their efforts
to deepen community unity and find collective solutions. A
tireless advocate for those living with landlessness and poverty in
Honduras explains, "until we change this system, all the charity
in the world won't take us out of poverty. How can we ever get
out of poverty if we can't get a piece of land to work?"[8]

D. **Sweatshop Workers:** Resource-limited countries are home to
a great many sweatshops—factories that abuse human rights.
These abuses include child labor, violence against workers,
forced birth control, sexual harassment, and forced overtime.
People are often so desperate for jobs that they endure inhumane
working conditions in factories organized by multinational
clothing, shoes, toys, and electronics companies. For example,
maquiladora (assembly) factories in Mexico are located near
the US border and produce for US companies. The workers face
higher rates of TB, hepatitis A, measles, salmonella, and typhoid
compared with Mexico at large.[9] Importantly, "worker health and
safety can only be improved when workers organize to collectively
confront and resolve the conditions of work that injure us and
make us sick".[10] Invited outsiders can assist workers in organizing
groups for health and safety monitoring and advocacy. Inspired
workers can push for better conditions, as well as the right to
create a union to promote their health care and other rights.

E. **War, Violence, and Migration:** War has obvious and disastrous
effects on access to food, water, shelter, health care, and
health in general. Drs. Barry Levy and Victor Sidel write that
"activities by public health professionals to prevent war and its

health consequences are, in our view, an essential part of our professional obligations."[11] Levy and Sidel recommend preventing war through observation and documentation of abuses, human rights advocacy, and getting involved with nonviolent conflict resolution.[12] Some outsiders have given medical care abroad in the midst of active warfare both to save lives and to report war crimes.[13] Empowering local people to resolve ethnic, religious, or class conflicts dramatically promotes health by preventing violence and war. Those fleeing war and violence also have deep health and empowerment needs; we can seek them out and partner to support them.

Massive landslides blocked the road into Burma, so my wife and I crossed the river in a small motorboat piloted by a one-armed man. Amputees were everywhere; the civil war had left a heavy mark. We partnered with community health workers (CHWs) who dodge landmines to administer health care deep in the jungle. The government refused to organize health posts in the territories of ethnic minority groups that they oppose; as an act of defiance (and necessity), local people organized their own grassroots approach to medical care. These CHWs treated over 70,000 patients, delivered babies, trained other CHWs, organized clean water projects, and even amputated limbs when unavoidable. Their important work was born out of a community's refusal to accept health care injustice; outsider health and human rights groups have importantly supported their life-saving work.

Taking the Power Back

Paul Farmer points out common ways in which "suffering is 'structured' by historically given (and often economically driven) processes and forces that conspire...to constrain agency."[14] Such *structural violence* causes and perpetuates poverty, while leading to much of the large-scale physical violence of the world.[15] Until structures and systems are changed, the health of the poorest will remain the poorest.

Social injustice can be approached by empowering the poor *and* taking power away from those that hoard and abuse it. As I touched on in the last chapter, abusers of power often include governments, militaries, corporations, and international financial institutions. Local people in resource-limited countries have sometimes succeeded in taking power back from these abusers; examples from the last chapter are expanded on here.

1. Unfair Loans and Debt: Empowered resource-limited countries have declined new restrictive loans from international financial institutions. They have also fought for debt forgiveness on existing loans. When this can't be achieved, they've pushed the IMF and World Bank to remove loan conditions which force further cuts in health care and other social services.

2. Foreign Aid: Empowered resource-limited nations have resisted the temptation to accept large donations from more wealthy countries, freeing themselves of the many strings attached which would deepen dependency. Instead of planning revolving around international aid, some have fostered local interventions such as the organization of coops, village markets, small businesses, and low-cost but effective health and social inventions.

3. *Free* Trade, Not *Fair* Trade: Empowered local people have shunned *free trade* arrangements which largely benefit rich nations; instead, they've embraced the improved environmental and social standards of *fair trade*. They've successfully turned down money-making promises from large outsider groups and corporate structures, including trade relationships.[16] Local people have instead looked to their neighbors to buy and sell goods, while turning to local government, civic groups, and cooperative structures for economic and social opportunities.[17]

4. Corporate Abuse of Health: Nations such as Brazil and India made local production of HIV meds a priority, leading to a large drop in medicine costs and an expansion in treatment. This enabled these nations to curb their HIV/AIDS crises, yet this simple, logical approach was achieved only after a long and bitter fight with pharmaceutical corporations and the US government.[18] Mining and oil companies commonly trample on the land, human, and environmental rights of Indigenous peoples; yet affected people often fight back and force the greedy outsiders to leave.[19] When a transnational corporation entered Bolivia to privatize local water and then inflate water-user fees, empowered local people who could no longer afford water took to the streets and developed a strong movement

that forced the corporation to flee the country.[20]

> *I had trouble getting to my job interview in rural Puerto Rico, since the roads were crammed with cheering protestors carrying placards and dreams of a less imperial future. A US company had set up an oil refinery right in the middle of their town; they were gagging from the stench of its emissions and they wanted it out. Local people blamed the refinery for their respiratory disease and cancer, so I helped them organize a study that indeed documented much higher rates of respiratory disease and cancer compared to the rest of the island. This company came from the US mainland and caused harm in this semi-autonomous island which has for too long been treated like a colony. I felt it my responsibility to report on the harm being done, so I collected data with the local protest movement, and they used it to shape their own future.*

People living in poverty can take their power back from the outsiders who are abusing theirs. Yet it's critical to point out that not all outsiders abuse their power; many chose to empower local people so that communities can improve their living conditions. Outsider groups have partnered with resource-limited countries to fight for just loan conditions and debt forgiveness. Outsider groups have stood with local people fighting for their health against pharmaceutical companies that kept HIV medicines prohibitively expensive.[21] Still other outsiders have partnered with Indigenous communities standing up to mining and oil giants.[22]

Socially-conscious outsiders can play a helpful role in promoting social justice so long as those efforts are initiated, led, and sustained by local people. Outsider health professionals can partner in these efforts only if invited to do so. If we are moved by injustice and attempt to change local systems ourselves, we would have less chance of "success" and would also contribute to the disempowerment of a community that could otherwise address its own problems. As I outlined in the chapter *Power to the People*, outsiders should limit ourselves to being facilitators—or catalysts—for local ideas, dreams, plans, and actions to improve community life. Just as we facilitate discussions with local people on health systems strengthening and clinical capacity-building, we can do the same with concerns about social justice.

Facilitating Social Justice

In a subtle but important way, we outsiders can begin to promote social justice in resource-limited countries simply by paying more attention to those living in poverty; through partnership, they may find more hope, confidence, and opportunity. We can promote social justice by reinforcing the message that local communities have the knowledge, skills, and tools to better their own lot. As community members successfully run, expand, and improve their clinical and public health programs, they not only become less dependent on foreigners but also on national organizations and government leaders who may be abusing their power.

Outsider groups often seek out and partner with those most excluded or living in the deepest poverty. This allows for a deliberate promotion of social justice, although many may not identify or label it as such. Outsiders often shy away from sociopolitical discussions with local people, and avoid or change the subject when community members raise such themes. Yet ignoring expressions of a deeper analysis when it's important to local people is a missed empowerment opportunity. When we try to avoid the recognition of social injustice, we may be unwittingly encouraging local people to do the same.

When we meet with health workers and impoverished communities, discussions on poverty and its causes naturally arise. This is especially true when conducting an *assets and needs assessment,* given that poverty and related needs come to the fore. The chapter *Community-Based Health Programs* will explore methods that promote the brainstorming of problems, their ranking and prioritization, and the search for potential solutions. Such a methodology of analysis unavoidably calls out the "elephants in the room:" poverty and social injustice.

Local people are almost always acutely aware of the ways in which inequitable systems exclude them, keep them poor, and keep them unhealthy. When this isn't the case, local facilitators can initiate important discussions to develop these themes. Outsiders can encourage this, and may be asked to co-facilitate some discussions on social justice. Discussing access to clean water, jobs, and health care leads directly to the question of *why* some have better quality or easier access to them. Injustice comes into plain sight when varying access is identified as based on one's level of poverty, power, opportunities, and/or rights. As open discussions dig deeper towards root causes, an internal awakening surfaces issues of social injustice.

Local and outsider facilitators can encourage creative community analysis of social injustice and how it blocks community members' attempts to be healthier. The causes and influence on health of social injustice can be explored with much utility; people living in poverty can be empowered by collectively analyzing these factors.[23]

As local people discuss and identify injustice together, they can analyze *why* it exists and *how* it's perpetuated. Unequal power relationships and ability to meet needs can be explored as a group. Community members can brainstorm whether they want to address injustice, and if so, how. Acting on the ideas expressed can lead them to improve their systems and living conditions.[24] As with health problems, injustices can be prioritized through local group discussion to provide direction on which abuses to try to counter first. Local social justice initiatives and groups may emerge from these discussions. Alternatively, existing health programs may develop more depth and inclusivity after acknowledging the influence of social injustice on their work.

I don't believe outsiders should tell communities where injustice lies. Not only can we easily be wrong given our limited local knowledge, but the organic, local realization of power imbalances is a necessary component of empowerment. Importantly, a "people-centered approach to health education... [aims] not to change the poor, but to help them gain the understanding and skills needed to change the conditions that cause poverty and poor health."[25]

To recap, poverty must be defined and approached as being a *state of disempowerment*. It follows that empowerment work offers a path on which both local people and outsiders can promote poverty-alleviation, as well as health and social justice. People living in poverty often have to change the structures of their society—its social determinants of health—in order to improve health in a lasting way.

A grim history and ongoing abuses can leave local people feeling locked into a state of poverty. Reversing the unjust tide of history is a mammoth task which can easily overwhelm our imaginations. It is worth remembering that large changes start small.

Change may start as simply as an enthusiastic chat under a mango tree where community members talk about their strengths, resources, and dreams. They can own their problems, imagine solutions, and ultimately take increasing control over their lives and health. Although conventional medical education tends to ignore it, social justice is the foundation of public health. Further, public health serves as the bedrock of global health, as addressed in the next chapter.

9

Global Health is Public Health

Global health is primarily a field of public health. While medicine plays an important role in global health, it's actually a small and dependent piece of a larger, public health-driven effort. The field of global health was born out of the merger of *international health* and *public health*; both are population-based, systems-based, and multidisciplinary, and they both focus on prevention, health equity, and people living in poverty.[1] Global health is concerned with these same areas, largely as public health applied to communities living in poverty throughout the world.

This entire book has demonstrated the application of public health priorities, methods and activities, so this chapter is far from being the beginning of the story! Public health is rooted in reacting to social injustice, health care inequity, and the unfairness of forcing people to live in poverty. It centers on the evidence-based interventions of empowerment, capacity-building, integrating with and strengthening local health systems, and organizing community-based programs.

Public health workers use assets and needs assessments to guide health program design, as well as continuous monitoring and evaluation. Public health planning models center on local people prioritizing their health problems.[2] In the chapter *Disaster Strikes: Outsiders Arrive*, I reviewed how interventions in both disaster relief and areas of chronic poverty primarily apply public health methodologies. The only non-public health *approaches* reviewed here are suitcase medicine and health facility-building (see *Appendices A and B* for a detailed review).

So how will this chapter be any different from the earlier ones? In addition to public health methods, I'll explore public health *topics* such as indoor smoke exposure, agriculture, scholarships, immunizations, water, sanitation, and hygiene. I encourage my medical professional readers to shift from the traditional clinical agenda to a public health agenda—an agenda capable of addressing these and other topics.

This chapter also explores the sixth approach to global health work: *public health capacity-building*. While I explored *clinical* capacity-building in *Part I*, this chapter will address public health topics by applying the same effective approaches: local health system integration, partnership, Train-the-Trainer practices, and bidirectional teaching on a locally-determined set of topics. Like clinical capacity-building, public health training is evidence-based, helpful, empowering, and sustainable (see Table 1 in *Global Health Approaches*). Public health can also stretch beyond capacity-building into the realm of Community-Based Health Programs (as the chapter with that title will address).

What Do Local People Want?

It was rainy season in Sierra Leone and the dirt "highway" was littered with puddles and full-out ponds. Like a Venus flytrap, various vehicles entered these ponds and couldn't get out. In each village, I joined a local facilitator in encouraging community members to brainstorm their health problems in focus groups. Youth leaders, women's group members, and everyday people put their heads together. Nearly every village discussion group came up with an identical problem list, including lack of sufficient clean water, sanitation, income-generating options, education, and health care.

In Burma, we brainstormed assets and problems with a similar focus group; its members then went ahead to vote on and prioritize community problems. Clean water was ranked #1, followed by health care and then infrastructure. In Honduras, it was a larger community meeting with leaders from each village brainstorming and ranking their problems: 1) clean water access, 2) education, 3) health care access, and 4) malnutrition.

These examples show community members on all three continents listing very similar public health problems as their health priorities. This is not a coincidence, but is typical of problem-ranking sessions in resource-limited places.[3]

Outsider physicians usually assume that local people primarily want more health care services, clinics, medicines, and supplies. However, when asked about medical needs, community members are often more concerned with basic human needs—accessing safe housing, food, clean water, and employment opportunities. These *social determinants of health* are critical components of public health. Local people are acutely aware of their importance although our outsider medical teams may not focus on them.

What do local people want most? Every community may have a

different answer, yet this question can only be answered appropriately by local people. Asking community members to list and prioritize *medical* resources and problems may provide us with a short list of physical problems, such as malaria and lung infections. Yet global health needs assessments should go deeper than clinical issues and address the social determinants of health.[4] By asking community members to brainstorm and then prioritize anything and everything that affects their health, the resulting list will surely include both medical and public health problems. This will be a richer and more meaningful list to work with, and it often proves to be as enlightening for local people as it is for us outsider health care workers.

We may feel overwhelmed by this broader range of problems. We may be made uncomfortable by exploring *non-medical* health challenges. Yet the struggles for health of people in resource-limited countries don't change because of our uncomfortable feelings. Just as health inequalities are socially-determined, many of the key solutions to health problems are found in a social context beyond medicine bottles and surgeries. However, the priorities and responses of local people may place unrealistic expectations on us outsiders, and this mismatch should be discussed during the early stages of our partnerships.[5] We need to be honest about which areas of public health we're comfortable working on in partnership, based on our levels of training, experience, and commitment.

Will You Do Public Health Work?

Schools of the health professions prepare us to attend to individual needs and problems by focusing on one patient at a time. While such a focus is practical for *patient care*, it's insufficient for holistic *community health*—and especially global health work. Major health needs are often missed by having a laser focus on individuals. For example, attending individual cases of measles in refugee camps is important, yet it misses the larger public health approaches which can prevent its spread: mass vaccination, and alleviating insufficient and congested housing.

An unfortunate gap has been created between public health and clinical medicine. Knowledge and skills should be shared between clinicians and public health professionals to better prepare practitioners of each field.[6] I believe all clinicians would benefit from a basic knowledge of public health, and that a minimum of one-fifth of all clinical education should be taught by public health professionals. Given that global health is primarily a field of public health, outsider clinicians should obtain significant training in global public health before travelling abroad.

Doing public health work is an oft-neglected best practice standard for medical service teams abroad.[7] Some of these teams have acknowledged the need to be multidisciplinary,[8] as well as the importance of focusing on preventive health interventions.[9] However, outsider medical volunteers usually have less interest in this work and most avoid doing it.[10]

Regardless of preference, seeing public health problems on the priorities list of communities in low resource settings can clarify important barriers to health promotion, disease treatment, and follow-up. Insufficient access to clean water can explain frequent gastrointestinal illness, while food insecurity can explain malnutrition and vitamin deficiencies. Lack of sufficient education can alert providers to high rates of illiteracy and suggest the need for alternative ways of providing health messages and medication instructions to ensure effectiveness.

A broad local health problems list should be a wakeup call for outside medical providers. It should push us to explore *non-medical* health problems such as poor access to clean water and sanitation, indoor smoke pollution, and limits to education, encouraging us to move beyond our traditional clinical training and enter the realm of public health and the root causes of ill health.[11]

Do clean water and sanitation projects lie outside of the job descriptions, comfort level, and training provided by the Western medical system? Usually this is the case, and it demonstrates a humbling inadequacy in our training. This is because anyone interested in helping to improve lives and prevent deaths should be involved in these and other public health projects. If we are prepared to treat a million cases of malaria rather than taught how to prevent people from getting it in the first place, then we as individual caregivers are falling woefully short in promoting health.

Yet we don't have to know it all or do it all ourselves; a great solution is to work on multidisciplinary teams that include public health professionals. When clinicians are uncomfortable or unprepared to do public health work, then public health professionals can be invited to join—and better yet, to lead—our outsider teams. In order to maximize health promotion, these complementary fields must work together closely. Common goals and aligned leadership, as well as a shared approach of community engagement, can bridge the clinician-public health gap.[12] Outsiders trained in public health can accomplish much by sharing knowledge with *local* clinical and public health workers.

Training in Action

*She smiled proudly despite many missing teeth. With
two metal cylinders and a large metal plate bound together
by twine on her back, and supported by a strap around her
forehead, she was hiking five miles to the mud and stick
structure that she called home. She had always cooked meals
inside for her family, but the indoor cook-fire produced
thick smoke that worsened her daughter's asthma and gave
her husband emphysema. She will use the stove parts she
was carrying to build an improved cookstove: food and pots
will sit on the metal plate over a fire, and the chimney will
channel smoke out of the house. Because it burns fuel more
efficiently, it will also mean fewer trips up and down the
steep volcanic slopes in search of wood.*

Improved cookstoves lower fuel consumption and reduce indoor air
pollution.[13] Household air pollution from indoor smoke is one of the
largest risk factors for disease in the world: in 2010 alone, it caused 3.9
million premature deaths from emphysema, pneumonia, heart disease,
stroke, and lung cancer.[14]

Yet improved cookstoves weren't in the medical school curriculum!
Still, we partnered with Honduran and Guatemalan community

members, all of us finding these stoves surprisingly easy to construct. My global health mentor demonstrated to village craftspeople an effective way to make them cheaply and easily, and together they adjusted the design based on community preferences and resources. Families wanting an improved cookstove would attend a training session on their construction and use, while contributing US$5 to the cost of materials. They were also required to contribute two days of community work, which might include helping other families build stoves.

> *I brushed past larger-than-life plantain leaves and saw a marvel down the winding path ahead of me. In the most unlikely of places, between slabs of rock on a steep slope, there were rows of maize fed by drip irrigation tubes running like IV lines. Growing tall against all odds, again and again I happened upon mini-plots of crops hidden among the mountain's 45-degree slopes. Elsewhere, some farmers dug a hole near their homestead and piped spring water to fill it. They introduced tilapia eggs, and after six months of feeding mango and corn to the growing fish, they could access high protein food for their family. The surplus from their fish farms also generated badly needed income.*

My global health mentor, Dr. Doug Stockman, taught me about nutrition and agriculture interventions in Honduras, including fish farming, drip irrigation, fertilizer, and crop rotation. Fish farming can offer an important and sustainable protein source,[15] while successfully generating family income.[16]

Crop yields can be expanded by irrigating, reducing pests and plant diseases, and applying fertilizer and manure.[17] *Drip irrigation* places thin tubes close to crops either above or below ground; these tubes have *emitter* holes which allow water to slowly drip to the roots of crops with minimal evaporation. Drip irrigation increases crop yields while minimizing water use.[18]

Training sessions on increasing agricultural yields have successfully increased food production, especially when combined with empowering farmers to do their own research on successful methodology; for example, rice yields in Thailand and Cambodia have been greatly expanded by changing the soil, compost application, weeding, and pest management, and altering seed age, spacing, and rate.[19] Crop yield can also be increased by rotating crops grown in the same field, growing two crops at the same time, and including tree growth in the cropping system; further, increased soil fertility and crop yields can be achieved by planting *cover crops* such as grasses or beans in the same fields during the off-season.[20]

> *These smart children lived in poverty and couldn't afford books, uniforms, shoes, supplies, or middle-school exam fees, so our joint local-outsider scholarship program endeavored to give them an opportunity. Housing was provided for those with over a three-hour walk to school. We met with parents who applied for a scholarship, talked with school administrators, and went apartment-hunting with kids and their parents. We supported a dozen more kids each year and set up focus groups with all of the families so they could help each other organize supplies, study, and housing. We encouraged them to create a local scholarship committee and they elected leadership to guide the program internally. One scholarship recipient graduated, became a teacher herself, and tutored community middle-schoolers.*

By organizing scholarships in partnership, we didn't directly do public health capacity-building; nonetheless, we supported local schooling which would indirectly expand health knowledge and health status. The higher our general educational level, the lower our risk factors for poor health become.[21] Systematic reviews show a consistent relationship between higher education levels and improved health outcomes, such as lower mortality rates.[22]

Immunizations are perhaps the most familiar public health intervention to outsider medical volunteers. Vaccine-preventable infectious diseases are the fourth most common cause of loss of *disability-adjusted life years* in resource-limited countries;[23] they cause one-fifth of all deaths under 5 years of age worldwide.[24] Existing vaccination programs for measles, pertussis, and tetanus prevent over two million deaths from these three diseases every year.[25] Vaccine-preventable child deaths are also commonly caused by haemophilus influenzae B, rotavirus, and pneumococcal infections. We outsiders may feel good about *treating hundreds* of patients in temporary volunteer clinics abroad, yet we should feel much better about *preventing thousands of deaths* by supporting local vaccine programs.

Although desperately needed in resource-limited countries, vaccine programs must be conducted in an empowering way. If local people do not believe in their importance and participate in their planning and roll-out, vaccine programs will flounder and breed distrust.[26] Community participation expands vaccine coverage rates.[27]

When needed and requested by local people, outsiders can offer a valuable service though vaccine capacity-building. Training topics can include safe injection practices, supplies, storage and the cold chain, transport, ordering, scheduling, documentation, side effects, and adverse events. These sessions can also cover outreach, promotion, vaccine drive organization, and fostering community trust. Promoting local vaccination is one of the areas in which short-term medical service teams can make a substantial and positive contribution.[28]

Safe Water, Safe Life

Since I have more experience in water, sanitation, and hygiene, they will serve as the main examples of public health work in this chapter and the two that follow.

> *This is where the boy's bathing was forever interrupted by the unforgiving, heavily-muscled jaws of the crocodile. His mother described his disappearance beneath the surface vividly as if she had watched the whole taking. This was their reality; water is life and there was no safer option than to come here. The river's gentle rhythm lapped at her forearms, her hands submerged rubbing clothes. Her daughter gathered drinking water downstream while her remaining son relieved himself in the water around the bend.*

Clean, safe water is critical to life, yet communities in resource-limited countries often suffer health problems due to a low quantity and quality of water. After pneumonia, diarrhea is the world's second leading cause of death for children under age five years.[29] Diarrhea is the most common cause of child death in Africa and the second most common in Southeast Asia.[30]

What can outsider medical professionals do beyond treating diarrhea and dehydration with oral rehydration solution and zinc (with or without IV fluid and antibiotics)? We can also offer vitamin A and promote safe pregnancy, breastfeeding, and nutrition.[31] Further, rotavirus vaccination prevents roughly half of all hospital admissions for diarrhea.[32]

Yet when fecal contamination of water and food is at the center of the diarrhea problem, these interventions will only scratch the surface. Child diarrhea can be *greatly impacted* through improvements in water quantity and quality, latrine access, and hygiene improvements—especially in combination.[33] Some 90% of all cases of diarrhea are caused by fecal contamination of water and/or food, or otherwise attributable to poor sanitation and hygiene.[34]

Shockingly, an estimated 55% of *all* child deaths in resource-limited countries could be prevented by making one or more improvements in sanitation or water safety.[35] For instance, hand-washing can reduce diarrhea risk by 47%.[36] In these ways, *non-medical* public health interventions are the most critical in saving children's lives in resource-limited countries.

I saw case after case of typhoid on my first trip to Sierra Leone. I gave out a lot of antibiotics, but what was really needed was prevention by improving water safety, sanitation, and hygiene. My next two trips focused almost entirely on related public health capacity-building and community-based program work. Only 22% of Sierra Leoneans have access to safe drinking water,[37] and waterborne disease is a major cause of child mortality there.[38]

> *I joined community facilitators as we strained our voices to overcome the roar of heavy rain pounding our tin roof. At the Train-the-Trainer session, we covered the tops of water buckets with pieces of clean cloth; they were used as filters for turbid water. Next, we passed around empty water bottles to practice with. We all pretended to fill them with water to the three-quarters mark, put the lids on, shook them for 20 seconds, and then put them on the tin roof for "solar disinfection." Then we reviewed "sedimentation." We practiced storing water for two days in a pot, transferring it to a second pot for two more days, and then a third one for two more days until drinking it. Water at the bottom of each pot was avoided by all in this hands-on training.*

Unclean containers and handling often introduce contamination before water reaches the home, so treating water at the *point of use* serves as an important training topic.[39] Filtering turbid water through a clean cloth filter is a helpful first step, increasing the success of other methods of disinfection. Through *solar disinfection*, leaving water out on sunny day for six hours actually disinfects it; ultraviolet light inactivates pathogen DNA.[40] Sedimentation via the *three pot method* can be helpful in settling bacteria to the bottom, while half of them die after two days.[41]

Boiling and chlorinating water serve as more expensive and less useful treatment options, since lack of fuel and unpleasant taste serve as common barriers.[42] Water pathogens can also be separated and settled out through a chemical process called *coagulation and flocculation*. Alum and iron compounds can be added to bring on this process, or else ground-up seeds from the moringa (or "horseradish tree") can be used.⁴³ Filters offer another option.

> *We passed PVC pipes and saws back and forth to fifteen community members in rural Sierra Leone. A man started with the hacksaw and was surprised when a woman reached for it, finishing the job. Men and women both grabbed glue and drills as we built a "slow sand filter" together. It was a chaotic but empowering hands-on teaching session!*

Slow sand filters consist of plastic drums with the top removed and PVC piping placed within it, leading up to a faucet. Holes are drilled into the PVC pipe at the bottom, so that water can be drawn up. Clean gravel is placed at the bottom, followed by a layer of clean sand, and then a layer of large rocks on top. Water is poured into the top, and nearly all pathogens are removed through sand filtration and biological inactivation from algae which grow in the sand layer.⁴⁴ The main ingredients are sand, gravel, and larger rocks, making these filters cheap and easy to construct—even without electricity.

> *After the Train-the-Trainer sessions, we passed on posters, maps, and teaching props that we'd made together. Local clean water leaders were encouraged to use them to teach others in their communities. We set up "field*

trips" to visit every local water source, asking government water organizers to join us and teach about each well that had mechanical problems; during these visits, they also chlorinated community wells with local people, shared their methods, and left behind chlorine powder for community members to continue the process.

In addition to training on water treatment options, capacity-building can focus on fixing or constructing new safe water sources. These projects expand both the quantity and quality of water and they include protected springs, piping systems, wells, boreholes, and rain water collection and storage systems. Through *Train-the-Trainer* sessions, local people can be prepared to serve as clean water engineers for their villages.[45] Some outside NGOs train local people in the basics of clean water engineering, encouraging them to prioritize community water problems and manage local systems.[46] As community members engage in planning, design, and construction, they build the skills and confidence needed for project replication and future repairs.

Each of these projects has long-term maintenance requirements, so they shouldn't *simply* be thought of as one-off training programs; rather, they need to be part of a long-term Community-Based Health Program (see chapter 11).

Latrines: Gifts or Goals?

Bamboo walkways rose above flooded village paths and through dense clouds of flies. In this area of Burma, just about everybody visited the bush to pass stool. The houses hovered on poles above the murky water, but they weren't high enough to get people away from the smell of their stool below.

Open defecation refers to leaving stool exposed, so that flies and other insects and animals can contact it and then expose people to it. Open defecation also allows stool to be carried by rainfall into streams, rivers, ponds, fields with crops, and other sources of drinking water or food. The pathogens in stool infect people through contact with contaminated fluids, fields, food, flies, and fingers. A deeply successful sanitation program will result in a village becoming *open defecation free*.

Latrines offer a low-cost and low-tech way to separate stool from human contact. Improved sanitation can reduce diarrhea by 34%.[47] However, resource-limited countries are a long way from achieving the Millennium Development Goal on sanitation; at the pace of change in 2011, it would actually take two centuries to meet this goal.[48] As of 2015, there were 2.4 billion people in the world who lacked access to an improved sanitation facility, such as a latrine.[49]

*The government came to the quiet mountain communities of Honduras and imposed a sanitation solution. They built **pour-flush** latrines for many families, but there were two reasons that these "gifts" weren't used: 1) communities didn't lead and "own" this project, and 2) there was no water to flush them! Lacking water for most of the year, we thought that **pit** latrines and **compost** latrines would be more appropriate options; yet outsiders shouldn't pick the solution either.*

We raised sanitation awareness and organized skits. In Train-the-Trainer sessions, we explored the links between sanitation and safe water, while reviewing various latrine models and asking for feedback. Community members decided to build more pit latrines and they wanted to practice making the VIP model together. After building a few, they took over. One particularly handy man tipped his cowboy hat and mumbled some fast Spanish before expanding the latrine project throughout the villages. He was a natural local leader. Inspired by the project, he was lit up enough to spread it like wildfire.

In skits to raise sanitation awareness, the promotion of latrines as convenient, modern status-symbols seems to influence community decisions more than promoting them as vehicles to improved health.[50] Another effective theme is promoting the physical safety of women. Latrine construction is best taught in a hands-on and active process rather than in a classroom.[51] As with all community projects, latrine models shouldn't be prescribed by outsiders but rather decided on by communities themselves.[52]

All latrine types require significant long-term maintenance,[53] so outsiders shouldn't construct them *en masse* and leave them as gifts. When done this way, such latrines were used for storage and other activities,[54] while open defecation continued nonetheless.[55] In Bangladesh, a government campaign to provide free latrines led to only 1% of households using them.[56] The hard-learned lesson is that latrines will only be used and maintained long-term if local people lead the process and view them as being a desirable *goal*. One or a few can be built for training purposes, but this often isn't needed since their construction is simple and the techniques are typically better known to local people than to outsiders.

Another alternative to outsider latrine construction is an empowerment-based activity called Community-Led Total Sanitation (CLTS). It aims to increase community desire to be *open defecation free*, and then to reach and sustain this state. It uses a community group model with empowering participatory techniques such as village walks, community sanitation mapping, and water testing homework assignments.[57]

> *In a remote corner of Sierra Leone, we hovered over a mess of colored markers on a tabletop. There was an expanding map in the middle and a ring of lively local people dipping their hands onto it. We asked them to collectively draw a community sanitation map, showing wells and other water sources in blue and latrines in red. This map stimulated discussion about the proximity of the two, as well as fields used for open defecation at the edge of town. We asked community members to apply brown powder to this map as a way to illustrate where stool goes and how it contaminates their water and food sources. The final map was covered in brown powder, generating some laughs but also some deep analysis.*

> *Another fun (but troubling) activity involved pulling out a kit of US$0.50 coliform bacteria tests. Testing powder was added to water samples, turning them yellow. Bacterial contamination was demonstrated when water samples turned black within 48 hours. Local people took the tests to their water sources and watched as rainwater and some well water remained yellow. Meanwhile, water turned black from the river, streams, lake, spring box, and most wells. Since community members planned and did the testing themselves, they "owned" the results and it motivated much discussion and desire for change.*

> *Local people were excited about visiting and improving water sources, but they dreaded the latrine visits we insisted on. We deliberately paired these visits so we could walk to and test wells built near latrines. When testing showed all of these wells to be contaminated, local people decided to close these latrines and dig new ones farther from the wells. At first, community members thought it was odd to visit and*

analyze each latrine with a doctor, but later the message was
clear that latrines have even more to do with their health
than clinics.

As a result of these CLTS discussions and activities, the
communities decided to form clean water committees, chlorinate wells,
close certain latrines, dig more latrines, collect water fees to repair
wells, prohibit young children from gathering (and contaminating)
well water, and to collect more rainwater. These capacity-building
and *community awakening* sessions can create a snowball effect of
ongoing water and sanitation improvements.[58] Communities in over 50
countries have successfully become open defecation free using CLTS.[59]
In India alone, thousands of villages and even entire districts have
become open defecation free.[60] Over 15 countries have embraced CLTS
into their national water and sanitation policy.[61]

Although it often falls short of the goal to be open defecation
free, WHO has also developed a participatory capacity-building activity.
Participatory Hygiene And Sanitation Transformation (PHAST) also
uses community mapping and water and sanitation walks. Through
this process, local people explore diarrhea prevention methods and
choose desired clean water, sanitation, and hygiene projects which they
also evaluate over time.[62] PHAST has been shown to empower local
people and induce hygiene behavior change; yet compared to CLTS, it's
more time-consuming[63] and more top-down in practice.[64]

How these *participatory approaches* work is the subject of the next
chapter.

10

Participation to Empower

Introduced in the previous chapter, our Community-Led Total Sanitation (CLTS) effort brought local people together to draw a *community sanitation map* and then to complete hands-on water testing *homework assignments*. Then we took a *community water and sanitation walk* together. These participatory activities led villagers to make impressive changes in their sanitation practices.

Yet how exactly did these changes happen? This chapter will serve as a brief guide on how participatory activities—such as CLTS—work. I encourage my readers to study, apply, and adapt community activities with your local partners.

Community walks, mapping, and other hands-on activities all involve the active participation of local people: an essential step on the road toward empowerment. The activities also encourage them to take ownership of local strengths, problems, and related solutions. Community members do the investigation, discover the results, make realizations, and become inspired to work toward solving their problems. Meanwhile, outsiders work on the sidelines as co-facilitators of and consultants to the process.

Inspiring Change: Maps and Walks

CLTS will be the first example of participatory empowerment explored here. Local people can create a *community sanitation map* to show the relationship between their water sources and stool contamination of them.[1] Mapping often awakens some families to the fact that many people pass stool near their homes and water supply. The flow of fecal contamination to rivers and ponds, colored on the map with increasing areas of the infamous brown powder, raises the level of collective concern and stimulates further disgust.

Through a *community walk*, local people can visit existing latrines as well as the informal areas of open defecation for women, men, and children. Through the uncomfortable time spent there together, the sight and smell of stool in the open generates disgust and the desire to do better. These ends are actually intermediate goals of CLTS; uncomfortable community members react strongly by refusing to continue open defecation.[2] Next, some tend to quickly build makeshift latrines and encourage others to do the same. Villages often have discussion and conflict over this and we outsiders shouldn't get involved. After all, their discomfort stimulates awareness, motivation, and movement toward a community-led sanitation program.[3]

At a later point, a village map of households using latrines can be displayed publicly; it's colored in as each subsequent house makes a latrine and *joins the club*. Again, those not making and using latrines feel pressure to do so. Although unconventional, the CLTS approach is usually very effective and can be expected to save more lives than more top-down outsider health initiatives.

CLTS is just one application of empowerment techniques through the use of participatory *community mapping* and *community walks*. Local and outside facilitators can guide local people to make their own community maps using available materials. They can be drawn in colors on paper, constructed as three-dimensional models, or simply scratched into the ground with sticks.[4] Importantly, community members without the ability to read or write can still pool their knowledge with their neighbors.[5] The highly participatory activity of creating such maps as a community has a variety of uses: to inventory health problems, to locate local assets such as skilled craftspeople, to identify areas dangerous to children, etc.

Community health maps can be drawn to show the location of treatment facilities and houses in relation to health risks such as areas of mosquito breeding. Health maps can identify the homes of those with chronic medical problems and disabilities, senior citizens, public nuisances, pregnant women, and single-parent households; they can also identify homes with child laborers, children under age five, orphans, malnourished and unvaccinated children, those with the worst housing, and those living in the deepest poverty.[6] For these higher risk community members, such maps can be used to identify needed initial health care access and follow up care.[7]

It's quite empowering to identify and discuss *assets* publicly through group mapping sessions. For example, *skills and leadership maps* illustrate where people with different skills work—including health workers, engineers, teachers, and local leaders. *Education maps* demonstrate the location of all types of schools and the level of literacy of community members.

*It was an abstract scene; it seemed that ghosts were
swaying between trees, quickly in and out of focus. Like an
impenetrable fog, malnutrition hovered everywhere in this
place. There were 12 community members in a focus group
and we asked them to draw a map of their villages and food
sources. They pointed out foods which were accessible and
those which were difficult to access. The local community
health worker (CHW) was chosen to be the main artist
and, with feedback from the group, he plotted village food
resources and problems. He noted the typical places to find
crabs, frogs, fish, shrimp, snakes, mice, livestock, eggs, veggie
gardens, fruit trees, potatoes, and rice. Some foods were
accessible to all, while others could only be found in stores or
neighboring towns. Expensive and less plentiful foods were
marked with 1 to 3 stars based on difficulty of access.*

*We asked them to draw conclusions from their map
regarding local food assets and problems, and what the
map showed about malnutrition. We were shocked to learn
that rice was actually their least available food! Despite rice
paddies being ubiquitous in this part of Burma, villagers
only worked the land and grew the rice; they neither owned
the paddies nor could afford the rice growing in them.
The CHW learned from this discussion that community
members weren't aware of the different "food groups" and the
importance of a balanced diet, so that was added to his list of
important teaching topics!*

Community mapping can be paired with community walks since
they reinforce each other. A town stroll for a tourist involves an
outsider and a community member walking around together to look at
whatever interests the outsider. By contrast, *community empowerment
walks* feature a small group of local people and 1 or 2 outsiders as
they tour what's important to community members. Local resources,
opportunities, and problems are visited, seen in person, and discussed.[8]
On these walks, groups may visit the village center, remote jungle
houses, food sources, health care centers, water sources, or many other
sites or resources of interest.[9] A systematic visit to assets and problems
tends to stimulate ideas and discussion. In a very practical way, it
reminds community members of what they collectively have and lack.

*The sun found a keyhole to project a glowing shadow of
itself wedged between storm clouds. Later, the gates of the*

sky opened and a white-hot sea filled the valley. The rays illuminated the local group leader's forehead, inside which ideas and plans were heating up, swirling with discussion, and gathering momentum for change.

Other participatory methods include drawing diagrams of local problem causality, demographics, social realities, and disparities.[10] Community groups can make *pie charts* of diagnoses, family planning methods, or other variables. The health status of children can be evaluated and ranked using *stones as markers*. Meanwhile, *Venn Diagrams* explore local people's perceptions and relationship to health centers and health workers. These last three methods, just a small sampling of what is possible, are reviewed in *Appendix C*.

Participatory Rural Appraisal

Entire textbooks are devoted to participatory empowerment methods and it has even spawned a Development sub-field called Participatory Rural Appraisal (PRA).[11] PRA aims to empower local people through participatory group-based activities; while outsiders may facilitate these activities, they neither control them nor the agenda.[12] Questionnaires, interviews, and lectures are downplayed by Participatory Rural Appraisal. Rather, information-sharing and analysis is highly participatory and directed at empowering local people.[13] A strong emphasis is placed on visual and hands-on methods, with drawing, drama, and videos taking precedence over verbal presentations and written guides.

PRA gathers data through community mapping, walks, and other local activities; data is cross-checked, or *triangulated*, with group members for its accuracy. Local people analyze and use the resulting data to design their programs. Community members present data in discussion groups, as they analyze their assets and problems. After identifying their own resources and problems, people are encouraged to brainstorm, select, and implement their own solutions.

The goal of PRA is active community participation to enable local people to select and achieve their own goals.[14] Unlike top-down approaches, PRA gives *ownership* of information to the community, which can decide how to analyze and use it. PRA "is built upon community members identifying their own problems and discovering their own solutions."[15] It is revolutionary because it essentially involves local people "developing" themselves, rather than relying on outsiders to paternalistically "develop" their community. PRA is also referred to as PLA, or Participatory Learning and Action.

Robert Chambers, one of the main proponents of PRA, has shown that *development* isn't successful when it's controlled by outsiders; rather, community programs only work when outsiders are "enabling local people to be the analysts, mappers, diagrammers, observers, researchers, historians, planners, and actors, presenters of their analysis, and then in turn facilitators."[16] Chambers' work revolutionized the field of development, which had long focused on outsiders' research and priorities rather than the needs, desires, and long-term empowerment of local people. With a charity mentality, foreigners designed and implemented programs in a top-down way that was usually inappropriate and often created dependency.[17] Beyond health care, this unfortunate story repeated itself in multiple settings within resource-limited countries, involving agriculture,[18] housing,[19] clean water,[20] sanitation,[21] and vaccine[22] programs.

From Top-Down to Bottom-Up Development

Top-down development programs are destined to fail since we outsiders lack adequate awareness of communities abroad. While surveys emerged as a way to gather data on local people's needs, they are typically designed in rich countries with biases inherent in the selection and wording of questions; often their overvaluing of conciseness condemns them to poorly reflect the complex realities of resource-limited countries.[23] Local people often give answers that they know foreigners want to hear, and we tend to analyze surveys in ways that confirm our preconceptions.

First, *Rapid Rural Appraisal* was developed as a cost-effective alternative to rigid question-based surveys. It uses open-ended questionnaires and only partly-structured interviewing, leaving more room for local feedback. It also involves community walks with local guides, attending community groups, and talking with *local* experts— not solely with outsiders.[24]

Rapid Rural Appraisal was a step in the right direction, yet it did little to empower local people. Community participation was only encouraged in the initial data-gathering phase. Rather than sharing data with community members, it was used by outsiders to develop programs while local people were mostly passive recipients of these programs.

PRA has been a breath of fresh air. Evolving from Rapid Rural Appraisal, it has been successfully applied to development fields worldwide, including poverty alleviation, agriculture, clean water, sanitation, and health care. It has appropriately become the new standard replacing old paternalistic strategies.

Many donors acknowledge that non-participatory programs tend to fail, and development grants are often conditioned on the use of PRA methodologies. Even the World Bank embraced PRA in the 1980s.[25] PRA is accepted as an evidence-based best practice in the field of development as well as that of global health.[26]

PRA and Participatory Health Care

Despite such esteem, PRA is seldom used by outsider medical teams. However, we would benefit greatly by following lessons from the increasingly bottom-up field of development. Health groups can implement a variety of participatory empowerment activities, including patient support groups, team-building retreats, peer support programs, vocational training, and income-generating activities.

A small group of teens living with HIV in Botswana started meeting informally and supporting each other, answering each other's questions on the disease, its social challenges, and its treatments. The group grew organically until it became a large and thriving body, now for more than a decade. Members "graduated" as they became adults, while new members joined. I worked with a Botswanan nonprofit that recognized the importance of what these empowered teens were doing, so they began facilitating and formalizing these meetings. New themes have been addressed at each monthly meeting, including stigma, pregnancy, viral load, and adherence.

The success of this empowerment model has been replicated throughout Sub-Saharan Africa. In Tanzania, some 200 teens come together each month to learn more about living with HIV. They support each other, dance to loud music, act out skits, eat together, and have their medicines refilled simultaneously. There are also peer-led empowerment groups for caregivers of children living with HIV and for those who have high viral loads despite treatment.

Youth mentors who are living with HIV serve as staff members of the clinics and community programs. These peer mentors organize a camping experience for those with poor treatment adherence, with hands-on activities and games to encourage teamwork and adherence support, and a range of participatory empowerment activities. They also support each other through income-generating opportunities; they make and sell crafts together as they learn artisan and business skills in the process.

HIV prevention has been promoted in Kenya by applying PRA methods to community discussions of barriers and proposed solutions,[27] as well as through drama.[28] In Uganda, *24-hour activity clocks* for men and women were drawn in groups, identifying men's risky behaviors for HIV transmission.[29] A group in Thailand used a PRA activity to divide and redivide community members into HIV risk categories, thus raising awareness that no one in town was without risk.[30]

In additional to HIV care, every patient visit can be structured to also serve as an empowerment opportunity. Patient-centered care, self-management of chronic disease, and motivational interviewing are empowerment approaches that can be shared with health workers in resource-limited countries, and can be merged with participatory PRA methods.

Patient-centered care revolves around the needs and desires of patients, who are invited to take a more active role in their own care. The approach more effectively listens to, informs, respects, and involves people in their own medical decisions.[31] In areas where health worker access is limited, one application of this approach involves visiting pharmacies together, identifying antibiotic packages, and reviewing the uses and dangers of each. This hands-on activity is helpful where patients frequently buy antibiotics over-the-counter with little guidance regarding their use.

In the West, patient empowerment is also promoted through the *self-management of chronic disease*. People with diabetes in the US used to be told what to eat and how much insulin to use, but now they're increasingly encouraged to set their own diabetes care goals after learning about diet, exercise, interpretation of sugar readings, and safe medicine use.[32] These patients are empowered to take ownership of their disease and its management, and the same can be true in resource-limited countries. Self-management can also be applied to chronic diseases such as sickle cell, tuberculosis, and long-term malnutrition. Families can learn to keep records tracking their own health improvement, including, for example, their anemia levels, a calendar of days on anti-TB treatment, and a graph of improving child weights and heights.

Motivational interviewing (MI) serves as another effective method of empowering patients, encouraging the achievement of healthy behavior changes they value. MI is used effectively to promote adherence to HIV medicines, as well as to increase the use of chlorine for drinking water treatment.[33] MI doesn't involve giving advice; rather, health care providers follow a patient's lead toward a desired behavior change, using a careful mix of listening, questioning, and sharing information.

Changing behavior is difficult, complex, and necessarily involves ambivalence. When health care providers present good reasons for a healthy behavior change, then patients naturally go on the defensive and respond with reasons to oppose change. With MI, the trick is to bring out the argument for behavior change from the patients themselves by having confidence in their intelligence and motivation.[34] As with the self-management of chronic disease, patients can be encouraged to make diagrams which outline the ways they plan to achieve their health goals.

We can train local health workers in these participatory empowerment methods, and they can also be applied more generally to clinical capacity-building. Rather than lecturing about the health issues that we're concerned about, PRA methods can be used to identify the issues of concern to local health workers. In PRA discussion groups, health workers analyze community health problems as well as gaps in their own health education. PRA can boost health knowledge intake through storytelling, role play, drama, and health games. Participatory empowerment is also critical for the final *approach* to global health work, which is the subject of the next chapter.

11

Community-Based Health Programs

Disguised by layers of mud, I could barely recognize the man standing at the bottom of a well shaft, deepening due to his hard work. On my first trip to Eastern Uganda, the community asked us to fund well construction; we listened to their priorities and shifted our focus to clean water. We raised the funds and community members built the well, yet this health program was created and organized by us outsiders.

It wasn't born out of community efforts and we hadn't promoted the organization of a local clean water committee. Without such a committee, there was little hope that the well would be monitored, maintained, repaired, and sustained long-term. All pump handles for wells eventually break, and when this one did, there would be no committee to respond and repair it. Local people hadn't taken ownership of what was simply gifted and left on their doorstep. I felt good watching its construction, but realized that we had messed up. This was not a community-based health program.

Despite our good intentions, "technically well-designed engineering projects fail because local citizens are not key members in the development plan to design, build, and manage the projects."[1] Regardless of our intentions and overall level of knowledge, outsiders can't plan appropriately within the context of local needs and desires.[2] Given our lack of community knowledge, it follows that we don't know how to solve local problems. We shouldn't design health programs ourselves—and if we do, their failure should be expected.

Outside volunteers typically organize health programs abroad in a top-down manner, doing the thinking, organizing, and sometimes the work ourselves. External organization isn't only problematic given the outsider knowledge gap, but also because it:

1. Bypasses preexisting local ideas, dreams, leadership, resources, and programs;
2. Disempowers local people, leaving them with less control over their health; and
3. Nearly guarantees the collapse of a health initiative since it remains dependent on the outsiders who started it.

When local people design and organize their own solutions to health problems it is most likely they will be well-informed, appropriate, successful, and sustainable. *Community-based health programs* do just that, as they're created, developed, and led by local people.[3] A community's capacity to improve its own health can be expanded through bottom-up participatory approaches which empower communities and prioritize the use of their own assets.[4] Bottom-up approaches are also generally more efficient and effective.[5] Community-based health programs (CBHPs) are organized from the bottom-up and are sustained by local people.

An improvement over one-time teaching events, such as *Training-the-Trainer* workshops, CBHPs are ongoing services or interventions and are typically long-term efforts. The sustainability of health programs is achieved only when they're rooted in the community.[6] For a change to be long-lasting, it needs to be driven by an expansion in local people's confidence and overall ability to continue helping themselves. Community members can be empowered to create their own programs, maintain *ownership* of them, adapt and improve them over time, and to sustain them indefinitely.

CBHPs are also evidence-based, as I'll review throughout this chapter. Further, there is a wealth of examples of health improvement through community-based participation.[7] Although any program can have unintended negative consequences, this is far less likely with community-based programs.

In these ways, CBHPs are a most fruitful approach to global health work (see Table 1 in *Global Health Approaches*). They often involve public health initiatives, and sometimes clinical ones as well. Examples of CBHPs include organizing community health centers, long-term health worker training programs, disease prevention and/or treatment programs, and water and sanitation programs such as wells and latrines.

Hand-Me-Downs and Facilitation

Suitcase medicine and health facility-building are the polar opposites of CBHPs. The former is based on the outsider organizing; it is rooted in our work and the initiatives are dependent on us. Yet communities in resource-limited nations deserve to have ownership and control of their health programs, rather than ceding control of community health to some distant entity. The presence of outsiders is almost always temporary, so the programs based on us are equally temporary. All communities deserve *long-term*, not provisional, health programs.

Many outsider-led health programs are later *handed down* to community members and, to this end, local committee formation may be encouraged at a later stage.[8] This committee may eventually take the reins of a program, but only after the path has been set, the bulk of the organizing has been completed, and the program has already seen some success, as defined by outsiders. In this model, local people remain disempowered throughout the organizational process of program development and implementation. Community leadership, program management, and financing are all stunted at birth, therefore reducing chances of blossoming later on.

As *Appendix B* will further demonstrate, such *hand-me-downs* rarely find long-term success. By contrast, CBHPs belong to local people from the very beginning.[9] The formation of a local committee to organize and run the program is encouraged at the start. There is no need for an awkward hand-over when the outsiders determine that the community members are ready.

As long as community members take the lead, partnerships between outsiders and local people can be a very effective support to CBHPs.[10] In the *Power to the People* chapter, I suggested that outsiders alter our approach from being that of a volunteer who gives charity or otherwise *does things for* and *gives things to* local people; rather, I proposed that we can help more by *facilitating* local people to organize their own health initiatives.

In some scenarios, outsiders can fill an important role by serving as facilitators for local people as they start up CBHPs.[11] Even so, communities will ideally facilitate their own programs—from start to finish—and never need the assistance of outsiders in sparking their creation. For example, when local people are *already* successfully organizing a health program, then there's no need for outsiders to offer to assist in facilitating it.

By contrast, when communities are interested in starting, changing, or expanding health programs, then outsiders might offer important assistance when invited to do so. Many communities in resource-limited nations (or, for that matter, in wealthy ones) aren't accustomed to *community-based* facilitation methods. Health program organization is more often *top-down* and led by local health authorities or government leaders. Local people who have developed community-based programs previously are likely to do a good job at it once again. On the other hand, those that haven't done so might benefit from a facilitation partnership with outsiders, national or foreign, who have. It can be particularly supportive of local development efforts to train one or more local leaders in methods of facilitation through the co-facilitation of health program organizing groups. In my experience, simply explaining how facilitation can work is not nearly as effective as actually doing it together.

When outsiders effectively facilitate within a locally-led partnership, it can often successfully promote local *ownership* of health interventions.[12] Outsider facilitators have also served as helpful problem-solving partners for CBHPs, thus increasing program chances of success.[13] The rest of this chapter will explore potential ways outsiders can contribute by co-facilitating (with one or more local leaders) community groups as they create or improve CBHPs.

Reigniting the Embers

The *Power to the People* chapter explored the importance of empowering by seeking out and utilizing *preexisting embers;* these are local health workers, facilities, groups, programs, ideas, dreams, plans, and other resources present in the community before outsiders arrive. The glowing embers of a fire are ready to ignite into a nice active flame when more wood is placed on them. Just as CBHP work is rooted in facilitation, it also centers on identifying preexisting embers and it commonly uses Participatory Rural Appraisal (PRA).

> *Searching for preexisting embers in Sierra Leone, we had a series of meetings with local people, experts, and NGOs— as well as government water agencies. Next, we connected or reconnected these groups with community members in an effort to forge stronger bonds among local people; we aimed to make outsiders as irrelevant as possible. Most days, we led discussion groups hand-in-hand with government chlorinators and well pump mechanics. Rather than day-dreaming about **new** water sources, we picked their brains about how they could improve each **existing** water source. Working with community members, we improved an existing "spring box," which protects a spring from contamination; we also expanded an existing rainwater collection system, both as "demonstration projects."*

*These villages previously had organized a water
committee but it had stopped meeting. Our goal was to help
reignite the embers. So we reached out to the committee
members who already knew how to chlorinate and repair
wells. Local people also reached out to masons, carpenters,
teachers, and health promoters. These many preexisting
"assets" became the basis of a renewed community water and
sanitation program.*

Communities in resource-limited countries often have preexisting
water committees, which should be approached and supported by
outsiders.[14] Compared to constructing new water projects, it's more
sustainable to incrementally improve **preexisting** wells in a step-wise
manner;[15] the same is true of water storage tanks.[16] Similarly, it's
more empowering, practical, and economical to improve a preexisting
latrine rather than building a new one from scratch. If a latrine can be
expected to last at least three more years, then it should generally be
upgraded rather than being replaced by a new one.[17]

For those of us trained in Western Medicine, one of our initial
patient questions is all too often: *Are you having any problems today?*
Likewise, one of our initial community questions echoes: *What are
your biggest village health problems?* Medical professionals are taught
to search for and ask about problems, yet empowerment work calls on
us to take a very different approach.

Focusing on problems can be quite disempowering. The more we look for problems, the more we find, and the worse those with the problems tend to feel as a result.[18] Yet when we focus first on a community group or program's positive attributes rather than its deficiencies, the characteristics of empowering solutions start to emerge.

Local groups can be encouraged to imagine what an ideal health program would look like, envisioning this through the lens of prior program successes (health or otherwise). This empowering activity is called *Appreciative Inquiry*; it appreciates the best in what already exists locally, recognizing that local people will have more confidence in the future if it's crafted using existing resources and successes.[19]

Appreciative Inquiry aligns perfectly with the methods of another field called *Asset-Based Community Development (ABCD)*. As a grassroots activity for sustainable community development, it taps into and connects preexisting local assets including skills, time, energy, and dreams.[20] The ABCD founders recommend that outsiders "avoid the temptation to begin with a traditional 'needs survey,' since this will lead inevitably to a strategy largely dependent upon outside help."[21] Needs-based evaluations seek to find out what local people don't have, therefore concluding—by their very design—that we outsiders are needed to *save the day* by providing what's lacking. When a needs survey pushes us to do things, we often bypass or curtail local leadership and ownership.

In contrast to needs-based approaches, asset-based ones start with what already exists locally. ABCD maps local assets, from individual skills to organizational reach. It then focuses on further building relationships among local people and groups so predominantly internal solutions can be found. Outsiders facilitate "community residents to *identify and recognize strengths and capacities* which they may have overlooked or ignored in the past."[22] Consensus-building and planning occur at a broad community level, and outsiders are only invited to help—if needed—during the final stages; we're invited only *after* local people develop a plan which encompasses primarily community assets.

In Sub-Saharan Africa, ABCD has used asset-searching as an activity to boost the self-esteem of impoverished communities. Too often local people internalize the definition of their communities as hopeless places after hearing themselves characterized this way again and again by Western NGOs.[23]

In Burma's rice paddy villages, one community taught us about their lack of health care and clean water access. Rather

*than rushing in to solve community health problems, we
asked how local people envisioned a solution. They wanted
to train community health workers to serve their people,
and they wanted to filter and pipe water to each house. We
met nearby Burmese groups who organize health worker
training and clean water programs, and we then connected
them to this village. What followed was an empowering tale
of Burmese helping Burmese; local people did the planning
and work, while we outsiders co-facilitated this process in the
background.*

Although they may look "backwards" to outsiders, most
communities are not stagnant places. Many times, community groups
have been meeting regularly for years prior to our arrival. They've
already developed some level of empowerment, expertise, functioning
group dynamics, leadership, and trust. Community groups like the
farmers' union, women's group, or a local NGO can serve as key
preexisting embers for health programs. Successful and ongoing local
programs are glowing embers! When a preexisting group or program
meets success, community members gain much more confidence
knowing that they started it and designed it before the outsiders even
showed up.

Partially-organized and planned but inactive local programs provide
another bed of embers for key health programs. Even failed and
abandoned local programs can offer sparks that can be coaxed into a
flame. For example, an abandoned school tutoring program offers a
chance for empowering questions to be discussed:

What worked well with this program?

If it were started again, how could it work better?

Which community skills and resources could help this
program?

Would community members like to improve the program
and start it again?

Outsiders should not forget that health programs often fail in
wealthy nations too, and that extra support can help to reignite
them. In order to empower local people, abandoned local programs
shouldn't be viewed as failures but rather opportunities to design better
programs.[24]

*In rural Sierra Leone, some community members
envisioned potential solutions internally, yet most pointed*

*their fingers at the white guy fresh off the plane. I used
Participatory Rural Appraisal group activities to try to turn
this expectation on its head. I asked community members
to list their preexisting groups in one column, with visiting
outside groups in another column. Groups that were still
active were circled; not surprisingly, they were largely local
groups!*

*Even so, community members kept insisting that the
outside groups should organize their desired programs. I
asked them whether their clean water and latrine access
would be more sustainable if outsiders or local people had the
knowledge, skills, and ability to build, fix, and pay for it. They
answered "local people" to all the questions, except there
was some debate about project start-up funds. They became
troubled by the idea that they would always be dependent
on outsider presence and resources to keep their programs
going. Finally, a consensus emerged that health programs
created by local groups are ideal.*

ABCD resonates well with a third field that was the central theme
of the last chapter: *Participatory Rural Appraisal (PRA)*. While
Appreciative Inquiry and ABCD teach us to start with *preexisting
embers*, PRA offers methods of identifying these embers through
participation. Visual and hands-on participatory methods, such as
community mapping, stimulate local self-analysis, discussion, and
planning. Community walks have been instrumental in stimulating
CBHPs[25], as have other PRA methods.[26]

ABCD is commonly implemented with PRA activities, given that
they are complementary and overlapping.[27] Appreciative Inquiry, ABCD,
and PRA all use evidence-based approaches to organize successful
community-based health programs. Further, they're all implemented at
the level of the community, in discussion groups or focus groups.

Focus Group Meetings

Although outsiders can meet with local leaders and professionals, I
don't believe that these meetings should ever be the *heart* of health
program organizing. Rather, meeting the larger community across
lines of race/ethnicity, gender, education, and social class is critical
for empowerment work. Such meetings can be done in a circle
arrangement to promote participation and equality.[28]

Group meetings are loosely referred to as *focus groups* by PRA
advocates, yet these groups are quite different from the research-based

community focus groups often used by outsiders. Conventional focus groups gather qualitative data, as a moderator uses a written discussion guide to gather group perceptions, beliefs, and ideas.[29] Outsiders then use this data to develop programs and solve problems.

By contrast, *empowerment-based* focus groups use a moderator to *facilitate* local people to solve their own problems; perceptions, beliefs, and ideas are probed so that community members can listen to themselves and generate their own understanding of their assets, problems, and potential solutions.[30] There's no written discussion guide or outsider agenda, as local people direct the discussion to where they deem to be most important and useful.

If an outsider invites ten people to form a focus group, then we may become the *de facto* organizer and group leader. Instead, I believe we get the best results by approaching a preexisting local group as a guest in order to sit in on or perhaps co-facilitate an empowerment focus group. Community groups such as women's or youth groups can be approached for focus group discussions. Where local groups are few (or are disinterested), we can seek out neutral community gathering spaces—places where community members can meet, speak freely, and informally share ideas.[31] Examples include town squares, schools, under trees, or eating places. Obviously, appropriate options are culturally-dependent.

Through focus group discussions, facilitators can lead the search to identify the pre-existing successes, leadership, resources, and inspiration in a community. Outsiders might co-facilitate these groups, but local people should do the thinking and organizing. Planning done by community members has a chance of being successful; planning done by outsiders does not.[32]

Working as facilitators, we can moderate discussion by promoting a safe and open space for communication and full participation. We can promote respect for others' ideas, even where there is disagreement. To serve as an effective facilitator, we could prompt quieter members to speak, perhaps by breaking a larger group into smaller ones. Group participants can be asked to summarize their discussions, identifying their own key *take home points* as part of the process of finding their own solutions.

Good listening is critical for facilitators, as is afterwards making the participants feel heard and inspired to continue thinking and speaking with confidence. Community group "participants feel empowered when focusing on positives or reframing negatives in such a way that they can manage them."[33] In order to best promote empowerment, we can curtail tangential conversations and those involving blame and rehashing past baggage.

Developing Health Programs

Here is the step-by-step approach to co-facilitating CBHPs that I use. Obviously, my preferences need not be duplicated, but these same concepts and methods can be adapted to facilitate effective community-based programs.

Step 1: Brainstorming assets and problems

Start by approaching preexisting community groups and work with them to facilitate a brainstorm of local assets and problems. When outsiders from a rich nation arrive, local people often freely share a long list of problems with the implicit expectation that outsiders will solve them. This is the first reason that I don't start by soliciting a problem list.

To uncover preexisting embers, begin by asking community members to brainstorm and list local assets. Through focus group exploration, local people may learn about resources and skills in their community that they weren't aware of or hadn't considered for years. Men and women, and people of different ages and social conditions have different vantage points from which they identify assets, so it is important to take stock of the diversity in the group. Then, after an exhaustive list of local assets is generated, we can begin brainstorming local health problems. Community members often impress themselves (and me!) by generating an assets list which is longer than their problem list.

It is important to state clearly that brainstorming sessions aren't aimed at finding ways for outsiders to solve local problems, but rather activating local people to do so. In order to demonstrate this point, have the community members compare their *assets list* and *problems list* side by side. Ask how they can use local assets to solve problems. This question is *kindling* for community members to consider, using assets they have to design largely internal solutions to challenges they face. Such a discussion is but a preview for more in-depth ones to come after a community health problem of interest is selected at a later stage.

Step 2: Prioritizing problems

Problem brainstorming meetings have the potential of burdening the group with an immense list of local problems. This can feel overwhelming, especially if assets aren't also explored. A focus group discussion to rank the local problems, and therefore prioritize them, can trim down a long problem list to a few priority issues. This can immediately make the list feel less overwhelming.

Next, local people can collectively decide on which health problem(s) they want to address. Community members can be encouraged to work on the health program that they are most driven to resolve, even if it responds to a less profound health need. The success of this program will prove to the community that it has capacity; its success can then serve as a template for progressively more important health initiatives. PRA methods for community problem ranking are reviewed in *Appendix C*.

Community members in Burma voting on how to rank village health problems.

Step 3: Brainstorming solutions

After problems are ranked and one or more is selected, focus groups can further explore with these questions:

> Who does the problem affect?
>
> Is this problem seen in other communities?
>
> What other problems relate to this one?
>
> What are its causes and potential solutions?

Through participatory community brainstorming, solutions can be identified and implemented.[34] Often community ideas for solutions flow directly from focus group discussions of assets and problems.[35] Other times, facilitators will need to use other PRA methods to stimulate the brainstorming of solutions. *Appendix C* reviews four PRA methods which can be helpful here:

- *Risk maps* focus attention on nearby assets which can be used for problem-solving.
- *Flow charts* can be used to explore perceived or actual causes of health problems.
- *Problem trees* allow for analysis of how problems relate to their causes and effects.
- *Matrices* can be used to explore the strengths and weaknesses of local medical care, as well as the health conditions which are supported with sufficient or insufficient care. They can also highlight treatment and prevention options which are present or lacking for specific diseases.

Each of these activities deeply analyzes health problems and lends itself to discovering and planning solutions.

One community member in Sierra Leone said, "If there is no collective responsibility, then wells spoil." Dirty hands lowered a rope and bucket into wells that were chronically contaminated and rarely chlorinated. Clothes were washed at well sites, as dirty water seeped underground. Kids jolted well pump handles and broke them; then they stepped into the pool of spring water to collect what the family would later drink. Adults left latrine holes uncovered and hands unwashed. Miners and farmers passed stool directly into streams, while women downstream gathered water for cooking. Patients with vomiting, diarrhea, and abdominal pain filled the clinics.

Local people wanted to make rules to prevent these problems, and they wanted to set up committees to enforce them. They decided that newly-elected committee members would regularly check on wells, clean and chlorinate them, and curb abuses. Responsibility for clean water would be taken out of the hands of the village leaders and given to local women, who primarily collect and use water. Empowered community members saw that they were the key to sustainable water and health solutions.

Community members aimed to start collecting minimal water fees, which would be used to cover and repair their wells and spring box. They wanted their own tools, to avoid calling on and paying NGOs, foreigners, and their government. We provided them with no more than the training, facilitating, and the handheld tools to construct and repair their water and sanitation projects; rejuvenated community water and sanitation committees took care of the rest!

Step 4: Forming a program committee

After local people brainstorm health solutions, they can be encouraged to compare proposals, decide on a course of action, and then develop a full health program. The formation of local program committees is a critical part of implementing sustainable CBHPs.[36]

Outsiders often create program committees afresh, but I believe they should ignite from preexisting embers. Program committees can sometimes emerge as outgrowths of empowered focus groups, which have already brainstormed assets, problems, and solutions. Alternatively, the focus group members most interested in designing the program may then continue meeting to become this committee. In still other cases, communities may elect committee members from among focus group attendees.

Focus group participants have already explored their problems and possible solutions together. Hopefully this process allowed them to bond, become inspired, develop leadership, and spurred them to start a health program committee. As outsiders, we may offer to co-facilitate the process, but local people actually create their own committees and programs.

In the villages of Sierra Leone, leadership and a sense of collective responsibility emerged from the "regulars" who came to most Train-the-Trainer sessions and focus group meetings. Community members decided that only those who attended most meetings could qualify as committee members; then they voted, and their water and sanitation committees were born!

Outsiders can serve an important role by facilitating local committee elections[37] and discussions on local water fee payment systems.[38] Such groups and systems can lead a fruitful path through various water programs over many years, yet it is not always smooth sailing. Comparing health proposals, deciding on a program, and structuring fees often are not easy tasks for committees, and there are bound to be disagreements. Conflict is natural, and when it is avoided, then the progress gained by developing a consensus will be avoided too. Facilitators can help by encouraging groups to express conflict openly, yet we should remain neutral.[39] When further discussion is no longer fruitful, we can remind the group of previously-identified common values, goals, and health priorities as way to help discussion move forward constructively.

Outsider participation in facilitation may enable local program committees to get past conflicts and achieve health program goals.[40] Facilitators should identify and work through group conflict patterns such as sabotage, blaming and shaming, scapegoating, dividing into factions, and *groupthink*. When disagreements get personalized, we can help blunt them by quickly distinguishing between the person and the issue. Facilitators can encourage the group to break down complex issues into smaller, more manageable parts. Identifying common needs and fears can provide opportunities for resolution, and we can encourage participants to search for *win-win solutions*. Where there are differences of opinion about how to proceed, alternative proposals should be brainstormed; teasing out areas of overlap between proposals can often lead to eventually reaching consensus.

Step 5: Monitoring and evaluation

After successfully designing and implementing a health program, local health committees can adapt it as they see fit. In order to progressively improve a program, committees need to monitor and evaluate it on a regular basis. As reviewed earlier, *participatory evaluation* can be facilitated using various PRA methods—yet this need not be done just by outsiders! We should aim to inspire and train local people to make participatory empowerment methods their own. PRA trainings involving health care workers from resource-limited countries may be formal 2 to 5 day events,[41] or they can simply involve community members participating in and co-organizing various group meetings using these facilitation methods.

Step 6: Program success!

When a CBHP achieves success and seeming sustainability, the community has proven to itself that it has the ability to further help itself. This inspiration often fuels future successes in health programs —with or without outsider involvement. For local people, the only step remaining is deciding what to do next! Community members can decide whether to expand or duplicate successful health programs. We can encourage them to share their success story with other communities as well,[42] so that a chain reaction spreads confidence and health improvements elsewhere.

In all stages of health program development, outsiders should stress: we won't design or lead programs, and we won't be there forever. This discourages dependence on us, as well as feelings of abandonment when we leave. We can climb onto our home-bound plane feeling good about our role in facilitation. Then we can stay in touch with the community, and perhaps be invited back to check in or to help in the event of a community or program crisis.

In supporting CBHPs, I've stressed the potential role of outsiders in facilitating empowerment through a locally-led organizing process. At the same time, I've downplayed the role of outsiders in doing, building, and funding things. I'll explore outsider contributions further in the next chapter, called *Less is More*.

12

Less is More

People arrived single-file on mountain paths from all directions, like spokes on a wheel. It was rare to find a lick of flat land in the Andes, especially one that hadn't been quickly repurposed into a soccer field. In  *one spot, pile after pile of PVC piping was carefully placed and then hoisted onto the shoulders of program designers contentedly heading towards home.*

I didn't understand the whole of this program until the full-day clothes-drenching hike. First we descended to the valley; the cows were stooling into the river where much of the water collection was happening, but our hike continued up the other equally steep valley wall where a spring was largely coated in concrete as a sort of public health shrine. Protected spring water was then carried by pipe to house after house through a dizzying network of PVC which made sense only on a map.

The community had created a spring box, organized a committee, and collected some funds and materials. Yet they just didn't have enough PVC to finish the job; this was the missing ingredient and we provided it, given that all of the other boxes were ticked.

In resource-limited communities, there are often a few items needed that can't be found or realistically purchased locally. Without these key ingredients, the program would never start or it would quickly collapse after starting. When requested, and when appropriate, outsiders can

help by providing these needed ingredients missing from the recipe.
Yet the majority of resources for health programs can and should be
found locally. If outsider groups contribute too many resources, we can
discourage empowerment and locally-based sustainability. In order to
be effective facilitators, we would best minimize our role as donors.
In this chapter, I'll review why this is the case and why *less is more*
regarding resource contributions.

Empower and Sustain

Prior chapters have reviewed how preexisting local resources provide
the ideal components for health program creation and maintenance.
When outsiders enumerate the resources we have or can access in our
home country, it can prematurely end local brainstorming sessions and
curtail ideas regarding home-grown solutions. When we offer resources
which haven't yet been requested, we are essentially offering solutions.
Further, when those resources are accepted by a community living in
poverty, as they almost inevitably are, we are essentially starting and
designing the programs ourselves.

Outsiders who lack feedback from community members should
arrive empty-handed on our initial trips abroad; showing up with
medicines, teaching tools, supplies, or other resources at this stage just
isn't appropriate. We would best only bring and donate resources after
learning about a community's needs, planned programs, and resource
requests. In this way, local people will only receive what they know
they need and therefore have asked for; importantly, they keep control
over the process. These are the seeds of empowerment, and they're
needed for effectively facilitating—or catalyzing—change. After all,
"an effective catalyst…is extremely cautious: the premature arrival
of external resources can overwhelm local efforts… Communities
experience internal power by mobilizing their own resources."[1]

Using local resources is not only more empowering, but also
generally more sustainable. Compared to imported resources, local
ones tend to be more economical, reliable, and easier to access long-
term.[2] Initially we may be able to create a program by providing items;
yet after we leave, a program will collapse unless these same items
can later be found locally. (Perhaps isolated *start-up* resources are
the exception to this rule.) When programs are founded without local
resources, it *proves* that local resources weren't needed for the health
program. This leads to less motivation to find them locally afterwards.
A program based entirely on outside resources is rarely sustained by a
community.

Local Ingredients First

Sweat dripped down my neck despite the air conditioning in the airport. We were frantically racing to make our flight across the Atlantic. I was attracting many strange looks since the large microscope box I was carrying was heavy and it was hard to run while carrying it. Nonetheless I zoomed along while holding it up on my head. The microscope was an important tool missing from the town we were traveling to; the clinic staff had searched for one locally without success. They decided it was what they needed the most and asked me to bring it.

Outside resources should be provided reluctantly and cautiously in order to minimize their adverse impacts and maximize the use of local resources. When possible, most if not all needed resources should be accessed locally from the very birth of a program. If they're not easily available, then the search for them should be ongoing until they are either located or determined to be definitely lacking. In the previous chapter, I reviewed the importance of brainstorming local resources and other assets *before* brainstorming problems and solutions; in this way, local resources get a leg up as potential solutions to community problems.

When brainstorming starts, it often appears that a community living in poverty lacks most if not all needed resources; yet these same resources may well become visible through a deep search. Outsiders often need to press local people in this exploration of resources; it's naturally easier to avoid searching and just accept gifts. Local resources, especially in conditions of scarcity, may be hidden or otherwise not disclosed to justify accessing goods from abroad. Similarly, when outsiders have a resource, then it will often be easier for us to quickly provide it rather than starting a difficult search for it in a resource-limited situation. It is important for both outsiders and community members to rein in these protective impulses in order to encourage real empowerment and program sustainability.

However, if all local problems could be solved entirely with community resources, then they likely would have been solved long before we arrived. After all, "resource-limited countries" are called that for a reason! Development specialists have pointed out that "outside resources are certainly needed, but they should be accepted only if they do not shift control outside the community."[3] While Asset-Based Community Development (ABCD) prioritizes local assets, it also acknowledges that resources from outsiders may be critical to program fruition.[4]

While community resource brainstorming tends to locate many or most needed inputs, it rarely finds them all. It can therefore pinpoint some resources critical for health program success which cannot be found or funded locally. Outsiders can then help by providing these few ingredients—ideally finding them in nearby towns or other parts of the resource-limited country. ABCD has established that the order of outsiders' facilitation and donation is very important: "First, outside resources will largely be wasted if the internal capacity of the community is not developed… The inside capacity must be there before the outside resource can be effectively leveraged."[5] As in the example of the previous chapter, there's no point in donating funding for well construction if there isn't already a local water committee that's engaged in supporting such a program.

Resources for Global Health

Suitcase medicine is heavily reliant on donating medicines, supplies, and equipment, while health facility-building often involves donating an entire clinic or hospital! In contrast, the empowering approaches to global health work aren't usually resource-intensive. Clinical and public health capacity-building approaches require few resources aside from teaching props. Health system strengthening often addresses the local stock of medicines, supplies, equipment, vaccines, and other resources, yet the focus is on the improvement of community-based supply systems rather than depending upon outside donations.

Professional disaster relief calls for resource donation more than other empowering global health approaches, yet it still aims to minimize these outside donations in order to avoid associated negative effects.[6] Finally, community-based health programs primarily utilize outsiders as facilitators rather than donors. However, in the chapter *Global Health is Public Health*, I did reference us outsiders buying improved cookstove parts and funding scholarships for middle schoolers. Even though empowering approaches to global health work minimize external resource inputs, they are often still necessary; for this reason, I'll briefly explore some clinical and public health examples, as well as the role for microloans.

Filling Clinic Shelves

In this small clinic in western Uganda, premature babies with difficulty maintaining their temperatures were kept warm in open-top foam containers. In another room, a very patient young boy had skin traction for a leg fracture; he was positioned on a bed with twine secured to his ankle and then to a box full of rocks dangling off of the bed. These were quick, easy, and inexpensive solutions using the resources at hand; there was rarely a need for complicated equipment imported from far-away nations.

Outsiders can minimize the need for donated medicines, supplies, and equipment by assisting in seeking out community sources, creating resources locally, and avoiding unnecessary use. We can learn from local traditions and teach and encourage the use of non-western medicine herbal (home) remedies when applicable, such as those for the treatment of viral respiratory infections.[7]

As addressed in *Part I*, a short list of safe, inexpensive, and critical medicines can be used in resource-limited health facilities. This can be adapted locally from the country's *essential drug* list, which in turn is rooted in the *WHO Model List of Essential Drugs*.[8] Outsiders should review these lists before traveling[9] and should generally avoid bringing medicines which are absent from these lists. We can ask local providers which meds they use frequently and which they lack, since unsolicited handouts are the most disempowering.

The same holds true for medical supplies and equipment. Outsiders frequently fly or ship them from our higher income countries. However, the most empowering place to get them is from the community itself—or as close as possible. Buying meds and supplies from local pharmacies contributes to the local economy and, perhaps as importantly, sends the message that solutions can be found locally.

There are many unfortunate stories of outsiders bringing unsolicited equipment abroad, without teaching about its use or how to repair it. I've even witnessed the shipping of dialysis supplies from the US to a rural African town which was hundreds of miles away from a dialysis center! In order to maximally empower community members, supplies and equipment should be low-cost, efficient, easy to use, and culturally acceptable; such *appropriate technology* should ideally be made of local materials and local abilities.[10] Community members must have the knowledge and tools to repair them when needed.

Medicines, supplies, and equipment can sometimes be created from scratch. For example, inexpensive, locally-available materials can be used to make scales for weighing babies, stethoscopes, timers for taking pulses and respirations, and *cold boxes* for vaccines.[11] Oral Rehydration Solution (ORS) packets can be purchased at pharmacies, and they serve as an effective alternative to IV fluid for most dehydrated children; yet further self-sufficiency is encouraged when caregivers are taught how to make their own ORS in the home using water, sugar or grain, and salt.[12] Outsiders all too often discourage local people from finding and using low-cost or home-made technologies, given that we "are unwilling to adopt standards that are inferior to those in developed countries."[13] This is unfortunate because low-cost options are often just as effective and more easily sustained in resource-limited nations.

What about buying medicines and supplies when needed? We could quickly clean out our wallet or purse while appeasing our conscience, but there are better ways. *Revolving drug funds* are especially empowering and sustainable, as they often only require start-up funds to purchase an initial supply of meds. When the medicines are sold, the resulting funds *revolve* to buy more medicine. The supply of medicine is maintained more or less indefinitely without dependence on outside resources.

Public Health Resources

Outsiders supporting Community-Led Total Sanitation (CLTS) work don't teach about sanitation or latrine models, and don't offer funding or materials; instead, we aim to trigger an internal and self-sustaining community process. After the desire to build latrines is stirred, it often starts with very basic US$3-4 pit latrines or even shallow holes in the ground with nothing more than ash and a lid to deter flies.[14] Ending *open defecation* is the central goal, while the quality of latrines is secondary; however, their quality gradually improves as community members invest more time and funding.

In contrast to CLTS, many other public health programs require a substantial investment in resources. Even so, much of the potential cost for public health programs can be recovered with *in kind* resources like local materials and labor.[15] Further, large and expensive public health projects can sometimes be avoided by making smaller stepwise improvements over time. The previous chapter reviewed how small improvements in water and sanitation programs tend to be more feasible and sustainable alternatives.

Outsiders can provide tools where needed but lacking, and these may be the most sustainable contribution that can be offered.[16] Tools can empower local people to repair or create various structural components of public health programs. In Sierra Leone, for example, we donated tools which were used for ongoing programs in latrine construction, well repair, rain water collection, spring protection, and slow sand filter construction.

Funding may be essential to program success, although offering needed tools or supplies is preferable and outsiders should be looked to only as a last resort. Local funding sources are preferable whenever possible. The previous chapter, for example, recounted how local water committees collected small program fees from their community members on a regular basis.

Where funds from outsiders are used, they ideally serve only as start-up program funds; long-term funding usually brings dependence. When more than one-quarter of the program budget is based on outsider funding, an inevitable shift to outsider priorities tends to occur.[17] Small contributions support sustainability, especially when they're offered as no-interest loans with realistic payback mechanisms.

Direct loans have been used successfully to build rain water collection systems[18] and spring water piping systems.[19] Program funding can also be accomplished sometimes without an initial loan. Revolving community water project funds have been used successfully to fund rainwater collection tanks: 12 households each contribute US$10 monthly for 1 year toward the cost of materials, while these community members construct one water tank each month at one of these 12 houses.[20] Essentially, they fund it themselves and share the labor.

Another alternative to direct loans involves paying back an initial loan for water and sanitation projects, and then using this same funding for another loan of this kind.[21] Such *revolving loans* have been used successfully to finance advanced latrine construction[22] and well construction.[23] A small amount of local funding can go a long way when it's recycled or shared in this way.

Microloans

In the mountains of Honduras, we put down our stethoscopes for two days and gave out microloans; this program supported health more indirectly, as small business earnings were used to fund family medical care, food, and schooling. We collected payment from prior microloans and used this to fund 15 new low-interest microloans. This had been done on a sustainable loop for 8 years. Supported businesses ranged from raising and selling pigs and chickens,

> *to baking bread for sale, to planting and marketing fruit. We*
> *joined successful former loan recipients in teaching basic*
> *business skills to new loan applicants.*

Microloans are small loans that can serve as an exciting and empowering alternative to direct donations. Low-interest microloans can help businesses start or expand, but they are most successful when paired with training programs on business skills and healthy living. Various nonprofits promote both health and economic empowerment by offering microloans for farming and raising livestock.[24] Some microloans even directly fund health care services[25] and health worker training programs.[26]

Yet for-profit banks and finance firms now serve the majority of microloan clients, rather than altruistic NGOs.[27] Many of these large institutions have amassed huge profits through corruption, fraud, and by charging interest rates up to 200% per year; with higher interest rates, community members living in poverty often fall deeper into debt, lose their jobs, and may even commit suicide due to the pressure to pay back loans.[28]

In order to avoid these dangers, microloans should be made only when there is a good chance they will be paid back. Only loans with low interest rates should be given, yet they may need to be adjusted for inflation. Small outsider health groups are well-situated to avoid the conflicts of interest of large for-profit businesses.

Success is encouraged when local people create *village banking* systems to sustain microloan programs in a community-based context. Village banks are credit and savings groups created and led by community members living in poverty; they're designed to collect, offer, and sustain microloans which serve their own community;[29] when successful, they can make loans and donations from outsiders unnecessary.[30]

Cash Payments

Finally, regular direct *cash payments* have yielded impressive health benefits when given either to families living in poverty or to caregivers of orphans and vulnerable children; some cash transfer programs have curbed teen pregnancy, while leading to improvements in diet and physical and mental health.[31] They have been used as incentives to keep children in school and delay their entry into the workforce.

Because of their cost and relationship to other services, cash transfer programs are typically organized by national governments and perhaps supplemented by loans or grants from large international NGOs. Smaller outside health groups are rarely well-positioned to make a substantial contribution through offering such payments.

In conclusion, small outsider health groups can maximize our role as facilitators of local empowerment by minimizing our role as donors. Our financial contributions would best only come into play when local people's resources are clearly insufficient or exhausted, and only through their request. When less is more, visitors can help community members to see the relatively small role that we played in achieving their health program's success:

> *Everything was planned and done by your community (A, B, C, etc.) and we only helped a bit with Y and Z. Almost all of the ideas, planning, tools, funding, supplies, work, and maintenance came from you. You're in control of your health, and you did a great job organizing this program!*

Doing Global Health Work
to *Really* Make a Difference

To conclude, I will summarize by asking the question posed by this book: How can I do global health work that *really* makes a difference? The quick answer is by:

1. Following **empowering approaches** to global health work:
   - Local clinical capacity-building
   - Strengthening local health systems
   - Professional disaster relief
   - Local public health capacity-building, and/or
   - Facilitating community-based health programs

Additionally, we can do so by:

2. Carefully minimizing or avoiding **traditional approaches** to global health work:
   - Suitcase medicine, and
   - Health facility-building

Tables 1 and 4 through 6 summarize all the main approaches to global health work, as well as the positive and negative work agendas that drive them (see the chapters *Global Health Approaches* and *Agendas We All Have*).

The longer answer to "How do I *really* make a difference" involves using the evidence-based, empowering strategies and methods outlined throughout this book. However, we can't do global health work on our own. So a more practical way to ask the question is: *Which global health group can I work with so I can really make a difference?* In choosing groups to apply to, we can ask ourselves: *What does a worthy professional outsider global health group look like and act like?* I propose the following criteria:

1. Positive Agendas are followed when outsider groups:

a. Don't primarily give things, build things, or do things for local people
b. Serve as facilitators of community empowerment
c. Build the capacity of local people
d. Work to strengthen community health systems
e. Avoid primarily following negative *work agendas* (tourism, education of outsiders, charity service, and charity construction)
f. Work to minimize the influence of *organizational agendas* in their work (religious, government, military, corporate, or donor-driven agendas)
g. Follow the lead of the community, whether it ventures into clinical care, public health, and/or social justice work (*sweeping health agendas*)

2. Professional Standards are followed when outsider groups:

a. Prepare thoroughly in a holistic manner before arriving abroad
b. Follow international, national, and local best-practices and standards
c. Perform evidence-based interventions in locally-led partnerships
d. Refrain from intervening in ways which can harm the community

3. Community-Led Processes are developed when:

a. Outsiders partner with a community, and the community leads the partnership
b. Local people control clinical care and health programs, rather than outsiders
c. Communities brainstorm assets, problems, and potential solutions
d. Communities prioritize their problems, decide on potential solutions, and organize their health programs
e. Outsiders encourage local people to start, lead, and sustain their own programs
f. Monitoring and evaluation is performed so that program impact can be understood, measured and improved upon
g. Health programs are constantly evolving based on local feedback and leadership
h. Communities lead programs with their resources while

outsiders supplement only needed but missing ingredients which have been requested

i. Health improvements and programs are sustainable
j. Outsiders avoid building dependency on their presence, actions, and resources

Beyond Improv

With this extensive list of criteria, I've set a high bar for what it takes to be a worthy professional outsider global health group. Yet I don't think it's an all or nothing proposition; I believe that all global health groups exist somewhere along a *spectrum of professionalism*; they range from the most improvisational to the most evidence-based, effective, and professional.

It's often quicker and easier to organize clinical and public health programs through *improv* groups since they simply do the best with what they have and what they know how to do; yet we can do much more than this. We need not reinvent the wheel by developing our own protocols, nor should we simply implement the methods we use in our home countries.

We often want to learn for ourselves what works and doesn't work, so we can then adjust health programs accordingly. Among those who follow this path, I've usually seen gradual progress along the way; however, I've also seen harm to and disempowerment of local people, as well as much wasted time, funding, and other resources. Trial and error can be fun, but I think we can do better for local people by seeking out and joining the most effective, evidence-based, and time-tested groups that are making a sustainable impact.

A worthy goal involves moving up the *spectrum of professionalism*, both personally as well as for the groups that we're part of and partner with. On a personal basis, we can keep up with the literature on evidence-based best practices in the clinical, public health, and global health fields; we can advance our training and contribute to various global health programs. These activities will not only serve to individually move us up the spectrum of professionalism; as we contribute our growing knowledge, skills, research, and experience, we will also influence and increase the professionalism of the groups with which we work.

Our global health groups can also increase their professionalism as they learn from their mistakes as well as from more professional groups. As we seek out professional *local* health groups with which to partner in resource-limited nations, our partnerships will assist in their training, facilitate community empowerment, and thus promote their professionalization as well.

Naturally, we all start as less worthy professional contributors to global health, and we may find ourselves with less professional groups initially. Yet this shouldn't take our eyes off the prize: *really* making a difference through our global health efforts. Every time we advance our awareness, knowledge, skills, and experience, we further deepen our ability to assist communities in resource-limited places. As we develop our capacities through experience, we also expand our ability to qualify for and positively contribute to the most worthy and professional of global health organizations.

You Can Improve Your Society

This book will conclude with one last push for us outsiders to approach people living in poverty as much more than passive recipients of our goodwill; they deserve to have ever-increasing control over their lives and their health. I believe we should aim to empower local people in all that we do, so that they appropriately take center stage.

> Women were fanning the flies off their kids while their husbands couldn't hide their expectant smiles. We were at a community meeting with all of the local leaders, and it seemed most of the village came too. They asked me to speak about why we'd travelled so far to be there; perhaps they wanted me to sound like most outside donor groups, but I gave them a very different speech. After the basic introductions and words of appreciation, I spoke to the core issue:

> We're not a donor group, and I'm sorry but we don't have any funds or equipment available to help your community. We're actually a small health group and we love partnering with communities in other countries to help them as they solve their own problems. I hope we can help you to meet your community's health needs. We don't know what your village needs, but I'm sure you will think deeply about this and figure it out together—if you haven't already. Please teach us how you'd like conditions to improve here and show us how we can support you in achieving your goals. We know that you can improve your own society, and we'd like to help you do it!

With this unconventional introduction, eager smiles faded and were replaced by many confused and pondering faces. At first, there seemed to be disappointment that we weren't just going to give them things. Then there was wonder: *Why exactly were we here?* Finally, once empowerment focus groups were in full swing, they understood that they would be the ones creating or expanding health programs, and they enjoyed building them as they thought best.

I try to share this message of empowerment when first connecting with communities abroad, and I repeat some version of it any time I'm asked to primarily give things and/or do things for local people. Changing expectations before beginning work often prevents local feelings of disappointment when various goods and services aren't provided.

From the very arrival of our outsider groups, the attitude projected should be humble, supportive, and empowering. This speech made it very clear that outsiders lack awareness of community problems and solutions; it also established that their community does have the answers. It stressed the importance of setting and meeting their goals rather than ours, emphasizing that we wanted to partner with them as they lead the partnership. Projecting confidence in them, this speech also underlined the small size and capacity of our group. This empowering approach offers an open invitation for community-based health program design.

The contagious effect of empowerment can inspire community members to take more control over their lives.[1] Confidence, positive attitudes, passion, and hope can have similarly contagious effects; these are the qualities that we should foster in communities in resource-limited nations. Each of these qualities can encourage the successful birth or expansion of a health program.

People who feel locked into a state of poverty can develop *learned helplessness.*[2] As a result, community members in resource-limited settings often have a sad refrain: *We can't do better; we can't do more because we're poor.* In this context, seeing new faces and hearing the new voices of outsiders can be refreshing and inspiring. Outsiders have a predilection for encouraging community members to think outside of the box; after all, we're coming from an entirely different box. Yet we can only work to inspire if our messages encourage local empowerment rather than dependence.

Finally, the speech established that we're primarily facilitators rather than donors or givers of charity. While this was only an introduction, local people should be further prepped on how an empowering partnership can function. Trainings in Participatory Rural Appraisal and Asset-Based Community Development can help us outsiders make the paradigm change from *volunteer* to *facilitator*, and the same is true for community members.

We'll also gain much from observing and inquiring as to how local groups organize and make decisions. In many cases, they're already working as facilitators in their own communities. Other times, community groups may be rigid, hierarchical, and overall difficult for outside facilitators to partner with. Both outsiders and local people need to embrace an empowering community-led partnership or else it just won't work.

Conclusion: A Sad Story?

There was a narrow cleft among massive boulders, and this became their home. It was a tight place to live for a mother and five children. Another opening created a perpetually open window that invited ever-replenishing lines of mosquitos to make sleep impossible. It was one bite after another until one child died of malaria and there was no money to treat the other child, who looked as feverish and pale as the child who died. Among the most thriving local businesses were the coffin shops immediately across from the hospital. Although she couldn't afford a coffin for her

daughter, she nonetheless had to pass by these shops again in two weeks on the way to visit the hospital for her own ailments.

Even among the peace of quiet boulders, she could no longer hide from the HIV thriving inside her. She had lost too much weight, and TB claimed her lungs and brain. She died in the hospital and her children returned to their rock refuge, now feeling quite alone and wondering if they would soon lie as still as their mother. They coughed all day and night, as the ominous grip of TB tightened on all the children caring for each other between the two slabs of rock. Little feet meandered over to the clinic, but the children had empty pockets and equally empty expectations.

This is typically where many outsiders end the story: the local context is overwhelming, the need is great, and therefore outsider intervention is critical if anything is to be done for these poor, suffering children. Yet the story ended quite differently.

*The children walked through the clinic door and a **local social worker** shared his morning "chapatti" bread as he ushered them into his office. He called other family members and found an **aunt** outside of town who would take them in. She came back with them two days later to review test results and collect the TB medicines they needed. **Local counselors and doctors** taught her how to give these medicines. Then after another week, she also started giving them daily HIV medicine.*

Yet they still didn't gain weight because the food the aunt had at home just wasn't enough for the extra mouths. A local nutritionist gave a peanut-based therapeutic food, and their waistlines and energy levels slowly expanded. She also taught the aunt some home gardening methods, and they began growing and eating more food at home. After a while, there was even enough food to sell the excess. A community-run microfinance group gave her a loan and her gardening business grew to where she could buy uniforms and books for most of the children. Now they could attend school and play with other kids, somehow finding joy in a seemingly cold and indifferent world without their mother, father, and sister.

The holistic solutions this family found extended far beyond the interventions we outsiders could successfully provide; in fact, all of the stars of this dramatic turnaround were local people. The ideal result is never for us outsiders to swoop in and put lost children like these on a healthy track; that is a job for an empowered community. We can—and in this case, did—support them in the background while they work their everyday miracles. This is an ideal yet not uncommon happy ending to a tragic story, and it should be what both outsiders and local people work toward. This is help in a way that *really* makes a difference.

Improving Suitcase Medicine

The most common clinical global health initiative involves volunteers traveling to resource-limited countries to provide medical care for one to a few weeks. Free health care is generally provided in makeshift clinic sites by teams which share medicines and supplies out of their suitcases. Our *suitcase medicine* trips are also commonly referred to as short-term medical service trips, medical missions, medical brigades, or medical volunteer trips.

These teams generally have great intentions and work quite hard under tough conditions. Although we can help individual patients in this way, unintended harm to patients and communities can result, though we outsiders may never be held accountable to local people. Suitcase medicine may not have a net positive effect on communities, and it tends to disempower them given the parallel care system created. It generally lacks an evidence base, and its temporary services are by definition not sustainable (see Table 1 of the chapter *Global Health Approaches*). This appendix will explore how we can improve the medical care that we give abroad, should we choose to still participate in the suitcase medicine approach.

Expanding Awareness

As was reviewed in the chapter *Reversing the Brain Drain*, we lack the cultural skills and knowledge of common community diseases and available health services, regarding which local health workers have an expert command. Local health workers are integral to providing appropriate and high-quality care, and, unlike us temporary visitors, they also hold the key to sustainable health services and needed follow-up and referrals. These advantages beg the question of whether we outsiders can expand our awareness enough to catch up to community health providers.

How can suitcase medicine teams do a better job regarding awareness?

First, extensive pre-trip preparation should be offered to all volunteers.[1] Preparation could include reviewing local health and social systems, culture, history, politics, language, partner organizations, and disease epidemiology, diagnosis, and treatment. An in-person orientation over multiple days can be organized, including lessons-learned from prior volunteers and international, national, and local best practice standards. There are a wealth of great reference books we can use to better prepare ourselves for the challenges of care in resource-limited nations.[2]

Basic global health clinical and public health education are excellent prerequisites for volunteering abroad, including tropical medicine familiarity for clinicians. The majority of team members could have prior global health volunteering experience from which to draw on. In order to reduce potential harm and shift the educational focus to local health workers, less than half of all team members could be trainees such as health professions students. Trainees could be invited abroad only if they're part of a long-term global health education program such as an international public health school or a global health residency track. Although these requirements would drastically reduce the number of potential outside volunteers, they would increase the likelihood of participants being more aware and causing less unintended harm.

This is clearly an area for growth, as extensive hands-on preparation is rarely done[3] and rarely matches our deficits in awareness.[4] Many Sub-Saharan Africans have had generally negative feedback on outsider preparation;[5] and this is a particular danger for medical students and other trainees.[6] Being unprepared upon arrival naturally sets us up to cause harm through our work.[7] In a survey of 117 US-based short-term trip organizations, 10% reported doing no orientation at all, while only half did an in-person orientation prior to departure.[8]

Screening of volunteers is another critical intervention that many organizations bypass, and therefore those accepted are not limited to the best-prepared or best-qualified.[9] US groups generally take almost all who apply.[10] Local health workers and community members would best be invited to screen potential volunteers so that only the best-qualified are chosen.

It's also troubling that many suitcase medicine groups perform care without adequate interpretation services, even when volunteers don't speak the language themselves.[11] Interpreters need to be utilized and care should never proceed without clear communication with patients. In addition to bridging the language gap, many interpreters can help bridge cultural gaps when they are from the same racial, ethnic, and social groups as the patients served.

Yet even with superb preparation, screening, and interpretation, our degree of awareness will never match that of local care providers. This is one of the central reasons it is critical for us to partner with local health workers and treat patients only within community health facilities, rather than our own makeshift ones. Disasters offer the only reasonable exception to this rule (see the chapter *Disaster Strikes: Outsiders Arrive*). Even so, partnership is still essential for post-disaster health care, and parallel health facilities should only be utilized when local ones are destroyed or overwhelmed.

Locally-Led Partnerships

As explored in the chapter *Reversing the Brain Drain*, many of the problems stemming from outsiders' lack of awareness need not arise given the inherent awareness of local health workers. It would be natural for outsiders to partner with local health workers to make up for this. Yet most short-term medical service trips fail to seek out and collaborate with local health systems and/or community groups.[12] Guatemalan doctors have seen many outsider medical teams offer services locally, while neglecting to visit nearby clinics to work with them or even ask what type of help is needed;[13] in Nepal, local clinics and hospitals are commonly avoided by visiting teams.[14]

> *A friendly village hugged the flooded roadside in Sierra Leone. Patients came in droves to an outsider-led one-day clinic. When needed, they were referred for further care at another outsider-led clinic 45 minutes away on the rockiest roads my imagination ever bumped over. My uneasiness took a nosedive, however, when I learned that there was actually a locally-operated clinic just two kilometers away. Shockingly, the organization I volunteered with was aware of this; yet they sought to draw patients away from the local care system for their supposedly "superior care."*

Duplication of medical services is quite common with suitcase medicine.[15] It's inefficient to have such *parallel services* and they detract from existing community health services. Parallel services have also occurred between two outsider groups who both serve the same area yet fail to coordinate.[16]

Another challenge comes when outsiders make a significant diagnosis with long-term implications, such as a new case of diabetes, HIV, or sickle cell disease. Each of these chronic conditions requires long-term follow-up that we visitors cannot provide. Harm can be caused by only briefly providing care for patients with chronic diseases.[17] For example, a patient with very high blood pressure may have a stroke after two months if they are only given one month of blood pressure medication by a visiting team.

In addition to chronic diseases, medical follow-up is also needed for various acute conditions. Even a simple case of bacterial skin infection may require a follow-up exam within 3 days, yet we outsiders may fly out the morning after diagnosing a patient with it. In a review of 92 articles on short-term medical service trips, only 11% of articles recommended integrating with local services, 7% recommended referring patients to the local system, and only 29% mentioned the need for a follow-up system.[18]

Given that most suitcase medicine trips do not collaborate with local health authorities, follow-up services for patients falls off the agenda.[19] Yet when we do collaborate closely with local professionals from the beginning, we are often able to arrange patient follow-up at community health facilities. A review of 67 studies showed that short-term medical service trips only followed up on patients for 1-3 days, while surgical trips did so for only 1-7 days.[20] Follow-up is especially important after doing surgeries abroad,[21] as departing surgeons can leave behind complications such as bleeding, infection, and blood clots occurring without proper diagnosis and treatment.

Keeping medical records and then passing them on to local health facilities is an important activity inappropriately neglected by our outsider medical teams.[22] A systematic review of articles suggested that most short-term volunteer teams do not use permanent medical records at all.[23] According to interviews with outsiders, 20% kept or destroyed medical records at the end of their trips rather than passing them on.[24] Lacking medical records, local health workers may be left to respond to future health challenges of patients without even knowing which diagnoses and treatments were given.[25]

How can suitcase medicine teams do a better job establishing local partnerships?

Conventional suitcase medicine establishes makeshift, temporary centers as a parallel system of care which neglects partnerships with local people; I think this creates an insurmountable problem. The only ethical and professional solution is to abandon the conventional model and partner with communities. Further, locally-led partnerships are the only types which should be allowed for any outside intervention;[26] we would best stay at home until we begin forging these partnerships with a community or its organizations or health facilities. Without a formal partnership, we essentially show up uninvited.

In an effort to avoid duplicate health care systems, we can *always* provide care at a local health facility except where none exist. Adequate follow-up with local providers should be planned for all patients who need it.[27] Medical records should be generated and passed on to local providers.[28]

We also need to do our due diligence regarding local group(s) that we partner with. It's important to understand their role within the community, as well as how they work with other groups and local government. We should shy away from working with groups that are corrupt, have ulterior motives, discriminate against certain community members, or that lack the respect of the community that they serve.

Improving Quality of Care

In rural Mexico, our medical team strolled past invisible walls of stench that formed an unpassable barrier for many other visitors. Beyond the hills of decomposing garbage was something almost unimaginably creative: a structure built from old and new trash, fitted together carefully to serve as bedrooms, kitchens, and in our case, a makeshift clinic. We also passed a cowhide drying on a clothesline. We marched in with our shoulders straight, gleaming stethoscopes around our necks, and faces clean and fresh, as if we'd come to save the day. Unfortunately, we were on a short-term medical trip and were only there for one day. So there was the illusion of good medical care for one day only; the rest of the year would be a different story.

This dramatic scene fed the high expectations of someone about to start med school at the end of the summer. Yet we didn't contribute anything substantial that day. The doctors gave a bit of health advice, and a few tubes of fungal cream were handed over. The head doctor sighed but then found a sliver of meaning when his eyes met an ingrown fingernail. The plan was to remove the nail but there was no lidocaine, and the fingertip is a goldmine of nerves and potential pain.

Nonetheless, the doctor ripped out the fingernail of this stoic man who hid his tears beneath the brim of his cowboy hat. I've never seen or heard of someone enduring the procedure without an injection of anesthesia. Feeling ashamed of my team, I wondered: Just how distant was the nearest Mexican clinic with anesthetics?

Inappropriate treatment may be given by us outsiders for many reasons.[29] These include deficiencies in procedural skills or the inability to adequately dispense medicines.[30] Critical treatments can be delayed or forgone by suitcase medicine teams if patients are seen on a first-come, first-serve basis, rather than being *triaged* to identify and treat the sickest patients first.[31] Quality of care can also be compromised by medicine expiration and improper use, bringing inappropriate supplies and equipment, failing to follow evidence-based treatment guidelines, and through the inappropriate use of surgery. I'll explore these concerns in depth here, since they haven't been covered in previous chapters.

Non-surgical groups rarely report on the harm that we outsiders cause. At the same time, it's well known that surgeries commonly cause harm on short-term medical service trips.[32] High complication rates have been noted when large outsider teams perform a high volume of surgeries abroad,[33] as well as when these surgeries are performed without adequate follow-up.[34] The death rate from hernia surgery is 20 times higher on short-term trips to Sub-Saharan Africa compared to the same procedure in the higher income countries where volunteers originate.[35]

Inappropriate surgeries have been recommended and done by outsiders, such as hip prostheses for people with social norms of frequent squatting, and cleft palate surgeries on malnourished children who died as a result.[36] Following the 2010 earthquake in Haiti, short-term surgery teams at one facility performed amputations in 1% of all surgeries while a team at another facility amputated in 45% of their surgeries; lacking any clear differences in teams or facilities (or other explanations), it's quite possible that many unnecessary amputations were performed during this horrible disaster.[37] It is also possible that truly informed consent for surgery may never be obtained given persistent language and cultural barriers.[38] Outsider surgeons have been known to practice their skills and develop new surgical techniques abroad, often at the expense of the health of local people.[39]

It was my birthday in a remote corner of Uganda. My "party" involved having 200 patients over at the house I rented with two other volunteers. Lacking a health facility, we used this house as a makeshift clinic for our suitcase medicine care. Although I was an idealistic, inexperienced med student, I somehow convinced some Ugandan medical students to join us. We asked a Ugandan medical officer to supervise the care we gave and we "paid" him with medical equipment. To add to this unprofessional scene, patient after patient faked symptoms of illness in order to get the free medicine we were providing. They wisely saved meds for the future, but I have my doubts they remembered how to properly use them even a few weeks later.

Medication errors serve as another threat to quality of care. Fewer than half of patients took medicines correctly as prescribed by us outsiders on short-term medical trips; patients often traded and shared medicines with others in their community.[40] According to one survey of American medical volunteers, 20% reported that they left medicines behind but not with health care workers or facilities.[41] One short-term medical team handed out all leftover medicines to patients at the end of the trip as if they were candy; this was done regardless of their diseases and potential adverse events.[42] Outsiders on suitcase medicine teams often donate medicines which aren't approved for use in the host country; after we leave, local providers can easily cause harm by using unfamiliar medicines.

When we donate expired medicines, they can become nothing more than a burden for local economies[43] as well as for local providers to sort out and dispose of.[44] The 2004 tsunami in Sri Lanka was followed by a flood of donated medicine, yet 80% weren't desired, 62% were labeled in an unknown language, and 50% had already expired.[45] Overwhelmed by donations, they were stored inadequately, which in turn may have caused the contamination of spinal anesthesia; three pregnant women died after receiving this anesthesia.[46]

Our supply and equipment donations can also work to inhibit the sustainability of local supply systems.[47] Equipment is commonly donated without related training and materials to maintain and repair it,[48] leading to 70% of all donated medical equipment in Sub-Saharan Africa remaining unused.[49] WHO has published guidelines on the responsible donation of medicines and medical equipment,[50] yet the majority of our short-term outsider teams do not follow them.[51]

Quality of care is also guided by the use of local, home-country, and international treatment guidelines. Suitcase medicine volunteers may not follow—or even be aware of—the evidence-based disease treatment guidelines of the host country.[52] Many outsiders prescribe treatments or perform procedures abroad which they'd never do in their home countries.[53] It's also commonplace for our suitcase medicine teams to neglect international care guidelines.[54]

Beyond care guidelines, local and national health care laws need to be explored and followed by us visitors.[55] For example, the medical licenses of outsiders are not automatically accepted by the credentialing authorities of other nations.

Inadequate supervision of outside trainees can easily harm patients on short-term trips.[56] Understaffed facilities in resource-limited countries may ask outside health professional students to perform tasks beyond their scope of knowledge and skill; many hold back on doing so, while others comply and put patients' health at risk. Unfortunately, very few of our outsider teams have stressed the importance of refraining from practicing unfamiliar skills abroad,[57] and this commonly includes the dispensing of medicines by non-medically trained volunteers.[58]

Data and accountability are needed to improve the quality of care, yet short-term medical trips typically avoid evaluations or only do self-evaluations with limited to no data.[59] Shockingly, there haven't been any comprehensive studies on direct physical harm to patients resulting from these trips, yet many articles document instances of such harm. In a review of 67 studies on suitcase medicine trips, only 19% reported on whether patient deaths occurred; these publications collectively reported on 59 deaths occurring overseas due to the interventions of outsiders.[60] However, the true scope of patients saved, harmed, and lost on these trips is unknown.

How can suitcase medicine teams do a better job improving quality of care?

As with the issue of limited awareness, partnering and working alongside local health workers is the main remedial intervention. Our short-term clinics would best serve local people when we and our partners set up *triage*—the speedy assessment of the acuity of illness when people first arrive. In this way, the sickest can be seen first and referral can proceed as needed.[61] Care should be limited to one's knowledge and skill set, and all trainees must be adequately supervised.[62] Prior to rolling up their sleeves, outsiders need to ensure that their organization has obtained acceptance of their license to practice medicine locally.

Safe use of medicines is paramount, and they should only be administered by or left behind with appropriately trained staff. We would do well to only donate medicines, supplies, and equipment if locally requested, appropriate, and approved on the national list (as well as following other WHO criteria as discussed in the chapter *Strengthening Health Systems*).

All short-term global health work would benefit from evaluating health outcomes on a regular basis,[63] yet no such oversight mechanisms now exist.[64] Monitoring and evaluation is needed on every trip, and could do much more than simply ask about the outsiders' experiences. Critiques by local people are far more important and should serve as the centerpiece of outcome evaluation. Local people can collaborate on evaluations, and ideally, they should lead them. We outsiders should create and pass on medical records and set up local follow-up *in order to* allow for local evaluation of our work.[65]

In addition to outcome evaluations, I believe that short-term medical volunteerism needs to be *regulated* on multiple levels. Currently, no international mandatory regulations regarding short-term medical service trips exist.[66] Best practice standards were identified in 2008 for suitcase medicine trips with the proviso that short-term organizations use them for self-regulation and self-evaluation. Little has been done to implement this for more than the decade which followed this report.[67] Important progress was made in 2022 when the Brocher Declaration proposed key guiding principles regarding partnership, cultural sensitivity, and accountability to local people, all designed to enable outsiders to limit the harm we cause, maximize the benefits we provide, and help shift power to local people.[68] Unfortunately, there is still nothing to compel outsider organizations to follow these critical principles.

Our global health care initiatives are fundamentally voluntary, and this largely explains how we get away with not being regulated by an international body. Suitcase medicine can be improved by the passage of international laws and regulation by WHO. Some have pointed out the irony of the intense regulation of research in resource-limited countries compared to the total lack of regulation of outsider-provided patient care in these same settings; the strict Institutional Review Board process for research abroad could be adapted and applied to medical service trips.[69]

However, it is our responsibility to act now rather than wait for international legislation and regulation. We would benefit from an organization to investigate and certify short-term service organizations as either being *best practices compliant* or not. This way, potential volunteers seeking to maximize the benefit and minimize the harm they might cause abroad would have a much easier time identifying groups to support them. Registration of all medical service organizations could serve as an important first step in this process. This has already been achieved by the British government for disaster relief groups[70] as well as those doing short-term capacity-building and health systems strengthening work within long-term partnerships.[71]

Local regulation at every site is also important. Evaluation by the main local partner group or health facility could ensure that community preferences are followed. A local regulator could have authority over our outsider organization, such that it can decide on service policies, health programs, and if or when we can be invited to return.

Finally, evaluation of trip cost effectiveness is also an important but largely unanswered question. Combining all short-term medical service trips, an estimated US$250 million is spent yearly.[72] Most of these funds are applied to outsider teams, rather than patient care; roughly half of all funds are spent on flights alone.[73]

Based on World Bank standards, two of the only three related studies to date suggested that outsider medical service trips are cost-effective.[74] Yet these studies assumed that absolutely no medical care was being provided locally until outsiders arrived; this research was therefore quite biased and actually failed to demonstrate the cost-effectiveness of temporary outsider medical services.[75]

One study compared orthopedic care in disaster settings with care given on short-term medical service trips; it found the latter intervention to be less cost-effective in terms of the improvement in quality of life (the cost per *disability-adjusted life-year* averted).[76] Another study compared surgical interventions on 1) short-term trips, 2) ship or plane-based care, and 3) at specialty surgical hospitals; short-term trips were again found to be the least cost-effective, have the lowest health impact, and to have the highest mortality rates.[77] This systematic review concluded that short-term surgical trips can only be justified in extremely remote corners of the world where surgical services could never be accessed without distant travel—and only for very simple surgeries.[78]

Some have understandably argued that the massive funds devoted to short-term trips should be rerouted to other global health programs.[79] *Opportunity costs* refer to health programs which aren't able to receive funds, staff, and supplies given that another program is simultaneously receiving them. For example, it's been noted that— with the same amount of funding—local surgeons could perform far more surgeries than visiting ones; alternatively, local nurses could be hired on a sustainable basis for what it costs to send one outsider team abroad.[80] One study of European medical volunteers showed that roughly 10 local staff members could be hired for the cost of hosting one of us outsiders.[81] While the net positive impact of short-term trips hasn't been shown to date, myriad global health interventions have dramatically expanded quality of life while reducing mortality; such programs could easily save countless lives with the lucrative promise of $250 million per year.

Longer, Repeated Trips with Fewer Patients and Volunteers

Another way of promoting the *quality* of patient care involves reducing both the quantity of patients seen and the number of outside volunteers. The same volunteers would best return multiple times for the sake of quality, and the trips could be longer in an effort to give more attention to partnership development, health outcome evaluation, trainee supervision, appropriate follow-up, and much more. Regular visits to the same partner community could certainly help more than an isolated visit. Although musical groups that are *one-hit wonders* leave us with a great song for posterity, suitcase medicine one-hit wonders leave no such legacy with a single trip.

Let's start with the quantity of patients seen. Outsiders often aim to treat large numbers of patients to the detriment of quality of care,[82] and this has been pointed out in interviews with local people.[83] Naturally, adverse medication reactions, treatment and surgery complications, and deaths are more likely to occur when we rush through treatment rather than working to give higher quality care. The consensus in the literature appropriately calls on suitcase medicine teams to treat fewer patients abroad.[84]

If patient care is to be better and less voluminous, then fewer volunteers are needed. Not surprisingly, local informants have requested smaller groups of us outsiders to wander through their villages.[85]

> *There were just three of us volunteering in Uganda that first summer. It felt like we'd accomplished much, so why shouldn't we multiply our effect? Why not expand from 3 to 30 the next summer? The math was attractive, but the end product was not! It seemed outsiders spent more time talking with other outsiders, rather than learning from and serving the interests of the community. New volunteers were less familiar with previously expressed community needs and goals, as well as the nuances of partner development up*

to that point. Further, Ugandans hadn't requested such an expansion. So we never should've considered it.

Rather than lively teams of 20 or more outsiders, groups of only 2 to 4 per trip have been recommended as appropriate.[86] Returning with the same volunteers over multiple trips can be very helpful,[87] and some have suggested that the overlap of prior volunteers should be at least 75%.[88] Bigger just isn't better; more outsiders working generally leads to fewer local people working, as well as less local control.

The horizon was roughly flat but far from constant. It was swaying with bobbing dark heads as the animals ran. Horns spanned across the plains like tiny saw teeth in the distance. Hundreds of wildebeests and zebras fanned out in front of us as we were surrounded. We felt like small dots engulfed by a world unto itself.

This is how I believe we foreigners should feel abroad. I don't think we should be part of a large intervention team of familiar people who look, think, train, and act as we might at home. When outsiders are a slim minority of the staff giving care, then local people can more effectively take center stage. I've also been on teams split up among various villages and among several projects so it never felt like an American invasion.

Finally, the length of trips can affect the quality of care provided. Most medical service trips are less than two weeks long; feedback indicates that outsiders generally want to travel for 1 to 2 weeks, while local people want us to stay at least 3 to 4 weeks.[89] Community members generally view less than two weeks as being insufficient, and recommend 2- to 12-month stays when surveyed.[90]

As a medical student, I had a full 6 weeks in rural El Salvador on a rotation. As the lone outsider, I had few distractions from expats and a generous amount of time to learn from and assist a Salvadoran doctor and nurse. I also had the time to work on long-term community-based programs such as those addressing alcoholism, HIV/AIDS, and the health impacts of mining operations.

According to local people who've hosted medical service teams, outsider volunteers who stay longer are more likely to be respectful, humble, adaptable, hard-working, and to have good technical and people skills.[91] The consensus in the literature now calls for longer medical service trips.[92] Reflecting this trend, various global health organizations have stopped accepting outside volunteers for short stints.[93]

Tipping the Balance: Benefits and Burdens

His warm, young smile contrasted starkly with his aged, wrinkling eyes which had seen far too much suffering and death. We felt perpetually welcomed by the hospitality of the people of this town. We took it as a proxy for their level of need; we took it as a compelling invitation and a convincing reason to fly back next year. Yet we understood what we wanted to as the mountain wind dashed through the town and the silence behind smiles continued unabated. Actually, we were never formally invited there, and they hadn't asked us directly to come back. After all, this hospitality was graciously offered to all guests and we were no different.

People in resource-limited nations often feel like they're in no position to ever refuse the presence of foreign medical guests, even if the terms of service aren't attractive to them.[94] Yet we shouldn't assume that the presence of outsiders is always welcome and potentially helpful; we can also serve as a serious burden on our hosts.

Community members often orient us and work out the logistics of our trips; yet by demanding their time and energy, our trips can cause local health services to become less efficient and profitable.[95] By occupying their public space and using up their patient care resources, we can adversely affect the ability of community members to treat patients themselves.[96] We may also use up scarce resources like food and water at volunteer sites.[97] The larger the outsider team, the more significant the host burden created.[98]

Patient follow-up is very important, yet it can serve as another burden on community members. Local medical providers are forced to do less surgery themselves given the need to identify possible surgery cases prior to the arrival of outsiders and to follow up with "our" patients after we leave.[99] Understandably, local surgeons are not always keen on following up with patients that foreigners had operated on,[100] and similarly the follow-up on non-surgical patients seen by outsiders creates another burden for community providers.[101] These burdens are exacerbated when partnerships with local facilities have been neglected and medical records have not been passed on.

The smooth and successful functioning of community health systems is often undermined by the temporary volunteer services provided by outsiders.[102] Local health workers in resource-limited countries usually don't have the ability to provide free health care to all; they are responsible for supporting staff, medicines, supplies, and facility operating costs to keep their doors open. The introduction of free outsider services draws patients away from local facilities which almost universally need to charge patients; this places outsider providers in direct competition with local ones—who inevitably lose this competition as they see fewer patients and earn less income to sustain services.[103] Guatemalan doctors have complained about this practice, insisting that outsiders collaborate with them more closely and charge all but the poorest surgery patients rather than providing free care to all.[104]

Similarly, clusters of outsider medical teams enter Honduras to provide desperately needed health care; ironically, our short-term service teams may be contributing to its health care shortage by keeping thousands of Honduran physicians unemployed.[105] This trend has also been seen in Haiti, among other nations, where local doctors lose their jobs as care is shifted to arriving outsiders.[106] The existence of outsider-driven health care also encourages local governments to invest less in their own public health services; therefore, while short-term medical service trips may expand health care access slightly in the short-term, they can have a devastating long-term impact.[107]

By their very nature, short-term medical service trips are unsustainable interventions since they only provide care from one to a few weeks. *Outsider-driven* health services cannot be sustainable without developing complete dependence on foreigners. Instead, efforts to make *local* health services sustainable should be a defining goal of these trips.

Dependency on outsiders is almost universally identified as a state to be avoided, although frequent short-term service trips encourage this.[108] Patients often elect to avoid their own health care systems given the associated charges, and many forgo needed care until the next short-term medical group arrives from abroad.[109] This rings several alarm bells warning about the harms of dependency.

Although physical and economic harm are quite concerning, I believe that the damage done to local confidence and empowerment may have more serious societal repercussions. For local health systems to thrive, communities need to own them, believe in them, and work hard to sustain and improve them. Unfortunately, the charity service agenda of suitcase medicine does not achieve this, but rather it systematically disempowers local people (see the expanded arguments in the chapters *Power to the People* and *Agendas We All Have*).

How can suitcase medicine teams do a better job of increasing benefits and lessening burdens?

As previously addressed, assets and needs assessments would best guide us to know *whether* our presence is desired as well as *how* we could best support the health programs that communities envision (including suitcase medicine). Community members—rather than we outsiders— should also be determining *where* we'll visit and *when*.[110] Local people deserve the authority to select volunteer trip dates based on their harvest season, work and holiday schedules, staffing, and space availability.

Yet local feedback is rarely sought by suitcase medicine teams[111] and community-based needs assessments and health outcomes evaluations are rarely performed by them.[112] Such assessments are critical and, for suitcase medicine, they can be an especially helpful means of looking into and preventing potential harm caused by our visits. For example, needs assessments can help tease out the *burdens* that we outsiders could place on a community should a partnership go forward.[113] The costs of food and housing, the time of the hosts, and many other factors should be considered in any comprehensive assessment. The negative impact of our free services on community health centers would best be considered in advance and prevented. Clear plans can be made in partnership for patient follow-up as well as ways that outsider medical care might alleviate strains on the local health system.

After all of this brainstorming on how we can improve the suitcase medicine approach, the main question remains: would all of these improvements make suitcase medicine an especially helpful approach to global health work? Although these changes would expand its benefits and reduce its potential harms, I believe that suitcase medicine would still serve as a *traditional* rather than an *empowering* approach for global health work. Even after many improvements, the approach still confronts two barriers inherent to this model:

1. Having limited awareness while providing very temporary, unsustainable medical care
2. Neglecting local health system partnership, thus creating a parallel care system

Still, by adapting the *traditional* suitcase medicine approach as this book recommends, we can increase its potential positive effect on the health of communities abroad. This requires local partnership, seeing patients at community health facilities, and only treating patients in tandem with local health workers (whose participation can ameliorate our limited awareness). We would be a health care supplement rather than the main face of care; importantly, we'd follow rather than lead.

Appendix B

Building Clinics... Or Confidence?

Appendix A explored how outsiders involved in suitcase medicine can improve the quality of health care they provide, and suggested how they might find *long-term* global health work even more fulfilling. What about outsiders who decide to start up a permanent presence by building and running a health care facility abroad? This *is* long-term work, but the approach of *health facility-building* also creates a parallel system to the locally-run system.

There may be a community clinic down the street from a new clinic built by foreigners. A town might have a district hospital and an outsider one as well, resulting in two emergency rooms, two TB treatment programs, two radiology services, two medication distribution systems, and so on.

Why is that a problem? Isn't it always good to have more clinics and hospitals in resource-limited countries? Not when one is redundant, unsustainable, disempowers the community, pulls staff and resources from the other, and inhibits local people's ability to provide their own medical care. This approach also isn't evidence-based and isn't particularly helpful in the long-term (see Table 1 in the chapter *Global Health Approaches*). This appendix will further develop the arguments, as well as propose more helpful scenarios for building facilities and passing them on to communities.

> *In the dry oven that is Botswana, I remember walking through open-air hospital walkways while dodging monkeys sprinting to raid the garbage. One patient was limping from the long walk to the hospital; the other stopped every 5 to 10 feet to convulse in a coughing fit. I was escorting both to the x-ray machine to confirm that TB had found a home in their lungs. We arrived and as the first patient approached the x-ray plate, the hospital power suddenly dropped. We waited patiently in the dark but the electricity never came back and I had only my imagination to draw pictures of what her x-ray might have uncovered.*

In settings such as this, it's quite easy and natural for us outsiders to assume that we can do a better job than the local hospital. We might point disparagingly at a run-down local hospital with intermittently functioning electricity, chronic understaffing, few or no gloves, and relatively empty pharmacy shelves. We may say: "We can make better facilities with more medicines, supplies, and equipment; we can make bigger rooms with more privacy and our systems can make the work-flow much nicer; we can have more reliable power and water sources; the standard of care can and should be better because we'll run it ourselves."

I've heard each of these claims many times, and they may well be true if resources permit. Yet they are irrelevant since they're answers to the wrong question. The issue isn't *who* can give better health care. Local facilities are independent places which were established to care for their own people; communities abroad need not be flooded with foreign facilities and programs which may or may not be able to do a better job at care than they can. The more relevant goal is for local people to do an even better job at giving the care they already provide.

The local hospital workers will agree with you that community members deserve better care. So why not work to assist a struggling hospital to find reliable electricity, gloves, and medicines? Why not assist with training and recruiting more local staff for the failing hospital? If the goal is to make a better facility, why start from scratch and build something new? Why raise and spend critical funding on construction and staff recruitment instead of using it to breathe new life into the hospital around the corner?

Separation Is Easier, Not Better

Health systems strengthening can be very helpful yet there are various reasons why partnering and integrating with local health systems abroad is often difficult. Many outsiders are professionals from cultures where individuality and independence are stressed, so we're not used to being told what to do or where to go. We like to just do what we believe is right and is needed; we tend to lead ourselves and to make our own programs. It takes much humility and flexibility to fit in to an existing system, let go of the wheel, and encourage local people to decide how we can help them.

Public facilities may also be home to language barriers, under-working *ghost staff*, unfamiliar bureaucratic methods, and stacks of required but redundant paperwork. Things often work very slowly and inefficiently. Standards of care may be low, evidence-based protocols neglected, and unfamiliar procedures followed. The acuity and volume of patients entering may be woefully mismatched to the scant resources and staff within the facility's doors. It may require a herculean test of patience for us outsiders to gradually understand how these places function, accept them as they are, and then slowly and in partnership work to improve their function over time (see the chapter *Strengthening Health Systems*).

A related challenge involves us outsiders preferring to do what's familiar and comfortable for us. We adjust ourselves to many unfamiliar realities volunteering abroad, so we love to have at least one constant: the structure of our daily routine of showing up and seeing a string of patients. We're also used to following our home country's standards of care; we like to use familiar tools inside of western-looking functional buildings with advanced technology.

Each of these familiar factors can be transplanted to a resource-limited country and a *parallel system* can be built. This comfortable and familiar approach is the *easy way*: to take the West and in a small way move it to another country. Yet if the tables were turned and some other society did this to us, it would certainly feel like an invasion. Clearly, this *easy way* is not the *best way*. Additionally, parallel systems disempower local people and can harm their health systems and societies. As reviewed in the chapter *Strengthening Health Systems*, we outsiders can help a lot by integrating, adapting, and working in partnership to improve the function of local health systems rather than building our own.

Why New Buildings?

Outsiders tend to have an intense calling to build a structure or facility that·makes a visible change in how a place looks. We like to *leave our mark*. I've even seen outsider organizations build a clinic in every country that they volunteer in—regardless of whether it's at the top of a community list of needs and requests. I've met some that have made a career out of building as many clinics as they can in resource-limited nations.

Other times, the push to build new facilities comes from local people. My original NGO contact in Uganda requested: "Please build us a clinic right here." A village leader in Burma asked me: "Can you bring us a new clinic?" Oddly, in both places there was already a locally-run clinic down the road. Health workers in both places would have been quite upset with me if I had responded to these requests and potentially put them out of business through unfair health facility competition. First, the community clinic could collapse and then the outsider one could eventually lose funding and attention—and collapse as well. There are numerous non-functioning health facilities, schools, and development projects throughout the world built by outsiders with the best of intentions.[1]

The motivations of outsiders and local people tend to be sincere when they propose outsider-led health facility construction. Yet this is often a knee-jerk response to one of the most common refrains heard by outsider medical teams upon arriving in remote communities: *"Please build us a clinic! We need it!"*

When focus groups tease out what this need for a clinic really means, it usually represents a general request for more and better medical care in the community. Oftentimes, both local people and outsiders equate improved medical care with clinic-building. Much can be learned by asking this *chicken or the egg* question:

> *What's more important for improved health care locally: a new clinic space to see patients, or new health workers to fill the clinic and provide care?*

Both goals can be justified and important, but the question itself has an inherent flaw in the use of the word *new*. The chapter *Power to the People* argued that successful and sustainable health programs tend to emerge from preexisting local facilities, people, ideas, and dreams (*preexisting embers*) rather than the new ones of outsiders. In the same way, the question about prioritizing a new clinic or new health workers is less relevant than the question: *What are existing clinics and the current health workers doing (or what could they be doing) to improve health?*

This is again where *assets and needs assessment* fits in. Asking about and seeking out preexisting health facilities, workers, and other assets is a critical initial activity for us outsiders to do with the community. Its steps involve meeting with them, forming a partnership, and learning about what they have, what they lack, and how they want to improve the health of their community. Finally, outsiders in partnership may work out *if* and perhaps *how* we can contribute in a locally-led way.

However, our outsider teams often skip these key steps. We may see minimal—or no—medical care facilities and assume that the community must therefore need and want one; at the very least, we may want one and then build it. Meeting with the community allows us outsiders to come to understand how they prioritize and rank their main health challenges, which may or may not include a new clinic.

I've seen eager outsiders build a clinic without asking about and visiting preexisting health facilities. I've also watched outsiders who were aware of preexisting clinics and hospitals decide to ignore them as they broke ground for their own. Some finished construction only to discover that a new facility wasn't needed in the first place. Creating a new outsider facility abroad when there are local ones nearby is quite an inappropriate activity.[2]

> *I passed an empty clinic on my morning walk; it was abandoned because some outsiders wrongly assumed that they built a clinic where it was needed most. One meeting with the Ministry of Health (MOH) could have quickly clarified where a larger need existed, and perhaps where the MOH was planning to construct a facility themselves.*

Outsider vision tends to focus on the worst in communities abroad, noting what they lack rather than what they have—including health facilities. We foreign professionals are conditioned to see medical care occurring only in hospitals and clinics, while other lay facilities and modes of care may be invisible to our eyes. For example, medical care is often given in pharmacies in resource-limited countries; lay pharmacists may question symptoms, do testing, and give a corresponding medicine without involving a health worker, nurse, physician, or other professional. The use of home-based medical care and traditional healers often goes unnoticed by outsiders, who may see a village with no clinic as a village without health care.

Why Not Empower?

Part I reviewed the many ways in which existing local facilities serve as the ideal environment for health worker training and systems strengthening. In light of these helpful approaches, it's hard to justify creating a separate facility which may take something away from a community. For example, *Appendix A* explored how free outsider health services can cause economic harm and the closure of local health services.

A new clinic built by outsiders will naturally be viewed by local people as *the foreigners' clinic*. It can become a daily visual reminder of how outsiders can create and maintain a system that the community hasn't yet achieved. In this way, the building of an outsider health facility can simultaneously tear down local self-confidence, disempowering the local health system and the community at large. We outsiders often do the planning for clinic construction, while local people do the physical work. This arrangement enlists community members simply as construction workers rather than people with a central and holistic role in improving their medical system.

Our outsider facilities can further disempower if they have a separate staff and system of medicines, supplies, and equipment provision. This essentially demonstrates that local tools and networks aren't needed to get the job done. If all staff members are outsiders, there is no local capacity-building. If all medicines and supplies come from the outside, then none would be purchased locally in a way that benefits the community's economy. When outsider-run clinics run completely independently from local people, it hurts them the most and creates complete dependency for local patients. When all services, staff, and resources come from outside the community, local people will be left high and dry if the spigot is turned off. Empowered communities, by contrast, can and do sustain care themselves.

A final empowerment issue involves *opportunity costs*. Since we only have so much time, energy, and funding, choosing to do or fund one thing means not being able to do or fund something else. Building a clinic may take several months or years. Yet this lost time could have been devoted instead to the community's top *to do list* items, such as distributing mosquito nets or expanding access to clean water. Building a clinic also takes large sums of money, even when community materials and volunteer labor are used; this funding is then not available to jump-start local people's higher priority programs. Finally, there tend to be significant *opportunity costs* after clinic construction is completed; time spent running a new clinic could be better spent strengthening the systems of existing ones and training health workers.

"Chicken or the Egg" Answer

We can re-approach the *chicken or the egg* question after removing the word *new*:

> What's more important for improved health care locally: a clinic space to see patients, or health workers to fill the clinic and provide care?

On the surface, the question isn't easily answered since both space and personnel are central to the provision of health care. Yet while every community is different, the typical answer is that more and better-trained health workers are needed far more than additional space to see patients. The chapter *Reversing the Brain Drain* explored the critical shortage of health workers in resource-limited countries; in light of this dire reality, health workers typically represent the deeper need.

Even when formal space isn't available for patient care, it usually doesn't limit the amount of health care given. After all, villages may contain empty buildings, community centers, and existing clinics in which to see patients. Community health workers (CHWs) often operate out of their own homes or visit patients' homes rather than using clinics; home-based care also tends to be more empowering for patients.[3] Since travel to a busy clinic for care may be costly or inconvenient, *community-based health care* aims to move the focus of care from medical facilities to homes; only the sickest patients are encouraged to visit clinics and hospitals.[4] Therefore, having minimal health facilities can actually encourage empowering patient care when sufficient health workers are present.

Ideally, we should ensure the presence of adequate CHWs, the primary providers of health care in many resource-limited countries, before considering clinic construction.[5] When there are none or few CHWs, we outsiders can assist more by organizing a training program for them. In this sense, the people should precede the place.

Patient outcomes are affected more by health workers than by the availability of space for health services. The presence of sufficient medical facilities is "not causally related to better health outcomes… [and] the evidence indicates only a weak link."[6] The quality of the *process* through which health professionals interact with patients determines health outcomes far more than the presence of facilities; process can be improved by supervising medical care, following or developing guidelines for quality care, organizing health worker re-training, and doing peer review of health care work.[7] Care is largely improved through the presence of health systems which communicate better with each other, train their staff better, and apply evidence-based medicine systematically.[8] In other words, we need to invest more in the people and less in the place to provide quality health care.

Leading global health organizations and development goals have never called on us outsiders to focus on health facility-building, yet they have consistently highlighted the need for expanded local health worker training and numbers. None of the Millennium Development Goals (MDGs) from 1990 through 2015 focused on building clinics, hospitals, or other health care infrastructure. The three health-related MDGs centered on improving maternal health, reducing child death, and treating major diseases like HIV and malaria. Building more facilities would have done little toward achieving these goals. By contrast, the Director of the Global Health Workforce Alliance pointed out that further progress on the MDGs was largely held back by health workforce limitations.[9]

The post-2015 Sustainable Development Goals (SDGs) also fail to include a goal or target of clinic-building; yet they do establish a renewed focus on achieving universal health coverage through an expansion of the health workforce.[10] As addressed in the chapter *Strengthening Health Systems*, the WHO strategy for reaching universal health coverage minimizes infrastructure contributions like building clinics and hospitals; attention is instead given to increasing the numbers and training of health care professionals, information about health needs, access to needed medical products, health policy leadership, and accessing sustainable funding.[11]

Concrete and Confidence

> *Cracks in long-neglected concrete gave it some life. The skies opened up season after season, extending an enthusiastic invitation to grow. First it was weeds, flowers, and then shrubs that grew out of the cracked floor of the clinic. Abandoned by outsiders, the human-made structure would continue to submit to the onslaught of nature reclaiming the unused space. Across town, another clinic had even wider cracks as entire trees pushed their way through the crumbling concrete; this one had been abandoned by community members, but it had also been built by foreigners with strange accents.*

Outsider involvement in a health facility abroad just isn't sustainable, whatever the background story which eventually draws us very committed outsiders away from it: kids, marriage, deaths, other family responsibilities, a lost job, a new job with relocation, lack of work approval to travel, loss of grants or other economic problems, natural disaster, war, or a host of other events. It isn't necessarily a bad thing that we can't sustainably run a facility abroad, given that local people should be the main actors anyway. Yet loss of outsider support can crush community hope if we start building a health facility and don't finish it, or finish building it without having developed plans to sustain operations long-term.

How can these common challenges be resolved? Outsiders can pass on the facilities we've created to local communities as soon as we can responsibly do so. That works most successfully when we pass clinics and hospitals on to capable hands with sufficient staff, resources, and funding to sustain them well. If outsiders build and staff a clinic in a remote area, community members may need to be trained to serve as the health workers within it. Otherwise, it could easily become little more than a nursery for stray plants growing over time. Ministries of Health, community groups, and other local health or training facilities may be instrumental in helping us outsiders plan a responsible turn-over for the facility; one or more of these *preexisting embers* may start, lead, and finish the process successfully.

So we should pass it on if we build it, yet the ideal would have been never to have created a parallel system in the first place. Such facilities are like *leftovers* which have sat out for a while and are quite cold and unappealing; a family with empty shelves will often gladly accept leftovers, but understandably, they'd be much happier with a warm meal of their choosing. Local people can be disempowered as they watch us build something beautiful and then pick up the leftovers.

We can expect community members to prefer owning the success themselves and building a facility their own way. Being less excited about a clinic than its creators, there's a risk that the project—and the health improvement it was built to support—comes to a screeching halt. Just as important, local people will not have *learned by doing,* so they won't easily be able to fix the facility when it has problems. Further, they won't feel empowered to create a similar program in the future when it's needed and when there may be no visitors offering help.

> *There was finally effective medicine to treat HIV and it was safe for children, but few resource-limited nations had pediatric care programs. I worked with a very professional outsider nonprofit that partnered with communities and MOHs in these settings to create the first national pediatric HIV care program as well as the first related clinic in-country. These facilities were set up in existing buildings or else constructed with community partnership. Rather than running such clinics as parallel systems, they were built on public hospital grounds or adjacent to them; these facilities were never passed on to local people because they were run by them from day one.*

In some situations, outsider clinic-building can be a helpful program when it is led by local people and merely *facilitated* by outsiders (see the chapter *Power to the People*). As addressed in *Part II*, a deep participatory assessment, priority ranking, and locally-led programming is needed first. For a clinic to be sustainable and successful, the impetus for its construction needs to flow from the deep desires of local people, rather than knee-jerk outsider reactions of compassion, desire, or misunderstanding. New clinic creation is best led by local people in every phase of the process, from the project's conception to drafting plans, construction, use planning, staffing, and its everyday operations. Construction projects in resource-limited countries should always flow from the impetus and participation of local people.[12]

In an effort to strengthen health systems, it's sometimes helpful to move existing health facilities or to add new ones in locations lacking access.[13] Yet these decisions should be made by the MOH, not by outsiders with our limited awareness of local health systems. Any health facilities we construct should become property of a public health care system rather than private property.[14]

As reviewed in the chapter *Disaster Strikes: Outsiders Arrive*, disaster relief is the most likely setting where outsider construction of health facilities can be helpful. Natural and human-caused disasters such as war and genocide are a specific scenario of global health work, through which parallel health care systems and outsider-built facilities are more likely needed. When existing systems are overwhelmed, building new and temporary facilities may be a critical means of saving and improving many lives. Importantly, professional outsider organizations working in areas of chronic poverty and those working in disaster relief *both* refrain from routinely setting up parallel systems and constructing health facilities.

If we're not usually building or running health facilities abroad, then how can we best help with them? As reviewed in the chapter *Strengthening Health Systems*, helping with community facilities rather than our own is a great starting point. When there are existing local health facilities, fixing and upgrading them can be a helpful activity—if we're called on to do so by local people.[15] For empowerment to occur, preexisting health facilities and modalities could be improved, expanded, or better supported. Systems strengthening work can do much to build community confidence and improve the quality of local health care. True success lies with supporting local people in gaining the confidence, power, and tools to help themselves.

Appendix C

Participatory Rural Appraisal

Participatory Rural Appraisal (PRA) was introduced in the chapter *Participation to Empower*, where community maps and walks were described. This appendix will explore other practical applications, including those used to brainstorm solutions to local health problems. I have mentioned using PRA methods to rank and prioritize health problems several times, and will review these techniques first.

Ranking Problems

The brainstorming of problems in focus groups is a good way to begin to understand the range of issues of concern to a community; however, it can generate an overwhelming list. Ranking these problems can be a helpful way to identify priorities and key first steps. Here are four participatory options for ranking problems:

1. List and Vote for Three

A facilitator can go around the room various times asking each person to identify a key local health problem; each response can be listed for all to see, and when everyone's contributions are exhausted, similar problems can be consolidated.[1] Next, each person can vote for three problems from the list that they think are the most important. The problem with the most votes is ranked number one, the one with the second most votes is ranked number two, and so on. If two problems receive an equal number of votes, then further discussion and a vote can be held between the contending options.

2. Vote and Assess Timing

In addition to ranking the importance of problems, the timing of which problem(s) should be addressed first can also be explored.[2] For example, lack of income-generation may serve as problem number 3, while malnutrition is ranked as problem number 1. Yet in order to address malnutrition, income-generation may be needed first. In this way, a community may decide to start with number 3 rather than number 1.

3. Four-Variable Method

A multidimensional approach can also be used for health problem ranking. Each problem can be scored by participants according to how 1) serious, 2) common, 3) important, and 4) appropriate for action it is; these four variables can each be given a score from 1 to 3, allowing for a total problem score between 4 and 12.[3] The problem with the highest score would be prioritized.

4. Compare Pairs

Pair-wise ranking is another method of systematic prioritization. After group brainstorming of problems generates a list, each problem can be labeled twice on a matrix—once in each axis (see Figure 4). Then each problem is compared against the others, as local people come to a consensus or vote on which member of each pair is more important. The winner of each comparison is listed in this matrix space.

The comparison of each pair of problems is done only once (proceeding left to right OR top to bottom) in each space of the matrix, except those where a problem would be compared against itself. Next, community members count how many times each problem won the duel, and list this total in a separate column to the right. The highest priority problem has the most wins, while the second priority problem has the second most wins, and so on. Reasons for ranking one problem over another should then be explored through in-depth discussion.[4]

Often groups of up to ten people can participate fully in such participatory problem ranking. However, one group of ten may come up with very different answers from another. More well-to-do local people would likely come up with a different problem list than those living in deepest poverty; groups of men often identify different priorities than groups of women. So repeating this activity and comparing differences can be very telling.[5] If different demographic groups rank the same problem as being *most important*, then it can be seen to be especially compelling.

While these ranking methods add an objective quality to local problem prioritization, there is no obligation that communities must work on that number one problem. Local people lead health program development, and while they may choose to tackle the highest-ranking problem, they might for a variety of reasons decide by consensus or vote to focus on a different problem entirely.

Figure 4. Pair-wise Ranking of Agricultural Problems[6]

Types	Seeds	Tools	Insecticide	Canals	Markets	Pipes	Transport	Training	Road	Score	Rank
Lack of seeds		Tools	Seeds	Canals	Seeds	Seeds	Seeds	Training	Seeds	5	3
Lack of tools			Tools	Canals	Tools	Tools	Tools	Training	Tools	6	2
Lack of insecticide				Canals	Insecticide	Pipes	Transport	Training	Insecticide	2	6
Canals					Canals	Canals	Canals	Training	Canals	7	1
Lack of markets						Pipes	Markets	Markets	Markets	3	5
Lack of pipes							Pipes	Training	Pipes	4	4
Transport								Transport	Transport	3	5
Training									Training	6	2
Road										0	7

PRA Methods to Explore Health

A. Health Status by Stone

In addition to problem ranking, there are many other hands-on PRA activities—most of which don't require literacy. For example, Figure 5 illustrates an activity in which facilitators ask community members to use different stones to represent children who are *very healthy*, of *average health, sometimes sick,* or *always sick.*[7] The results show that 9 children were found to be *sick sometimes,* while 11 were *always sick.* These rankings give valuable clues for outsider and local health workers regarding *community diagnosis,* individual pediatric diagnosis, and needed follow-up. They can help to get everyone on the same page regarding children's health status despite differences in literacy.

Figure 5. Stone-based Ranking of Children's Health Status in Ambari, Meghalaya[8]

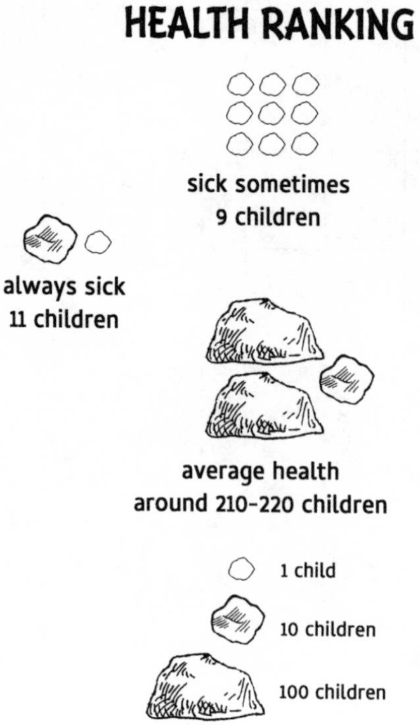

HEALTH RANKING

sick sometimes
9 children

always sick
11 children

very healthy
10 children

average health
around 210–220 children

1 child

10 children

100 children

B. Pie Charts

Pie charts are a PRA method more familiar to Westerners. Lines radiate from the center of a circle to the outer border, dividing the "pie" into different sized slices proportional to the whole. This circle can be drawn on paper or constructed using sticks as adjustable pie chart lines. Pies may represent actual quantitative data, community perceptions, or estimations of numbers.

For example, community members may estimate that one-fourth of households have chronic cough and fever, while three-quarters don't. Alternatively, pie diagrams can illustrate community preferences for various family planning methods.[9] They can be used to explore how often local people seek out health care for various medical problems; for example, community members with arm and leg pains may see health workers roughly 60% of the time and traditional healers the other 40%. Pregnant women may self-deliver around 5% of the time, use birth attendants or midwives 40% of the time, and deliver in hospitals the remaining 55%.

C. Venn Diagrams

Venn diagrams are particularly useful in exploring local people's perceptions of and relationship to clinics, hospitals, pharmacies, healthcare organizations, and traditional healers.[10] First, ask community members to discuss and agree upon which are the more important health care sources. Next, ask them to cut out circles of various sizes, with the more important sources larger than the less important, and to write the name of each health institution in each circle. Then ask the local people to place their circles on a large piece of paper with their community's name drawn in a big circle in the center; their smaller circles are placed various distances away from their central *community circle*, with closer circles representing more effective health care sources.

The degree to which circles overlap represents how much healthcare groups communicate and collaborate. For example, the circles of two clinics would overlap if they were co-organizing a TB program; a clinic could also overlap with traditional birth attendants if they held skills improvement classes or helped them with supplies. Discussion of the relative importance of health centers may show one center being favored for general care, while another is favored for deliveries or specialist care.[11] Reasons for variable preferences and effectiveness can be explored as well. Figure 6 illustrates an example of a Venn Diagram, where the larger circle represents a village and the other circles represent local sources of health care with variable importance to the village (depending on the size of the circle); overlapping circles show close contact and cooperation.

Figure 6. Venn Diagram, Village Example

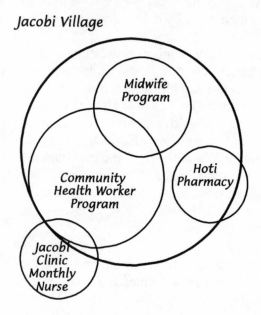

Jacobi Village

PRA Methods to Brainstorm Solutions

1. Risk Map

PRA methods are excellent for envisioning and designing locally-led solutions. By focusing on one or more locally identified priority problems, community members can physically locate the problem(s) in specific areas and then draw a *risk map*.[12] Participatory mapping can focus attention on where risks are clustered, how many nearby people are affected, and it can depict local assets which can be mobilized to address the problems.

2. Flow Charts

The perceived and/or actual causes of health problems can be explored as a community by drawing a *flow chart* (see Figure 7). Circles are placed around social and public health problems, diseases, and disease vectors; lines with arrows are drawn between these circles showing the direction of causality. It can be helpful to draw each problem or factor on a separate piece of paper that can be moved around as the group discusses and develops a common understanding of the relationships among the parts. Flow charts have been used to explore causes of child mortality and water-borne diseases[13] as well as alcoholism.[14] They are also quite useful in exploring the natural history of a disease and the potential interventions at each disease stage.[15]

Figure 7. Flow Chart for Disease Causation[16]

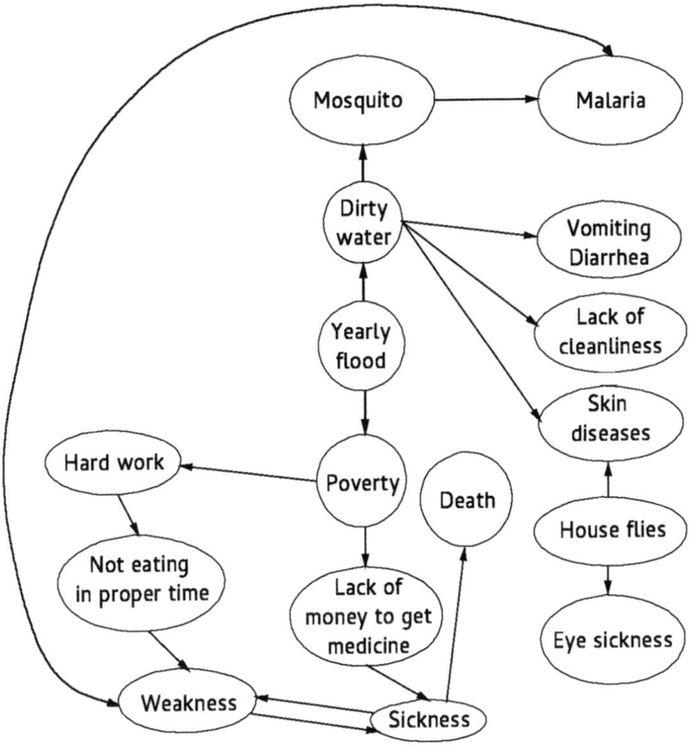

3. Problem Tree

Both the causes and effects of health problems can be visually explored using a *problem tree*.[17] A large tree is drawn, where the trunk is the main problem being addressed, roots are labelled as the causes, and branches are labelled as the effects of the problem. Solutions can be more effectively crafted by a group when it understands and addresses causes as well as effects.

4. Matrices or Grids

Local people can create a matrix listing health facilities on one axis and diseases or other health problems on the other. Discussing the relationships among the items and showing them visually can help develop a better understanding of the strengths and weaknesses of local medical care, and then support the brainstorming of solutions. A similar comparison involves listing medical problems on one axis and medical care access and utilization on the other.[18] For example, such a matrix may show sufficient care for malaria yet a dearth of care for heart problems.

Diseases of concern to community members may also be listed on one axis, and then compared against the types of treatment and prevention available for each. This activity may illustrate important assets as well as *missing links* in disease prevention and cure. Such missing links may include clean water, nutritious food, mosquito nets, health education, medical supplies, medicines, etc. Visual brainstorming activities such as these lend themselves to discovering home-grown health solutions.

Don't Just Do Something:
Stand There
by Robin Young, MBA, and Jessica Evert, MD

Global Health Education and Work for Students and Trainees

We enter into global health work because we feel strongly about taking action to eliminate health disparities. So why should we advocate just standing there and not doing? Counterintuitively, to make sustainable reduction of health disparities in low-resource settings, we first have to sit on our hands. Often, we have to sit on our hands even as veteran physicians, mid-career nurse practitioners, or any kind of health worker, especially if it is our first time in the community we are visiting. We have to sit on our hands for longer and with more restraint when we are students and trainees.

> *We started our journey to visit Dr. Mbabazi, a traditional healer, early that morning... We were very warmly received by the traditional doctor [who] has a great relationship with Dr. Atim (lead physician at the health organization where I am placed). Dr. Atim had helped create a book for Dr. Mbabazi that includes the names of different plants (both in English and Rukiga, the language spoken in that part of Uganda) and their common uses. Dr. Mbabazi explained how this has enabled him to use consistent products and he can also send his grandchildren to the garden with this book and they will know exactly what plant or even the specific part of a plant to bring back to him. They are also able to run drug-drug and drug-disease interaction reports between natural products and Western pharmaceutical products.*

> *Dr. Mbabazi discussed how he mainly treats psychosocial*
> *issues and generally does not attempt to treat complications*
> *in pregnancy or infectious diseases such as HIV/AIDS, TB,*
> *malaria, and typhoid. Instead, Dr. Mbabazi refers these*
> *patients to Dr. Atim. Given the stigma surrounding mental*
> *health, I am so impressed by the way these doctors work*
> *together to incorporate people's health beliefs with Western*
> *medical practices. I hope more healthcare providers can*
> *move towards treating patients as whole beings.*
>
> —Third-year pharmacy student (PharmD)

Before health professionals become professionals, they are students and trainees. Our work in CFHI with these passionate trainees centers on helping them to engage, learn, and build solidarity and equity through global health experiences. Kirk Scirto's book provides a great text reinforcing appropriate guidance and program frameworks that explicitly tear down colonial approaches to global health work, helping them to both learn from and contribute to their host communities. As we structure experiences that "do no harm" into short-term segments to accommodate academic calendars, we find many commonalities in the way we suggest Doing Global Health Work.

There are many ways for visitors to cause harm in global health settings, even for the most enlightened and well-meaning among us. Scirto lays them out comprehensively: from usurping power, prestige and much-needed funding and resources away from local healthcare systems (formal and informal) and workers, to operating outside of local legal and regulatory frameworks such as medical licensure boards and ministries of health, to offering substandard care to patients or training to healthcare workers due to lack of knowledge, skills, and relevant cultural and language training.

Scirto delineates ways that health workers and other professionals can do better than they have in the past in global health settings, by collaborating with local leaders and workers to co-offer capacity-building and training, offer initiatives to strengthen health systems, and facilitate community-based programs. Of course, as he highlights, the devil is in the details: capacity-building is most effective when it focuses on local needs as identified by local leaders and community members, and within long-standing relationships with a track record of trust and transparency. In Chapter 8: Poverty and Empowerment, the section Taking the Power Back highlights the role of Fair Trade in commerce; similarly, Fair-Trade Learning Principles[1] offer a rubric for student engagement in Global Health Service Learning activities that can serve as a baseline for developing strong partnerships with Fair Trade principles at their core.

How does all of this relate to students and trainees (from undergraduate to postgraduate levels)? Should they be in the same roles as trained visiting professionals? The stakes related to students and trainees seeking global health experiences can be even higher than for professionals. The dangers caused by students engaging in global health experiences without appropriate training and without carefully structured and supervised programs are now well documented.[2] They range from generating cultural misunderstandings and program service interruptions, to accidentally causing disability or death to patients. As Scirto critiques in his discussion of Suitcase Medicine, many programs and trip-providers to resource-poor settings believe that sub-standard care or education from an unlicensed foreign volunteer must be better than whatever health system exists locally (or they provide misinformation that no system exists locally!). This foundation for global health programs is tremendously dangerous for all involved, none more than vulnerable patients and service-seekers.

The role of occupational therapy looks very different depending on the country you visit. In the United States, we function more on the medical model because that is what our payment system supports. In other countries the occupational therapist may advise patients in a transitional state, such as refugees or individuals experiencing homelessness, focusing more on mental health and the development of meaningful roles and routines. As I shadowed a physical therapist at her clinic in Oaxaca, Mexico, she used many interventions I had learned in school, such as kinesiotaping and massage. She seemed to fill the role of both a physical therapist and occupational therapist, providing interventions for areas like the hands, that are typically treated by occupational therapists in the States. Patient conditions ranged from musculoskeletal injuries such as a supraspinatus tear to sciatica and arthritis. I was extremely impressed by this young physical therapist's confidence and professionalism, given that she is only 22 years old and has been practicing for only 7 months. I loved her emphasis on patient education, drawing pictures and using playdough to demonstrate the cause of a patient's injury. She told me that while this clinic lacks a lot of the modern technology she learned about in school, she likes being creative with her interventions and the resources available.

—Occupational therapy doctoral candidate

For students and trainees, unintended harm can happen in the name of helping, volunteering, learning, "giving back," and more evenly distributing resources. As the oath many plan to take vows to "Do No Harm," students are often horrified when they have epiphanies similar to those in the narratives shared by Scirto: "Is this whole experience solely intended for my own personal growth and benefit? Will I come away from this experience thinking I helped, when really I didn't help at all? Will I actually make things worse while trying to help?" What may have initially seemed simple to a student seeking a global health experience suddenly becomes much more complex when examined.

Facilitating organizations and leaders must ensure these experiences are ethical, safe and appropriate for students; students themselves cannot confirm these safeguards are in place. Though there is a growing awareness around these concerns, including a recent flowering of literature focused on "decolonizing global health,"[3] global health organizations and those facilitating student experiences are not always well-versed in these considerations, sometimes with dire consequences for the communities they visit as well as for visiting students.

Partly in response to the increased awareness about inappropriate activities that students sometimes undertake in global health settings, US-based medical and health professions schools are increasingly adding nuance to their entry requirements, and residencies are becoming more discerning as well. For example, whereas in the past it was common for medical schools to state that demonstrated "hands-on" experience in clinical settings was a requirement or at least a highly desirable experience on an applicant's resume, many institutions are now clarifying that these experiences must be primarily observational in nature, for legal and ethical reasons; and that students should undertake these experiences within existing organizational structures, under appropriate supervision, and with proper permissions granted by national and local authorities whether at home or abroad. This is just one step in how medical and health professions schools must make changes in instructing trainees to do global health work.

Given these concerns, limitations, and pitfalls, anyone would be justified in wondering if they should bother seeking out a global health experience at all. But for students to skip global health experiences altogether would be a major loss. Students need global health experiences now more than ever, and our world needs students to have these experiences. Why? Because global health education experiences have the potential to equip students with the fundamental competencies to address many of our most pressing shared challenges: climate change, lack of access to essential healthcare, global pandemics, hate and discrimination, and protecting the rights of the most vulnerable, to name just a few. While research shows that it is neither desirable nor expected for students to fill gaps in healthcare systems,[4] long-standing partnerships and programs can provide students with the opportunity to become learners, secure in the knowledge that they are indeed "helping" as much as they are learning, because everyone involved in their program has been intimately involved in its design and is being fairly compensated for their time, teaching, and preparation work. Students and trainees may only realize later how important it was that they created health education materials about safe sex under the close supervision of their Ugandan mentor, for example, given local cultural realities related to sex and contraception, and how relieved they are that they were not the sole individual responsible for delivering that training, but instead served in a supporting role.

In an era of new technology, rapid innovation and "build the plane while flying" ethos, we consciously advocate the "don't just do something, stand there" approach when it comes to student engagement in global health situations. For example, observing clinical patient interactions in another language is an exciting and humbling experience, and offers trainees deep insight into the lived experience of their future patients or clients who may not understand the primary language spoken at the clinic or service center. Similarly, shadowing a midwife in rural Oaxaca, Mexico for several days or weeks offers trainees the opportunity to keep a detailed professional journal and develop insight into the value of integrating indigenous healing modalities with biomedical approaches to achieve better patient outcomes. When traveling in a group or with visiting health professionals, so much can be gained from observing and contributing to thoughtful intercultural collaborations, with community members setting the agenda and everyone working toward shared goals.

My four-week trip to New Delhi, India was transformative as it influenced my passion for medicine and public health. These experiences allowed me to witness individuals and organizations lobbying on behalf of patients and community

members. I saw the direct yet far-reaching impact my
own voice could have in protecting patient rights and
ensuring healthcare access. Throughout medical school
and during residency, I have continued to focus on serving
the underserved community, primarily focusing on health
education.

—Emergency & Family Medicine Resident

These experiences help trainees to become more thoughtful, humble, curious, and empathetic, all skills that host communities, when surveyed, do list as desirable in visiting trainees.[5] Through their own hard work and that of their mentors, preceptors, and educators, students come to deeply understand local healthcare systems, the burden of disease, and determinants of health including environmental and socioeconomic factors. They observe the practice of public health or medicine in settings that are likely differently resourced than what they are accustomed to and differently resourced than what the remainder of their training is likely to provide. They will approach their future patients and clients differently, more empathetically, and with a greater appreciation for how what happens outside the clinic or agency impacts everything that happens inside. In short, a global health experience for students is nothing less than an investment in better healthcare, better public health systems, better social service safety nets, and more culturally-informed and creative approaches to address the factors that influence health outcomes, such as access to safe, adequate, and dignified food, water, shelter, and work. As educators, healthcare workers, researchers, and program providers, our charge is to model humble, ethical, and compassionate behavior when we engage in global health work; the trainees learning from us will be the ones to not just to eventually fill gaps in local and global healthcare and public health systems, but to effect much-needed paradigm changes and build Health for All.

So stand there, sit on your hands, examine assumptions, confront bias, and work toward being informed enough to do something that will really make a difference in global health.

Robin Young, MBA
Executive Director, Child Family Health International
Jessica Evert, MD
Medical Director, Child Family Health International

Endnotes

1. https://www.cbglcollab.org/ftl
2. https://www.cfhi.org/extent-nature-and-consequences-of-performing-outside-scope-of-training-in-global-health; https://www.cfhi.org/how-the-social-contract-can-frame-international-electives; https://www.cfhi.org/advisor-perspectives-of-pre-health-students-experiences-abroad; https://www.cfhi.org/practising-beyond-ones-scope-while-working-abroad; https://www.cfhi.org/special-collection-short-term-experiences-in-global-health-steghs-urgent-need-for-a-legal-and
3. https://annalsofglobalhealth.org/collections/special/decolonizing-global-health-education/; https://www.cfhi.org/decolonizing-global-health-education-rethinking-institutional-partnerships-and-approaches-o
4. https://www.cfhi.org/visiting-trainees-in-global-settings-host-and-partner-perspectives-on-desirable-competencies
5. *Ibid.*

Endnotes

Part 1: Health Care, Systems, and Training

1. World Health Organization (hereafter WHO) 2021b.
2. Duvivier, Burch, and Boulet 2017.
3. Tankwanchi, Vermund, and Perkins 2015.
4. de Vries, Steinmetz, and Tijdens 2016.
5. WHO 2016b.
6. Campbell *et al.* 2015.
7. WHO 2016b, p. 11.
8. *Ibid*, p. 9.
9. Nullis-Kapp 2005.
10. Agyepong *et al.* 2017.
11. WHO 2016a.
12. Agyepong *et al.* 2017.
13. Budy 2015.
14. Abuagla and Badr 2016; Labonté *et al.* 2015; Lowe and Chen 2016.
15. Kitzito *et al.* 2015.
16. Budy 2015.
17. Abuagla and Badr 2016; Tankwanchi, Vermund, and Perkins 2015.
18. Duvivier, Burch, and Boulet 2017.
19. WHO 2016b.
20. Moszynski 2011.
21. WHO 2016b.
22. Nullis-Kapp 2005.
23. WHO 2016b.
24. WHO 2018.
25. WHO 2021a.
26. WHO 2021c.

1. Reversing the Brain Drain

1. Wall, Arrowsmith, Lassey, and Danso 2006.

2. Asgary and Junck 2012; Bezruchka 2000; Bishop and Litch 2000; Crump and Sugarman 2008; St. Clair *et al.* 2017; Wilson, Merry, and Franz 2012.
3. Laleman *et al.* 2007.
4. Jesus 2010; Lasker 2016; Van Hoving, Wallis, Docrat, and DeVres 2010; Wilson, Merry, and Franz 2012.
5. St. Clair *et al.* 2017.
6. Crump and Sugarman 2008.
7. Seager 2012.
8. Martiniuk, Manouchehrian, Negin, and Zwi 2012; Wilson, Merry, and Franz 2012.
9. Laleman *et al.* 2007.
10. Bishop and Litch 2000; Crump and Sugarman 2008; Jesus 2010.
11. Laleman *et al.* 2007.
12. Bezruchka 2000.
13. Wright, Walker, and Yacoub 2007.
14. Schultz 2010.
15. Victora, Hanson, Bryce, and Vaughan 2004.
16. Hill 2002.
17. Wilson, Merry, and Franz 2012.
18. Rozier, Lasker, and Comptom 2017.
19. Laleman *et al.* 2007.
20. Dupuis 2003.
21. Maki, Qualls, White, Kleefield, and Crone 2008.
22. Sykes 2014.
23. Gedde 2009.
24. Powel, Gilliss, Hewitt, and Flint 2010.
25. Heck, Bazemore, and Diller 2007.
26. Lasker 2016.
27. Abdullah 2008; Patel et al. 2012.
28. Eberlin, Zaleski, Synder, and Hamdan 2008; Ruiz-Razura, Cronin, and Navarro 2000.

29. Chapin and Doocy 2010.
30. Werner and Bower 2012.
31. Americares 2013; DeCamp 2011; Eberlin, Zaleski, Synder, and Hamdan 2008; Powel, Gilliss, Hewitt, and Flint 2010; Wilson, Merry, and Franz 2012.
32. Maki, Qualls, White, Kleefield, and Crone 2008; Suchdev et al. 2007; Wall, Arrowsmith, Lassey, and Danso 2006.
33. Chapin and Doocy 2010; Dainton, Chu, Gorman, and Cherniak 2019.
34. Dainton, Chu, Gorman, and Cherniak 2019.
35. Pfeiffer et al. 2008.
36. Lough 2015.
37. Maki, Qualls, White, Kleefield, and Crone 2008.
38. Rozier, Lasker, and Comptom 2017.
39. WHO 2016b.
40. WHO 2018.
41. Laleman et al. 2007.

2. Training Health Workers

1. Mills, Rasheed, and Tollman 2006.
2. Roche, Ketheeswaran, and Wirtz 2017.
3. Jordan and Davis-Floyd 1992.
4. Hongoro and Normand 2006.
5. Seager 2012.
6. WHO 2005a.
7. Schellenberg et al. 2004.
8. Victora, Adam, Bryce, and Evans 2006.
9. WHO 2005a
10. WHO 2013b.
11. Reisman et al. 2016.
12. Versantvoort et al. 2019.
13. Jokhio, Winter, and Cheng 2005.
14. Suchdev et al. 2007; Wilson, Merry, and Franz 2012.
15. Joralemon 1999.
16. Seager 2012.
17. Gedde 2009.
18. Kuehn 2013.
19. Ibid.
20. Styles 2010.
21. Lassi, Cometto, Huicho, and Bhutta 2013.
22. Eyal, Cancedda, Kyamanywa, and Hurst 2016.
23. Ellard et al. 2016.
24. Wise, 2011.
25. Ibid.
26. Lankester 2019d.
27. Campbell et al. 2015.
28. Kinfu, Dal Poz, Mercer, and Evans 2009.
29. Haines et al. 2007.
30. Lankester 2019d.
31. Seager 2012.
32. Werner and Bower 2012.
33. Werner 1992.
34. Burns, Lovich, Maxwell, and Shapiro 1997; Dickson 2006; Jailer, Lara-Meloy, and Robbins 2015; Lankester and Grills 2019; Werner and Bower 2012.

3. Strengthening Health Systems

1. WHO 2007.
2. Nambiar et al. 2017; Zarocostas 2010.
3. Mills, Rasheed, and Tollman 2006.
4. Ibid.
5. Pfeiffer et al. 2008.
6. Mills, Rasheed, and Tollman 2006.
7. Travis et al. 2004.
8. Tollman, Doherty, and Mulligan 2006.
9. English, Lanata, Ngugi, and Smith 2006.
10. Gedde 2009.
11. Green, Green, Scandlyn, and Kestler 2009; Lasker 2016; Seager 2012; Wright, Walker, and Yacoub 2007.
12. WHO 2007.
13. Gedde 2009.
14. Travis et al. 2004.
15. Nyamtema, Urassa, and van Roosmalen 2011.
16. Pfeiffer et al. 2008.
17. Mills, Rasheed, and Tollman 2006.
18. Travis et al. 2004.
19. Nambiar et al. 2017.
20. Mills, Rasheed, and Tollman 2006.
21. Comninellis 2012.
22. Whitney, Stevens, and Bearman 2011.
23. Mills, Rasheed, and Tollman 2006.
24. Travis et al. 2004.
25. St. Clair et al. 2017.

26. Travis *et al.* 2004.
27. Zarocostas 2010.
28. Victora, Hanson, Bryce, and Vaughan 2004.
29. Travis *et al.* 2004.
30. Pfeiffer *et al.* 2008.
31. Green, Green, Scandlyn, and Kestler 2009; Roberts 2006.
32. WHO 2011a.
33. WHO 2000.
34. Wilson, Merry, and Franz 2012.
35. Travis *et al.* 2004; WHO 2007.
36. Buekens, Keusch, Belizan, and Bhutta 2004; Victora, Adam, Bryce, and Evans 2006.
37. Wilson, Merry, and Franz 2012.
38. Zarocostas 2010.
39. Pfeiffer *et al.* 2008.
40. Klarreich and Polman 2012.
41. Hill 2002.
42. Travis *et al.* 2004.
43. Gedde 2009; Powel, Gilliss, Hewitt, and Flint 2010.
44. Collins 2014.
45. Crump, Sugarman, and Working Group on Ethics Guidelines for Global Health Training 2010.
46. Green, Green, Scandlyn, and Kestler 2009.
47. Lasker 2016.
48. Wall, Arrowsmith, Lassey, and Danso 2006.
49. Heck, Bazemore, and Diller 2007.
50. Mills, Rasheed, and Tollman 2006.
51. Pfeiffer *et al.* 2008.
52. Collins 2014; Lasker 2016; Mills, Rasheed, and Tollman 2006.
53. Southall, Cham, and Sey 2010.
54. Pfeiffer *et al.* 2008.
55. Hongoro and Normand 2006.
56. Kuehn 2013; Labonté *et al.* 2015.
57. Hongoro and Normand 2006.
58. Duvivier, Burch, and Boulet 2017.
59. Budy 2015.
60. Tankwanchi, Vermund, and Perkins 2015.
61. WHO 2010.
62. WHO 2010.
63. Abuagla and Badr 2016; Labonté *et al.* 2015; Tankwanchi, Vermund, and Perkins 2015.

4. Disaster Strikes: Outsiders Arrive

1. Burkle 2006.
2. Médecins Sans Frontières (hereafter MSF) 1997.
3. Bygbjerg 2012.
4. MSF 1997.
5. Ciottone 2016.
6. Ketchie and Breuily 2010.
7. Eyal 2016.
8. Markenson and Reilly 2011.
9. Perrin 1996.
10. Dainton, Chu, Gorman, and Cherniak 2019.
11. Perrin 1996.
12. Koenig and Schultz 2012.
13. Peleg and Kellermann 2012.
14. MSF 1997.
15. MSF 1997; Perrin 1996.
16. MSF 1997; Pan American Health Organization (hereafter PAHO); Perrin 1996.
17. *Ibid.*
18. PAHO 2003.
19. MSF 1997; Perrin 1996.
20. Perrin 1996.
21. *Ibid.*
22. MSF 1997; PAHO 2003.
23. MSF 1997.
24. Perrin 1996.
25. MSF 1997.
26. Perrin 1996.
27. Giannone, Hilmi, and Anderson 2018.
28. Olu, Usman, Woldetsadik, Chamla, and Walker 2015; PAHO 1999.
29. International Federation of Red Cross and Red Crescent Societies and International Committee of the Red Cross 1994, p. 4.
30. Jahre, Kembro, Adjahossou, and Altay 2018.
31. *Ibid.*
32. Cullinan 2001; Kuehn 2013; MSF 1997.
33. Perrin 1996.

34. MSF 1997.
35. MSF 1997.
36. Ooms 2006.
37. MSF 1997; United Nations High Commissioner for Refugees (hereafter UNHCR) 2007.
38. Aschkenasy and Cranmer 2016.
39. Sphere 2018.
40. Aschkenasy and Cranmer 2016.
41. Office for the Coordination of Humanitarian Affairs 2012.
42. Humanitarian Accountability Partnership 2010.
43. *Ibid.*
44. PAHO 1999.
45. WHO 2013d.
46. WHO 1993.
47. MSF 1997; Perrin 1996.
48. Collins 2014.
49. Asgary and Junck 2012; Seager 2012; St. Clair *et al.* 2017.
50. WHO 2011a.
51. UNHCR 2007.
52. Perrin 1996.
53. Shah 2011.
54. MSF 1997, p. 38.
55. MSF 1997; Perrin 1996; Stockman 1994.
56. Asgary and Junck 2012; Martiniuk, Manouchehrian, Negin, and Zwi 2012.
57. MSF 1997; Perrin 1996.
58. Perrin 1996.
59. Ndomoto *et al.* 2018.
60. Lasker 2016; Lupton 2011; Wilson, Merry, and Franz 2012.
61. Blanchet *et al.* 2017.
62. PAHO 2001.
63. Langowski and Iltis 2011; Lupton 2011; Shrime, Sleemi, and Ravilla 2015; Wilson, Merry, and Franz 2012.
64. Chackungal *et al.* 2011; Redwood-Campbell *et al.* 2011; VanRooyen, Greenough, and Venugopal 2005.
65. WHO 2013a.
66. Ahmed, Grade, Malm, Michelen, and Ahmed 2017; Asgary and Junck 2012; St. Clair *et al.* 2017; Wilson, Merry, and Franz 2012.

5. Power to the People

1. Yunus 1999, p. 249.
2. Lupton 2011.
3. Ginwalla and Rickard 2015; Lasker 2016; Lupton 2011; Seager 2012.
4. Lupton 2011; Seager 2012.
5. Asgary and Junck 2012; Bishop and Litch 2000; Green, Green, Scandlyn, and Kestler 2009; Lasker 2016.
6. Friedmann 1992.
7. Hunter, Bailey, and Taylor 1995.
8. Bailey 1995.
9. Hunter, Bailey, and Taylor, 1995.
10. Hogan 2007, p. 22.
11. Chambers 1997.
12. Lupton 2011.
13. Ginwalla and Rickard 2015.
14. Dupuis 2003; Green, Green, Scandlyn, and Kestler 2009; Martiniuk, Manouchehrian, Negin, and Zwi 2012.
15. Lasker 2016; Lupton 2011; Wilson, Merry, and Franz 2012.
16. Rozier, Lasker, and Comptom 2017.

6. Agendas We All Have

1. Chui, Weng, Chen, Yang, and Lee 2012.
2. Lasker 2016.
3. Crump and Sugarman 2008.
4. Crump and Sugarman 2008; Dupuis 2003; Lasker 2016.
5. Ahmed, Grade, Malm, Michelen, and Ahmed 2017; Merlin *et al.* 2011; St. Clair *et al.* 2017; Wall, Arrowsmith, Lassey, and Danso 2006.
6. Rozier, Lasker, and Comptom 2017.

Part II: Social Justice and Public Health

1. Ruiz-Razura, Cronin, and Navarro 2000.
2. Biddle 2021; Lasker 2016.
3. Green, Green, Scandlyn, and Kestler 2009.
4. D'Adesky 2004.
5. Peterson 2002.
6. Lasker 2016.

7. Victora, Hanson, Bryce, and Vaughan 2004.
8. Langowski and Iltis 2011.
9. O'Dempsey and Munslow 2009.
10. Victora, Hanson, Bryce, and Vaughan 2004.
11. O'Dempsey and Munslow 2009.
12. Kim, Millen, Irwin, and Gershman 2000.
13. Hill 2002.
14. Klarreich and Polman 2012.

7. Exotic Diseases and Social Injustice

1. Human Rights Watch 2013.
2. WHO 2017, p. 2.
3. From "Chart of GDP per Capita" by the Global Education Project 2020, retrieved from https://www.theglobaleducationproject.org/earth/wealth-inequality/gdp-per-capita.
4. Rodney 2011.
5. From "Map of the Human Development Index (2005 version of this map)" by the Global Education Project 2005, retrieved from https://www.theglobaleducationproject.org/earth/development/the-human-development-index.
6. Bezruchka and Mercer 2004, p. 11.
7. Gish 2004.
8. Rodney 2011.
9. Infant deaths reflect estimated 2020 figures, while Absolute poverty and No water access reflect 2015 data. Adapted from "Reference map," "Absolute poverty," "No water access," and "Infant deaths 2020," by Worldmapper 2022a-d, retrieved from https://worldmapper.org/. (See references for link to and reference for each map). Copyright 2022 by Worldmapper.
10. Farmer 1999, p. 266.
11. Turnock 2016.
12. Marmot, Friel, Bell, Houweling, and Taylor 2008.
13. Shepherd et al. 2014.
14. Turnock 2016.
15. Marmot 2005.
16. WHO 2017, p. 1.
17. Marmot, Friel, Bell, Houweling, and Taylor 2008.
18. Sadana and Blas 2013.
19. Ibid.
20. Turnock 2016.
21. Marmot, Friel, Bell, Houweling, and Taylor 2008; Sadana and Blas 2013.
22. Lappe and Collins 2015.
23. Ibid, p. 4.
24. Gershman and Irwin 2000.
25. Schoepf, Schoepf, and Millen 2000.
26. Sachs 2005.
27. Easterly 2006; Korten 2012.
28. Korten 2001.
29. Olivera 2004; Shiva 2002.
30. D'Adesky 2004.
31. Iriart, Waitzkin, and Merhy 2004.
32. Schlesinger and Kinzer 2005.

8. Poverty and Empowerment

1. Friedmann 1992, p. 70.
2. Sen 1999, p. 87.
3. Narayanasamy 2009.
4. Rodriguez-Garcia, Macinko, and Waters 2001, p. 5.
5. Farmer 2005.
6. Yunis 1999, p. 205.
7. Kunitz 2000.
8. Alvarado and Benjamin 1989, p. 104.
9. Brenner, Ross, Simmons, and Zaidi 2000.
10. Jailer, Lara-Meloy, and Robbins 2015, p. 17.
11. Levy and Sidel 2000, p. 393.
12. Ibid.
13. Clements 1984.
14. Farmer 2005, p. 40.
15. Farmer 1999.
16. Korten 2001.
17. Cavanagh and Mander 2002.
18. D'Adesky 2004.
19. Gedicks 2001.
20. Olivera 2004.
21. D'Adesky 2004; Farmer 2005.

22. Gedicks 2001.
23. Freire 1970.
24. *Ibid.*
25. Werner and Bower 2012, p. 1-29.

9. Global Health Is Public Health

1. Koplan *et al.* 2009.
2. National Association of County and City Health Officials 2019.
3. Stevens *et al.* 2010; Suchdev *et al.* 2007.
4. Heck, Bazemore, and Diller 2007.
5. Gedde 2009.
6. US Department of Health and Human Services 2016.
7. Dainton, Chu, Gorman, and Cherniak 2019; Green, Green, Scandlyn, and Kestler 2009; Heck, Bazemore, and Diller 2007; Lasker 2016; Wilson, Merry, and Franz 2012.
8. Heck, Bazemore, and Diller 2007.
9. Lasker 2016.
10. Martiniuk, Manouchehrian, Negin, and Zwi 2012.
11. Stockman 1994.
12. de Beaumont Foundation 2017.
13. Pal 2016.
14. Smith *et al.* 2014.
15. Antwi, Kuwornu, Onumaha, and Ram 2017.
16. Cai, Quagrainie, and Hishamunda 2017.
17. Bontkes, van Keulen, and Kuyvenhoven 1999.
18. Savva and Frenken 2002.
19. Mishra, Kumar, and Ketelaar 2016.
20. Tilman, Cassman, Matson, Naylor, and Polasky 2002.
21. House *et al.* 1994.
22. Byhoff 2017.
23. Comninellis 2012.
24. Kamat and Fischer 2012.
25. United States Agency for International Development (hereafter USAID) 2003.
26. La Fond 1992.
27. USAID 2003.
28. Seager 2012.
29. United Nations Children's Fund (hereafter UNICEF) 2007.
30. WaterAid 2011.
31. Hutty, Morris, and Pisani 1997.
32. Kamat and Fischer 2012.
33. Waddington, Snilstveit, White, and Fewtrell 2009.
34. WHO 2005b.
35. Esrey, Potash, Roberts, and Shiff 1991.
36. Curtis and Cairncross 2003.
37. Jimmy *et al.* 2013.
38. Hodges 1993.
39. Skinner 2003.
40. SODIS 2011.
41. Mihelcic, Fry, Myre, Phillips, and Barkdoll 2009.
42. Bouman, Novalia, Hiemstra, and Willemsen 2010.
43. Mihelcic, Fry, Myre, Phillips, and Barkdoll 2009.
44. *Ibid.*
45. Gould and Nissen-Petersen 2008.
46. Ortiz, Perén, Escobar, and Cifuentes 1999.
47. Waddington, Snilstveit, White, and Fewtrell 2009.
48. WaterAid 2011.
49. UNICEF 2015.
50. Jenkins and Curtis 2005.
51. Werner and Bower 2012.
52. Brandberg 1997; Kar with Chambers 2008.
53. Winblad and Kilama 1985.
54. Mehta 2011.
55. Kar and Pasteur 2003.
56. Ahmed 2011.
57. Kar with Chambers 2008.
58. *Ibid.*
59. Institute for Development Studies (hereafter IDS) 2011.
60. Chambers 2011.
61. Ahmed 2011; IDS 2011.
62. Wood, Sawyer, and Simpson-Hebert 1998.
63. International Rescue Committee International Water and Sanitation Centre 2009.
64. Gonzalez, Gullemann, and Thyberghien 2010.

10. Participation to Empower

1. Wijk-Sijbesma 2001.
2. Kar with Chambers 2008.
3. *Ibid.*
4. Chambers 1992.
5. Chambers 1997.
6. Chambers 1992; Francis, Devavaram, and Erskin 1992.
7. Heaver 1992.
8. Narayanasamy 2009.
9. Appleton 1992.
10. Francis, Devavaram, and Erskin 1992.
11. Narayanasamy 2009.
12. Chambers 1997.
13. Alumasa 2003.
14. Narayanasamy 2009.
15. Comninellis 2012, p. 385.
16. Chambers 1997, p. 117.
17. Narayanasamy 2009.
18. Chambers 1997; Lappe and Collins 2015.
19. Schilderman 2010.
20. Gould and Nissen-Petersen 2008; Mihelcic, Fry, Myre, Phillips, and Barkdoll 2009; Oenga and Ikumi 1999.
21. Kar with Chambers 2008; Kar and Pasteur 2003; Mehta 2011.
22. USAID 2003.
23. Chambers 1997.
24. Appleton 1992.
25. Heaver 1992.
26. Comninellis 2012; Seager 2012.
27. Sellers and Oloo 1995.
28. Chamberlain, Chillery, Ogolla, and Wandera 1995.
29. Ssembatya, Coghlan, Lumala, and Kituusibwa 1995.
30. Duangsa 1995.
31. Epstein and Street 2011.
32. Funnell 2004.
33. Rollnick, Miller, and Butler 2008.
34. Miller 2013.

11. Community-Based Health Programs

1. Orr and Annis 2009, p. 31.
2. Chambers 1997; Heaver 1992.
3. Lankester 2019a.
4. Freudenberg, Pastor, and Israel 2011; Victora, Hanson, Bryce, and Vaughan 2004.
5. Unger, De Paepe, and Green 2003.
6. Lankester 2019a.
7. O'Toole, Aaron, Chin, Horowitz, and Tyson 2003.
8. Taylor-Ide and Taylor 2002.
9. Werner and Bower 2012.
10. Lankester 2019a.
11. *Ibid.*
12. McCoy, Hall, and Ridge 2012.
13. Lammerink, Bot, de Jong, and Schouten 1999; McCoy, Hall, and Ridge 2012.
14. Lammerink, Bot, de Jong, and Schouten 1999.
15. Gierke 2009.
16. Gould and Nissen-Petersen 2008.
17. Wegelin-Schuringa 2000.
18. Hammond 1998.
19. *Ibid.*
20. Kretzmann and McKnight 1993.
21. *Ibid*, p. 352.
22. Bergdall 2012, p. 4.
23. Russell and Smeaton 2009.
24. Taylor-Ide and Taylor 2002.
25. Orr and Annis 2009.
26. Kibuga, Bibby, and Sakafu 1999.
27. Russell and Smeaton 2009.
28. Duangsa 1995.
29. Edmunds 1999; Hennick 2007.
30. Chambers 1997.
31. Evans and Boyte 1986.
32. Taylor 1995.
33. Hogan 2007, p. 100.
34. Ahmad and Raza 1999.
35. Appleton 1992.
36. Gomez and Rojas 1999.
37. Oenga and Ikumi 1999.
38. Tayong and Poupom 1999.
39. Hunter, Bailey, and Taylor 1995.
40. Lammerink, Bot, de Jong, and Schouten 1999; McCoy, Hall, and Ridge 2012.
41. Mukherjee 1994.
42. Lammerink 1999.

12. Less Is More

1. Bergdall 2012, p. 8.
2. Werner 1992.
3. Taylor-Ide and Taylor 2002, p. 43.
4. Kretzmann and McKnight 1993.
5. *Ibid*, p. 376.
6. Perrin 1996.
7. Werner and Bower 2012.
8. WHO 2013d.
9. Seager 2012.
10. Mihelcic, Fry, Myre, Phillips, and Barkdoll 2009.
11. Werner and Bower 2012.
12. *Ibid.*
13. Pickford 1995, p. 120.
14. Kar with Chambers 2008.
15. Mihelcic, Fry, Myre, Phillips, and Barkdoll 2009.
16. Gould and Nissen-Petersen 2008.
17. Taylor-Ide and Taylor 2002.
18. Gould and Nissen-Petersen 2008.
19. Khadka, Paudyal, and Subba 1999.
20. Varley 1995.
21. Wijk-Sijbesma 2002.
22. Varley 1995.
23. Rodriguez-Garcia, Macinko, and Waters 2001; Yunus 1999.
24. Rodriguez-Garcia, Macinko, and Waters 2001; Werner and Bower 2012.
25. Yunus 1999.
26. Rodriguez-Garcia, Macinko, and Waters 2001.
27. MacFarquhar 2010.
28. Sinclair 2012.
29. Yunus 1999.
30. Rodriguez-Garcia, Macinko, and Waters 2001.
31. Glassman and Temin 2016

Conclusion: Doing Global Health Work to *Really* Make a Difference

1. Shields 1994.
2. Abramson, Seligman, and Teasdale 1978.

Appendix A

1. Dainton, Chu, Gorman, and Cherniak 2019; Lasker 2016; Redmond, O'Dempsey, and Taithe 2011; Snyder, Dharamsi, and Crooks 2011; Wilson, Merry, and Franz 2012.
2. Comninellis 2012; Drain, Pirtle, and Huffman 2009; Kamat and Fischer 2012; Osborn and Ohmans 2005; Palmer and Wolf 2008; WHO 2011b, WHO 2013c.
3. Asgary and Junck 2012.
4. Ahmed, Grade, Malm, Michelen, and Ahmed 2017; St. Clair *et al.* 2017; Wilson, Merry, and Franz 2012.
5. Laleman *et al.* 2007.
6. Crump and Sugarman 2008.
7. Van Hoving, Wallis, Docrat, and De Vries 2010; Wall, Arrowsmith, Lassey, and Danso 2006.
8. Lasker 2016.
9. Rozier, Lasker, and Compton 2017.
10. Lasker 2016.
11. Chapin and Doocy 2010.
12. Bishop and Litch 2000; Dupuis 2003; Green, Green, Scandlyn, and Kestler 2009; Lasker 2016; Martiniuk, Manouchehrian, Negin, and Zwi 2012; Roche, Ketheeswaran, and Wirtz 2016; Rozier, Lasker, and Compton 2017; Seager 2012; Van Hoving, Wallis, Docrat, and De Vries 2010.
13. Green, Green, Scandlyn, and Kestler 2009.
14. Bishop and Litch 2000.
15. Dupuis 2003; Van Hoving, Wallis, Docrat, and De Vries 2010.
16. WHO 2013a.
17. Jesus 2010; Lasker 2016.
18. Roche, Ketheeswaran, and Wirtz 2016.
19. Dupuis 2003; Green, Green, Scandlyn, and Kestler 2009; Jesus 2010; Langowski and Iltis 2011; Martiniuk, Manouchehrian, Negin, and Zwi 2012; St. Clair *et al.* 2017.
20. Sykes 2014.
21. Jesus 2010; Langowski and Iltis 2011.
22. Chapin and Doocy 2010; Green, Green, Scandlyn, and Kestler 2009.

23. Roche, Ketheeswaran, and Wirtz 2016.
24. Chapin and Doocy 2010.
25. Green, Green, Scandlyn, and Kestler 2009.
26. Dainton, Chu, Gorman, and Cherniak 2019; Gedde 2009.
27. Eberlin, Zaleski, Snyder, and Hamdan 2008; Green, Green, Scandlyn, and Kestler 2009; Heck, Bazemore, and Diller 2007.
28. Dainton, Chu, Gorman, and Cherniak 2019; Green, Green, Scandlyn, and Kestler 2009.
29. Bishop and Litch 2000.
30. St. Clair *et al.* 2017.
31. Jesus 2010.
32. Ahmed, Grade, Malm, Michelen, and Ahmed 2017; Ruiz-Razura, Cronin, and Navarro 2000; St. Clair *et al.* 2017.
33. Dupuis 2003.
34. Jesus 2010.
35. Shrime, Sleemi, and Ravilla 2015.
36. Dupuis 2003.
37. Redmond *et al.* 2011.
38. Ahmed, Grade, Malm, Michelen, and Ahmed 2017.
39. Ahmed, Grade, Malm, Michelen, and Ahmed 2017; Dupuis 2003.
40. Seager 2012.
41. Chapin and Doocy 2010.
42. Roberts 2006.
43. WHO 2011a.
44. Green, Green, Scandlyn, and Kestler 2009.
45. WHO 2011a.
46. *Ibid.*
47. Wilson, Merry, and Franz 2012.
48. *Ibid.*
49. WHO 2000.
50. WHO 2000; WHO 2011a.
51. Chapin and Doocy 2010.
52. Asgary and Junck 2012; Seager 2012; St. Clair *et al.* 2017.
53. Asgary and Junck 2012; Langowski and Iltis 2011.
54. Chapin and Doocy 2010; WHO 2013a.
55. Prasad *et al.* 2022.
56. Biddle 2021; Snyder, Dharamsi, and Crooks 2011; Wilson, Merry, and Franz 2012.

57. Lasker 2016; Roche, Ketheeswaran, and Wirtz 2016.
58. Roberts 2006.
59. Langowski and Iltis 2011.
60. Sykes 2014.
61. Dainton, Chu, Gorman, and Cherniak 2019.
62. Crump, Sugarman, and Working Group on Ethics Guidelines for Global Health Training 2010.
63. Eberlin, Zaleski, Snyder, and Hamdan 2008; Lasker 2016; Prasad *el al.* 2022; Suchdev *et al.* 2007; Wilson, Merry, and Franz 2012.
64. Sykes 2014.
65. Lasker 2016.
66. Americares 2013.
67. Maki, Qualls, White, Kleefield, and Crone 2008.
68. Prasad *et al.* 2022.
69. DeCamp 2011.
70. Redmond, O'Dempsey, and Taithe 2011.
71. Gedde 2009.
72. Sykes 2014.
73. Lasker 2016.
74. Sykes 2014.
75. Shrime, Sleemi, and Ravilla 2015.
76. Gosselin, Gialamas, and Atkin 2011.
77. Shrime, Sleemi, and Ravilla 2015.
78. *Ibid.*
79. Abdullah 2008; Dupuis 2003; Martiniuk, Manouchehrian, Negin, and Zwi 2012.
80. Dupuis 2003.
81. Laleman *et al.* 2007.
82. Dupuis 2003; Green, Green, Scandlyn, and Kestler 2009; Jesus 2010; Seager 2012.
83. Green, Green, Scandlyn, and Kestler 2009.
84. Dupuis 2003; Jesus 2010; Patel *et al.* 2012; Roche, Ketheeswaran, and Wirtz 2016; Seager 2012; Shrime, Sleemi, and Ravilla 2015.
85. Green, Green, Scandlyn, and Kestler 2009.
86. Dupuis 2003; Gedde 2009.
87. Abdullah 2008.
88. Eberlin, Zaleski, Snyder, and Hamdan

2008.
89. Rozier, Lasker, and Compton 2017.
90. Lasker 2016.
91. *Ibid.*
92. Dupuis 2003; Gedde 2009; Laleman *et al.* 2007; Lasker 2016; Patel *et al.* 2012; Rozier, Lasker, and Compton 2017; Shrime, Sleemi, and Ravilla 2015; Suchdev *et al.* 2007; Sykes 2014; Wall, Arrowsmith, Lassey, and Danso 2006.
93. Laleman *et al.* 2007; Lasker 2016.
94. Lasker 2016.
95. St. Clair *et al.* 2017.
96. Ginwalla and Rickard 2015.
97. Langowski and Iltis 2011; Van Hoving, Wallis, Docrat, and De Vries 2010.
98. Green, Green, Scandlyn, and Kestler 2009.
99. Shrime, Sleemi, and Ravilla 2015.
100. Dupuis 2003.
101. Asgary and Junck 2012.
102. Langowski and Iltis 2011; Lasker 2016.
103. Green, Green, Scandlyn, and Kestler 2009; Lasker 2016.
104. Green, Green, Scandlyn, and Kestler 2009.
105. Seager 2012.
106. Lasker 2016.
107. Green, Green, Scandlyn, and Kestler 2009.
108. Lupton 2011; Wilson, Merry, and Franz 2012.
109. Green, Green, Scandlyn, and Kestler 2009.
110. Ginwala and Rickard 2015.
111. Green, Green, Scandlyn, and Kestler 2009; Lasker 2016; Lupton 2011.
112. Lasker 2016; Lupton 2011; Wilson, Merry, and Franz 2012.
113. Dainton, Chu, Gorman, and Cherniak 2019.

Appendix B:

1. Munk 2013.
2. Lankester 2019c.
3. Werner and Bower 2012.
4. Lankester 2019a.
5. *Ibid.*

6. Peabody, Taguiwalo, Robalino, and Frenk 2006, p. 2.
7. *Ibid.*
8. Institute of Medicine 2001.
9. Campbell 2015.
10. WHO 2016b.
11. WHO 2007.
12. Schilderman 2010.
13. Travis *et al.* 2004.
14. Klarreich and Polman 2012.
15. Nyamtema, Urassa, and van Roosmalen 2011; Pfeiffer *et al.* 2008.

Appendix C

1. Taylor-Ide and Taylor 2002.
2. de Colombani, Borrini, Irshad, and de Melo 1992.
3. Lankester 2019b.
4. Narayanasamy 2009.
5. Wellbourn 1992.
6. "P.R.A.—Participatory Rural Appraisal: Concepts, methodologies, and techniques" by Cavestro 2003, retrieved from https://liberiafti.files. wordpress.com/2013/08/cavestro_ participatory-rural-appraisal-concepts-methodologies-techniques.pdf
7. Kumar 1992.
8. Adapted from "Trends in health care" by Kumar 1992, retrieved from http://pubs.iied.org/pdfs/G01444.pdf. (c) 1992 by International Institute for Environment and Development.
9. Campbell and Gill 1992.
10. Narayanasamy 2009.
11. Tolley and Bentley 1992.
12. de Colombani, Borrini, Irshad, and de Melo 1992.
13. *Ibid.*
14. Sahu and Tirkey 1992.
15. Chambers 1992.
16. From "Trends in health care" by Kumar 1992, retrieved from http://pubs.iied.org/pdfs/G01444.pdf. (c) 1992 by International Institute for Environment and Development.
17. Narayanasamy 2009; Smith, Shannon, and Vickery 2015.
18. Chambers 1992.

Bibliography

Abdullah, F. (2008). Perspective of West Africa: Why bother to 'mission'?. *Archives of Surgery, 143*(8), 728–729.

Abramson, L., Seligman, M., & Teasdale, J. (1978). Learned helplessness in humans: Critique and reformulation. *Journal of Abnormal Psychology, 87*, 32-48.

Abuagla, A. & Badr, E. (2016). Challenges to implementation of the WHO Global Code of Practice on International Recruitment of Health Personnel: The case of Sudan. *Human Resources for Health, 14* (Suppl. 1), S1-S10. doi:10.1186/s12960-016-0117-8

Agyepong, I. A., Sewankambo, N., Binagwaho, A., Coll-Seck, A. W., Corrah, T., Ezeh, A., ... Piot, P. (2017). The path to longer and healthier lives for all Africans by 2030: The Lancet Commission on the future of health in sub-Saharan Africa. *Lancet, 390*, 2803–2859. doi:10.1016/ S0140-6736(17)31509-X

Ahmad, T. & Raza, H. (1999). Pakora in Pakistan: Moving towards democratic management. *PLA Notes, 35*, 66-69.

Ahmed, F., Grade, M., Malm, C., Michelen, S., & Ahmed, N. (2017). Surgical volunteerism or voluntourism—Are we doing more harm than good? *International Journal of Surgery, 42*, 69–71. https://doi.org/10.1016/j.ijsu.2017.04.020

Ahmed, S. A. (2011). Community-led total sanitation in Bangladesh: Chronicles of a people's movement. In L. Mehta & S. Movik (Eds.), *Shit matters: The potential of community-led total sanitation* (pp. 25-38). Warwickshire, UK: Practical Action Publishing.

Alumasa, J. K. (2003). Hanging on the edge of a cliff. In A. Cornwall & G. Pratt (Eds.), *Pathways to participation: Reflections on PRA* (pp. 11-17). London, UK: Institute for Development Studies (ITDG Publishing).

Alvarado, E. & Benjamin, M. (1987). *Don't be afraid gringo: A Honduran woman speaks from the heart* (M. Benjamin, Trans.). New York, NY: Harper Perennial.

AmeriCares. (2013). Medical outreach best practices study: A literature review. Retrieved from https://medicaloutreach.americares.org/globalassets/_mo/resources/07_bestpractices/americares-medoutreachpracticesstudy-lit-review-final.pdf.

Antwi, D. E., Kuwornu, J. K., Onumaha, E. E., & Ram, C. B. (2017). Productivity and constraints analysis of commercial tilapia farms in Ghana. *Kasetsart Journal of Social Sciences, 38*(3), 282-290. https://doi.org/10.1016/j.kjss.2016.12.001

Appleton, J. (1992). Notes from a food and nutrition PRA in a Guinean fishing village. *RRA Notes, 16*, 77-85.

Aschkenasy, M., & Cranmer, H. (2016). Global disaster response. In G. R. Ciottone (Ed.), *Ciottone's Disaster Medicine* (2ⁿᵈ ed.). (pp. 105-110). Elsevier.

Asgary, R., & Junck, E. (2012). New trends of short-term humanitarian medical volunteerism: Professional and ethical considerations. *Journal of Medical Ethics*. doi:10.1136/medethics-2011-100488

Bailey, A. (1995). Anne Bailey: Interview. In D. Hunter, A. Bailey, & B. Taylor (Eds.), *The art of facilitation: How to create group synergy* (pp. 204-209). Tucson, AZ: Fisher Books.

Bergdall, T. (2012). Facilitating asset based community development. In T. Timsina & D. Neupane (Eds.), *Changing lives changing society: ICA's experience in Nepal and in the world*. Retrieved from https://resources.depaul.edu/abcd-institute/publications/publications-by-topic/Documents/Bergdall%20-%20Reflections%20on%20the%20Catalytic%20Role%20of%20an%20Outsider%20in%20ABCD.pdf

Bezruchka, S. (2000). Medical tourism as medical harm to the third world: Why? For whom? *Wilderness & Environmental Medicine, 11*(2), 77–78.

Bezruchka, S. & Mercer, M. A. (2004). The lethal divide: How economic inequality affects health. In M. Fort, M. A. Mercer, & O. Gish (Eds.), *Sickness and wealth: The corporate assault on global health* (pp. 11-18). Cambridge, MA: South End Press.

Biddle, P. (2021). *Ours to explore: Privilege, power, and the paradox of voluntourism*. Lincoln, NE: Potomac Books (University of Nebraska Press).

Bishop, R. A., & Litch, J. A. (2000). Medical tourism can do harm. *British Medical Journal, 320*(7240), 1017.

Blanchet, K., Ramesh, A., Frison, S., Warren, E., Hossain, M., Smith, J., … Roberts, B. (2017). Evidence on public health interventions in humanitarian crises. *The Lancet, 390*, 2287–2296. http://dx.doi.org/10.1016/S0140-6736(16)30768-1

Bontkes, S., van Keulen, H., & Kuyvenhoven, A. (1999). *Modelling the dynamics of agricultural development: A process approach: The case of Koutiala (Mali)*. (Doctoral thesis, Wageningen Agricultural University, Wageningen, The Netherlands). Retrieved from https://library.wur.nl/WebQuery/wurpubs/fulltext/164910

Bouman, D., Novalia, W., Hiemstra, P., & Willemsen, J. (2010). *Smart disinfection solutions: Examples of small-scale disinfection products for safe drinking water*. Netherlands Water Partnership. Amsterdam: KIT Publishers.

Brandberg, B. (1997). *Latrine building: A handbook for implementation of the SanPlat system*. Warwickshire, UK: ITDG Publishing.

Brenner, J., Ross, J., Simmons, J., & Zaidi, S. (2000). Neoliberal trade and investment and the health of *maquiladora* workers on the U.S.-Mexico border. In J. Y. Kim, J. V. Millen, A. Irwin, & J. Gershman (Eds.), *Dying for growth: Global inequality and the health of the poor* (pp. 260-290). Monroe, ME: Common Courage Press.

Budy, F. C. (2015). Policy options for addressing health system and human resources for health crisis in Liberia post-Ebola epidemic. *International Journal of Maternal and Child Health and AIDS, 4*(2), 1-7.

Buekens, P., Keusch, G., Belizan, J., & Bhutta, Z. A. (2004). Evidence-based global health. *JAMA, 291*(21), 2639-2641.

Burkle, F.M. (2006). Complex humanitarian emergencies: A review of epidemiological and response models. *Journal of Postgraduate Medicine, 52*, 110-115.

Burns, A. A., Lovich, R., Maxwell, J., & Shapiro, K. (1997). *Where women have no doctor: A health guide for women*. Berkeley, CA: Hesperian Health Guides.

Bygbjerg, I. C. (2012). Double burden of noncommunicable and infectious disease in developing countries. *Science, 337*(6101), 1499-1501.

Byhoff, E., Hamati, M. C., Power, R., Burgard, S. A., & Chopra, V. (2017). Increasing educational attainment and mortality reduction: A systematic review and taxonomy. *BMC Public Health, 17*(1). doi:10.1186/s12889-017-4754-1

Cai, J., Quagrainie, K. K., & Hishamunda, N. (Eds.). (2017). *Social and economic performance of tilapia farming in Africa. FAO fisheries and aquaculture circular no. 1130*. Rome, Italy: Food and Agriculture Organization of the United Nations.

Campbell, J. (2015). Investing in health workforce: The path towards the SDGs starts here. Retrieved from https://www.who.int/workforcealliance/media/news/2015/path-towards-SDGs/en/

Campbell, J., Cometto, G., Rasanathan, K., Kelley, E., Syed, S., Zurn, P., ... Andrea N. (2015). Improving the resilience and workforce of health systems for women's, children's, and adolescents' health. *BMJ, 351*, h4148. https://doi.org/10.1136/bmj.h4148

Campbell, L. & Gill, G. J. (1992). Extract from: Research report series no. 4, February 1991: Participatory Rural Appraisal for Nepal: Concepts and methods. A guide to slide presentation. RRA Notes, 16, 60-62.

Cavanagh, J., & Mander, J. (2002). (Eds.). *Alternatives to economic globalization: A better world is possible. A report of the international forum on globalization*. San Francisco, CA: Berret-Koehler Publishers, Inc.

Cavestro, L. (2003). *P.R.A. - Participatory Rural Appraisal: Concepts, methodologies, and techniques*. (Master's thesis). Retrieved from https://liberiafti.files.wordpress.com/2013/08/cavestro_participatory-rural-appraisal-concepts-methodologies-techniques.pdf

Chackungal, S., Nickerson, J. W., Knowlton, L. M., Black, L., Burkle, F. M., Casey, K., ... McQueen, K. (2011). Best practice guidelines on surgical response in disasters and humanitarian emergencies: Report of the 2011 humanitarian action summit working group on surgical issues within the humanitarian space. *Prehospital and Disaster Medicine*. 26(6). 429-437.

Chamberlain, R., Chillery, M., Ogolla, L., & Wandera, C. (1995). Participatory educational theatre for HIV/AIDS awareness in Kenya. *PLA Notes, 23*, 69-74.

Chambers, R. (1992). Actual or potential uses of RRA/PRA methods in health and nutrition. *RRA Notes, 16*, 101-106.

Chambers, R. (1997). *Whose reality counts? Putting the first last*. London, UK: ITDG Publishing.

Chambers, R. (2011). Spread and scale with CLTS: Past lessons, future paths. In L.

Mehta & S. Movik (Eds.), *Shit matters: The potential of community-led total sanitation* (pp. 245-260). Warwickshire, UK: Practical Action Publishing.

Chapin, E., & Doocy, S. (2010). International short-term medical service trips: Guidelines from the literature and perspectives from the field. *World Health & Population, 12*(2), 43-53.

Chiu, Y. W., Weng, Y. H., Chen, C. F., Yang, C. Y., & Lee, M. L. (2012). Perceptions and efficiency of short-term medical aid missions among key groups of health professionals. *Evaluation & the Health Professions, 37*(3). doi:10.1177/0163278712461503

Ciottone, G. R. (2016). Introduction to disaster medicine. In G. R. Ciottone (Ed.), *Ciottone's Disaster Medicine* (2nd ed.). (pp. 2-5). Elsevier.

Clements, C. (1984). *Witness to war: An American doctor in El Salvador*. New York, NY: Bantam Books.

Collins, E. M. (2014). Developing health care clinic partnerships in resource-limited regions. *Pediatrics, 133*(4), 574-576.

Comninellis, N. (2012). *INMED International Medicine & Public Health: Advanced preparation for healthcare professionals* (2nd ed.). Kansas City, MO: Institute for International Medicine.

Crump, J. A., & Sugarman, J. (2008). Ethical considerations for short-term experiences by trainees in global health. *JAMA, 300*, 1456–1458. https://doi.org/10.1001/jama.300.12.1456

Crump, J. A., Sugarman, J., & Working Group on Ethics Guidelines for Global Health Training (WEIGHT). (2010). Ethics and best practice guidelines for training experiences in global health. *American Journal of Tropical Medicine and Hygiene, 83*(6), 1178-82.

Cullinan, T. (2001). The problems of medical relief agencies. *The Lancet, 357*(9257), 713-714.

Curtis, V. & Cairncross, S. (2003). Effect of washing hands with soap on diarrhea risk in the community: A systematic review. *THE LANCET Infectious Diseases, 3*(5), 275-281.

D'Adesky, A. C. (2004). *Moving mountains: The race to treat global AIDS*. London, UK: Verso.

Dainton, C., Chu, C., Gorman, C., & Cherniak, W. (2019). Development of a theoretical framework for assessment of quality of primary care service trips in Latin America. *International Journal of Public Health, 64*(3), 333-342.

de Beaumont Foundation. (2017). The Practical Playbook: Helping public health and primary care work together to improve population health. Retrieved from https://www.practicalplaybook.org/

DeCamp, M. (2011). Ethical review of global short-term medical volunteerism. *HEC Forum, 23*(2), 91-103.

de Colombani, P., Borrini, G., Irshad, H., & de Melo, C. (1992). Exploring the potential for primary environmental care: Rapid appraisal in squatter communities in Salvador de Bahia (Brazil). *RRA Notes, 16*, 88-100.

de Vries, D. H., Steinmetz, S., & Tijdens, K. G. (2016). Does migration 'pay off' for foreign-born migrant health workers? An exploratory analysis using the global WageIndicator dataset. *Human Resources for Health, 14*(1), e1-14. doi:10.1186/s12960-016-0136-5

Dickson, M. (2006). *Where there is no dentist.* Palo Alto, CA: Hesperian Health Guides.

Drain, P. K., Pirtle, S. E., & Huffman, S. A. (2009). *Caring for the world: A guidebook to global health opportunities.* Toronto, Canada: University of Toronto Press.

Duangsa, D. (1995). A participatory approach to promoting AIDS awareness in Thailand. *PLA Notes, 23,* 66-68.

Dupuis, C. C. (2004). Humanitarian missions in the third world: A polite dissent. *Plastic and Reconstructive Surgery, 113*(1), 433–435.

Duvivier, R. J., Burch, V. C., & Boulet, J. R. (2017). A comparison of physician emigration from Africa to the United States of America between 2005 and 2015. *Human Resources for Health, 15*(1), e1-12. doi:10.1186/s12960-017-0217-0

Easterly, W. (2006). *The white man's burden: Why the west's efforts to aid the rest have done so much ill and so little good.* New York, NY: Penguin Books.

Eberlin, K. R., Zaleski, K. L., Snyder, H. D., & Hamdan, U. S. (2008). Medical missions for children. Quality assurance guidelines for surgical outreach programs: A 20-year experience. *Cleft Palate-Craniofacial Journal, 45*(3), 246-255.

Edmunds, H. (1999). *The focus group research handbook.* Chicago, IL: NTC Business Books.

Ellard, D. R., Shemdoe, A., Mazuguni, F., Mbaruku, G., Davies, D., Kihaile, P., … O'Hare, J. P. (2016). A qualitative process evaluation of training for non-physician clinicians/associate clinicians (NPCs/ACs) in emergency maternal, neonatal care and clinical leadership, impact on clinical services improvements in rural Tanzania: The ETATMBA project. *BMJ Open, 6*(2), 1-9.

English, M., Lanata, C. F., Ngugi, I., & Smith, P. C. (2006). The district hospital. In D. T. Jamison, J. G. Breman, A. R. Measham, G. Alleyne, M. Claeson, D. B. Evans, … P. Musgrove (Eds.), *Disease Control Priorities in Developing Countries.* (2nd ed.). Washington, D. C.: The International Bank for Reconstruction and Development / The World Bank; New York: Oxford University Press.

Epstein, R. & Street, R. (2011). The values and value of patient-centered care. *Annals of Family Medicine, 9*(2), 100-103.

Esrey, S. A., Potash, J. B., Roberts, L., & Shiff, C. (1991). Effects of improved water supply and sanitation on ascariasis, diarrhea, dracunculiasis, hookworm infection, schistosomiasis, and trachoma. *Bulletin of the World Health Organization, 69*(5), 609-621.

Evans, S. & Boyte, H. (1986). *Free spaces: The sources of democratic change in America.* Chicago, IL and London, UK: University of Chicago Press.

Eyal, N. (2016). Ethical issues in disaster medicine. In G. R. Ciottone (Ed.), *Ciottone's Disaster Medicine* (2nd ed.). (pp. 67-74). Elsevier.

Eyal, N., Cancedda, C., Kyamanywa, P., & Hurst, S. (2016). Non-physician clinicians in sub-Saharan Africa and the evolving role of physicians. *International Journal of*

Health Policy and Management, 5(12), 725–727. doi:10.15171/ijhpm.2016.80

Farmer, P. (1999). *Infections and inequalities: The modern plagues* (updated ed.). Berkeley, CA: University of California Press.

Farmer, P. (2005). *Pathologies of power: Health, human rights, and the new war on the poor.* Berkeley, CA: University of California Press.

Francis, S., Devavaram, J., & Erskin, A. (1992). Training workshop on participatory rural appraisal for planning health projects. *RRA Notes, 16,* 37-47.

Freire, P. (1970). *Pedagogy of the oppressed.* New York, NY: Bloomsbury Publishing Inc.

Freudenberg, N., Pastor, M., & Israel, B. (2011). Strengthening community capacity to participate in making decisions to reduce disproportionate environmental exposures. *American Journal of Public Health, 101*(Suppl. 1), S123-S130. doi:10.2105/AJPH.2011.300265

Friedmann, J. (1992). *Empowerment: The politics of alternative development.* Cambridge, MA: Blackwell.

Funnell, M. & Andernson, R. (2004). Empowerment and self-management of diabetes. *Clinical Diabetes, 22*(3), 123-127.

Gedde, M. (2009). *The International Health Links manual: A guide to starting up and maintaining long-term international health partnerships.* (2nd ed.). Retrieved from https://www.thet.org/wp-content/uploads/2017/08/Links-Manual-In-Full-Low-Res-72dpi.pdf

Gedicks, A. (2001). *Resources rebels: Native challenges to mining and oil corporations.* Cambridge, MA: South End Press.

Gershman, J. & Irwin, A. (2000). Getting a grip on the global economy. In J. Y. Kim, J. V. Millen, A. Irwin, & J. Gershman (Eds.), *Dying for growth: Global inequality and the health of the poor* (pp. 11-43). Monroe, ME: Common Courage Press.

Giannone, P. J., Hilmi, M., & Anderson, M. (2018). Camp management. In D. Townes (Ed.), *Health in humanitarian emergencies: Principles and practice for public health and healthcare practitioners* (pp. 244-256). Cambridge, UK: Cambridge University Press.

Gierke, J. (2009). Manually constructed and operated well. In J. Mihelcic, L. Fry, E. Myre, L. Phillips, & B. Barkdoll (Eds.), *Field guide to environmental engineering for development workers: Water, sanitation, and indoor air* (pp. 287-317). Reston, VA: American Society of Civil Engineers Press.

Ginwalla, R., & Rickard, J. (2015). Surgical missions: The view from the other side. *JAMA Surgery, 150*(4), 289–290. doi:10.1001/jamasurg

Gish, O. (2004). The legacy of colonial medicine. In M. Fort, M. A. Mercer, & O. Gish (Eds.), *Sickness and wealth: The corporate assault on global health* (pp. 19-26). Cambridge, MA: South End Press.

Glassman, A., & Temin, M. (2016). *Millions saved: New cases of proven success in global health.* Washington, DC: Center for Global Development.

Global Education Project. (2005). Map of the Human Development Index (2005 version of this map). Retrieved from https://www.theglobaleducationproject.org/earth/

development/the-human-development-index

Global Education Project. (2020). Chart of GDP per capita. Retrieved from https://www.theglobaleducationproject.org/earth/wealth-inequality/gdp-per-capita.

Gomez, C. & Rojas, A. (1999). Sparkling ideas in Campoalegre, Colombia: Managing the watershed to sustain the water supply. *PLA Notes, 35*, 59-62.

Gonzalez, L., Gullemann, H., & Thyberghien, H. (2010). Community led total sanitation (CLTS) in the red cross / red crescent movement. Retrieved from https://ifrcwatsanmissionassistant.files.wordpress.com/2018/10/clts-in-red-cross-discussion-paper-final.pdf

Gosselin, R. A., Gialamas, G., & Atkin, D. M. (2011). Comparing the cost-effectiveness of short orthopedic missions in elective and relief situations in developing countries. *World Journal of Surgery, 35*(5), 951–5.

Gould, J. & Nissen-Petersen, E. (2008). *Rainwater catchment systems for domestic supply: Design, construction, and implementation.* Warwickshire, UK: Intermediate Technology Publications.

Green, T., Green, H., Scandlyn, J., & Kestler, A. (2009). Perceptions of short-term medical volunteer work: A qualitative study in Guatemala. *Globalization and Health,* 5(4).

Haines, A., Sanders, D., Lehmann, U., Rowe, A. K., Lawn, J. E., Jan, S., ... Bhutta, Z. (2007). Achieving child survival goals: Potential contribution of community health workers. *The Lancet, 369*(9579), 2121-2131.

Hammond, S. A. (1998). *The thin book of appreciative inquiry.* Thin Book Publishing Co.

Heaver, R. (1992). Participatory Rural Appraisal: Potential applications in family planning, health and nutrition programmes. *RRA Notes, 16*, 13-21.

Heck, J. E., Bazemore, A., & Diller, P. (2007). The Shoulder to Shoulder model-channeling medical volunteerism toward sustainable health change. *Family Medicine, 39*(9), 644-50.

Hennink, M. (2007). *International focus group research: A handbook for the health and social sciences.* Cambridge, UK: Cambridge University Press.

Hill, P. S. (2002). The rhetoric of sector-wide approaches for health development. *Social Science & Medicine, 54*, 1725–1737.

Hodges, M. (1993). Diarrhoeal disease in early childhood: Experiences from Sierra Leone.   *Parasitology, 107*(Suppl.), S37-S51.

Hogan, C. (2007). *Facilitating multicultural groups: A practical guide.* London, UK and Philadelphia, PA: Kogan Page.

Hongoro, C., & Normand, C. (2006). Health workers: Building and motivating the workforce. In D. T. Jamison, J. G. Breman, A. R. Measham, G. Alleyne, M. Claeson, D. B. Evans, ... P. Musgrove (Eds.), *Disease Control Priorities in Developing Countries.* (2nd ed.). Washington, D. C.: The International Bank for Reconstruction and Development / The World Bank; New York: Oxford University Press.

House, J. S., Lepkowski, J. M., Kinney, A. M., Mero, R. P., Kessler, R. C., & Herzog, A.

R. (1994). The social stratification of aging and health. *Journal of Health and Social Behavior, 35*(3), 213-234.

Human Rights Watch. (2013). Letting the big fish swim: Failures to prosecute high-level corruption in Uganda. Retrieved from https://www.hrw.org/report/2013/10/21/letting-big-fish-swim/failures-prosecute-high-level-corruption-uganda

Humanitarian Accountability Partnership International. (2010). *The 2010 HAP standard in accountability and quality management*. Retrieved from https://www.humanitarianlibrary.org/resource/hap-standard-accountability-and-quality-management

Hunter, D., Bailey, A. & Taylor, B. (1995). *The art of facilitation: How to create group synergy*. Tucson, AZ: Fisher Books.

Huttly, S. R., Morris, S. S., & Pisani, V. (1997). Prevention of diarrhea in young children in developing countries. *Bulletin of the World Health Organization, 75*(2), 163-174.

Institute for Development Studies. (2011). The CTLS approach. Community-led total sanitation. Retrieved from http://www.communityledtotalsanitation.org/page/clts-approach

Institute of Medicine. (2001). *Crossing the quality chasm: A new health system for the 21st century*. Washington, DC: National Academy Press.

International Federation of Red Cross and Red Crescent Societies & ICRC. (1994). The code of conduct for the International Red Cross and Red Crescent Movement and non-governmental organizations (NGOs) in disaster relief. Retrieved from https://www.icrc.org/en/doc/resources/documents/publication/p1067.htm

International Rescue Committee International Water and Sanitation Centre and NETWAS International. (2009). *Report of the evaluation of the PHAST tool for the promotion hygiene & sanitation in the GOK/UNICEF programme of cooperation*. Nairobi, Kenya: UNICEF.

Iriart, C., Waitzkin, H. & Merhy, E. (2004). Managed care in Latin America. In M. Fort, M. A.

Mercer, & O. Gish (Eds.), *Sickness and wealth: The corporate assault on global health* (pp. 69-78). Cambridge, MA: South End Press.

Jahre, M., Kembro, J., Adjahossou, A., & Altay, N. (2018). Approaches to the design of refugee camps: An empirical study in Kenya, Ethiopia, Greece, and Turkey. *Journal of Humanitarian Logistics and Supply Chain Management, 8*(3), 323-345. https://doi.org/10.1108/JHLSCM-07-2017-0034

Jailer, T., Lara-Meloy, M., & Robbins, M. (2015). *Workers' guide to health and safety*. Berkeley, CA: Hesperian Health Guides.

Jenkins, M. & Curtis, V. (2005). Achieving the 'good life': Why some people want latrines in rural Benin. *Social Science & Medicine, 61*, 2446-2459.

Jesus, J. E. (2010). Ethical challenges and considerations of short-term international medical initiatives: An excursion to Ghana as a case study. *Annals of Emergency Medicine, 55*(1), 17-22.

Jimmy, D. H., Sundufu, A. J., Malanoski, A. P., Jacobsen, K. H., Ansumana, R., Leski,

T. A., ... Stenger, D. A. (2013). Water quality associated public health risk in Bo, Sierra Leone. *Environmental Monitoring and Assessment, 185*(1), 241-51. doi:10.1007/s10661-012-2548-6

Jokhio, A. H., Winter, H. R., & Cheng, K. K. (2005). An intervention involving traditional birth attendants and perinatal and maternal mortality in Pakistan. *New England Journal of Medicine, 352*(20), 2091-2099.

Joralemon, D. (1999). *Exploring medical anthropology.* Needham Heights, MA: Allyn & Bacon.

Jordan, B. & Davis-Floyd, R. (1992). *Birth in four cultures: A crosscultural examination of childbirth in Yucatan, Holland, Sweden and the United States.* Prospect Heights, IL: Waveland Press.

Kamat, D. & Fischer, P. (2012). *Textbook of global child health.* USA: American Academy of Pediatrics.

Kar, K. with Chambers, R. (2008). *Handbook on community-led total sanitation.* UK: Institute of Development Studies and Plan International (UK).

Kar, K. & Pasteur, K. (2003). *Subsidy or self-respect? Participatory total community sanitation in Bangladesh. IDS working paper 184.* Brighton, England: Institute of Development Studies.

Ketchie, K., & Breuilly, E. (2010). Our experience in earthquake-ravaged Haiti: Two nurses deployed with a disaster medical assistance team. *Journal of Emergency Nursing, 36*(5), 492-496.

Khadka, R., Paudyal, L. & Subba, H. (1999). Experimenting to solve water management problems: Lele community in Nepal. *PLA Notes, 35*, 56-58.

Kibuga, K. F., Bibby, S., & Sakafu, A. (1999). Participatory evaluation of a community water project in Tanzania. *PLA Notes, 35*, 70-73.

Kim, J. Y., Millen, J. V., Irwin, A., & Gershman, J. (Eds.). (2000). *Dying for growth: Global inequality and the health of the poor.* Monroe, ME: Common Courage Press.

Kinfu, Y., Dal Poz, M. R., Mercer, H., & Evans, D. B. (2009). The health worker shortage in Africa: Are enough physicians and nurses being trained? *Bulletin of the World Health Organization, 87*, 225-230.

Kizito, S., Mukunya, D., Nakitende, J., Nambasa, S., Nampogo, A., Kalyesubula, R., ... Sewankambo, N. (2015). Career intentions of final year medical students in Uganda after graduating: The burden of brain drain. *BMC Medical Education, 15*(1), e1-7. doi:10.1186/s12909-015-0396-0

Klarreich, K. & Polman, L. (2012). The NGO republic of Haiti: How the international relief effort after the 2010 earthquake excluded Haitians from their own recovery. *The Nation.* Retrieved from https://www.thenation.com/article/ngo-republic-haiti/

Koenig, K. L., & Schultz, C. H. (2012). Medical relief after earthquakes: Don't forget the local response! *Annals of Emergency Medicine, 59*(5), 448-448.

Koplan, J. P., Bond, T. C., Merson, M. H., Reddy, K. S., Rodriguez, M. H., Sewankambo, N. K., & Wasserheit, J. N., for the Consortium of Universities for Global Health Executive Board. (2009). Towards a common definition of global health. *The*

Lancet, 373, 1993-1995.

Korten, D. (2001). *When corporations rule the world* (2nd ed.). Copublication. Bloomfield, CT: Kumarian Press, Inc. San Francisco, CA: Berrett-Koehler Publishers, Inc.

Korten, D. (2012). Forward. In H. Sinclair, *Confessions of a microfinance heretic: How microlending lost its way and betrayed the poor* (pp. ix-xiii). San Francisco, CA: Berrett Koehler Publications, Inc.

Kretzmann, J. & McKnight, J. (1993). *Building communities from the inside out: A path towards finding and mobilizing a community's assets.* Chicago, IL: ACTA Publications.

Kuehn, B. (2013). Volunteer corps aims to improve training for clinicians in developing countries. *Journal of the American Medical Association, 309*(19). 1982-1983.

Kumar, A. (1992). Trends in health care. *RRA Notes, 16,* 48-52.

Kunitz, S. J. (2000). Globalization, states, and the health of indigenous peoples. *American Journal of Public Health, 90*(10), 1531-1539.

La Fond, A. (1992). Qualitative methods for assessing the acceptability of immunization in Somalia. *RRA Notes, 16,* 22-26.

Labonté, R., Sanders, D., Mathole, T., Crush, J., Chikanda, A., Dambisya, Y., ... Bourgeault, I.L. (2015). Health worker migration from South Africa: Causes, consequences and policy responses. *Human Resources for Health, 13*(92), e1-16. doi:10.1186/s12960-015-0093-4

Laleman, G., Kegels, G., Marchal, B., Van Der Roost, D., Bogaert, I., & Van Damme, W. (2007). The contribution of international health volunteers to the health workforce in sub-Saharan Africa. *Human Resources for Health, 5,* 19.

Lammerink, M. (1999). A detailed look at the PAD approach. *PLA Notes, 35,* 34-41.

Lammerink, M., Bot, E., de Jong, D., & Schouten. T. (1999). Strengthening community water management. *PLA Notes, 35,* 21-28.

Langowski, M. K., & Iltis, A. S. (2011). Global health needs and the short-term medical volunteer: Ethical considerations. *HEC Forum, 23,* 71–78. https://doi.org/10.1007/s10730-011-9158-5

Lankester, T. (2019a). Community-based health care: Setting the scene. In T. Lankester, & N. Grills (Eds.), *Setting up community health and development programmes in low and middle income settings* [Kindle version] (4th ed.). (pp. 3-20). Retrieved from https://www.amazon.com

Lankester, T. (2019b). Drawing up plans. In T. Lankester, & N. Grills (Eds.), *Setting up community health and development programmes in low and middle income settings* [Kindle version] (4th ed.). (pp. 109-122). Retrieved from https://www.amazon.com

Lankester, T. (2019c). Setting up and improving a community health clinic. In T. Lankester, & N. Grills (Eds.), *Setting up community health and development programmes in low and middle income settings* [Kindle version] (4th ed.). (pp. 205-228). Retrieved from https://www.amazon.com

Lankester, T. (2019d). The community health worker (CHW). In T. Lankester, & N.

Grills (Eds.), *Setting up community health and development programmes in low and middle income settings* [Kindle version] (4th ed.). (pp. 123-149). Retrieved from https://www.amazon.com

Lankester, T., & Grills, N. (Eds.). (2019). *Setting up community health and development programmes in low and middle income settings* [Kindle version] (4th ed.). (pp. 123-149). Retrieved from https://www.amazon.com

Lappe, F. M. & Collins, J. (2015). *World hunger: 10 myths.* New York, NY: Grove Press.

Lasker, J. (2016). *Hoping to help: The promises and pitfalls of global health volunteering.* Ithaca, NY: ILR Press.

Lassi, Z. S., Cometto, G., Huicho, L., & Bhutta, Z. A. (2013). Quality of care provided by mid-level health workers: Systematic review and meta-analysis. *Bulletin of the World Health Organization, 91,* 824-833.

Levy, B. & Sidel, V. (2000). Preventing war and its health consequences: Roles of public health professionals. In B. Levy & V. Sidel (Eds.), *War and public health* (updated ed.). (pp. 388-393). Washington, DC: American Public Health Association. (Original work published 1996).

Lough, B. J. (2015). A decade of international volunteering from the United States, 2004 to 2014. *Washington University Center for Social Development publication, 15,* 1-8. Retrieved from: https://openscholarship.wustl.edu/csd_research/15/

Lowe, M. & Chen, D. R. (2016). Factors influencing the migration of West African health professionals. *Pan African Medical Journal, 24*(1), e1-10. doi:10.11604/pamj.2016.24.237.9402

Lupton, R. (2011). *Toxic charity: How churches and charities hurt those they help (and how to reverse it)* [Kindle version]. Retrieved from https://www.amazon.com

MacFarquhar, N. (2010, April 13). Banks making big profits from tiny loans. *New York Times.* Retrieved from http://www.nytimes.com

Maki, J., Qualls, M., White, B., Kleefield, S., & Crone, R. (2008). Health impact assessment and short-term medical missions: A methods study to evaluate quality of care. *BMC Health Services Research, 8*(121). https://doi.org/10.1186/1472-6963-8-121

Markenson, D, & Reilly, M. (2011). Development of model medical care protocols for alternate care sites during pandemics and public health emergencies [Abstract]. *Prehospital and Disaster Medicine, 26*(Suppl. 1), S34.

Marmot, M. (2005). Social determinants of health inequalities. *Lancet, 365,* 1099-1104.

Marmot, M., Friel, S., Bell, R., Houweling, T. A., & Taylor, S. on behalf of the Commission on Social Determinants of Health. (2008). Closing the gap in a generation: Health equity through action on the social determinants of health. *The Lancet, 372,* 1661-1669.

Martiniuk, A. L., Manouchehrian, M., Negin, J. A., & Zwi, A. B. (2012). Brain gains: A literature review of medical missions to low and middle-income countries. *BMC Health Services Research, 12*(134). doi:10.1186/1472-6963-12-134

McCoy, D. C., Hall, J. A., & Ridge, M. (2012). A systematic review of the literature for evidence on health facility committees in low- and middle-income countries. *Health Policy and Planning, 27*(6), 449–466. https://doi.org/10.1093/heapol/czr077

Médecins Sans Frontières. (1997). *Refugee health: An approach to emergency situations*. London: Macmillan Education Ltd.

Mehta, L. (2011). Introduction: Why shit matters: Community-led total sanitation and the sanitary challenge for the 21st century. In L. Mehta & S. Movik (Eds.), *Shit matters: The potential of community-led total sanitation* (pp. 1-22). Warwickshire, UK: Practical Action Publishing.

Merlin, J., Morrison, G., Gluckman, S., Lipschik, G., Linkin, D., Lyon, S., ... Friedman, H. (2011). Medical students in developing countries. *Journal of General Internal Medicine, 26*(8), 833. doi:10.1007/s11606-011-1744-3

Mihelcic, J., Fry, L., Myre, E., Phillips, L., & Barkdoll, B. (2009). *Field guide to environmental engineering for development workers: Water, sanitation, and indoor air*. Reston, VA: American Society of Civil Engineers Press.

Miller, W. (2013). Motivational interviewing and social justice. *Motivational interviewing: Training, research, implementation, practice, 1*(2). Retrieved from http://www.mitrip.org/ojs/index.php/mitrip/issue/view/2

Mills, A., Rasheed, F., & Tollman, S. (2006). Strengthening health systems. In D. T. Jamison, J. G. Breman, A. R. Measham, G. Alleyne, M. Claeson, D. B. Evans, ... P. Musgrove (Eds.), *Disease Control Priorities in Developing Countries*. (2nd ed.). Washington, D. C.: The International Bank for Reconstruction and Development / The World Bank; New York: Oxford University Press.

Mishra, A., Kumar, P., & Ketelaar, J. W. (2016). Improving rice-based rainfed production systems in Southeast Asia for contributing toward food security and rural development through sustainable crop production intensification. *AIMS Agriculture and Food, 1*(2), 102-123.

Moszynski, P. (2011). Number of midwives is critically low in many poor countries, study shows. *British Medical Journal, 342*(7812), 1386-1386. doi:10.1136/bmj.d3881

Mukherjee, N. (1994). PRA training for health workers. *RRA Notes, 19*, 31-34.

Munk, N. (2013). *The idealist: Jeffrey Sachs and the quest to end poverty* [Kindle version]. Retrieved from https://www.amazon.com

Nambiar, N., Hargreaves, D. S., Morroni, C., Heys, M., Crowe, S., Pagel, C., ... Colbourn, T. (2017). Improving health-care quality in resource-poor settings. *Bulletin of the World Health Organization, 95*, 76-78. http://dx.doi.org/10.2471/BLT.16.170803

Narayanasamy, N. (2009). *Participatory Rural Appraisal: Principles, methods and application*. New Delhi, India: SAGE Publications India Pvt Ltd.

National Association of County and City Health Officials. (2019). Mobilizing for action through planning and partnerships (MAPP). Retrieved from https://www.naccho.org/programs/public-health-infrastructure/performance-improvement/community-health-assessment/mapp

Ndomoto, L., Hibble, A., Obuzor, G., Nthusi, N., Quine, A., Chahal, P., ... Tulinius, C.

(2018). Understanding the fundamental elements of global health: Using the sen capability approach as the theoretical framework for a health needs assessment in deprived communities. *Education for Health, 31*(1), 43-47.

Nullis-Kapp, C. (2005). Health worker shortage could derail development goals. *Bulletin of the World Health Organization, 83*, 5-6.

Nyamtema, A. S., Urassa, D. P., & van Roosmalen, J. (2011). Maternal health interventions in resource limited countries: A systematic review of packages, impacts and factors for change. *BMC Pregnancy and Childbirth, 11*(30). https://doi.org/10.1186/1471-2393-11-30

O'Dempsey, T. & Munslow, B. (2009). 'Mind the gap!' rethinking the role of health in the emergency and development divide. *International Journal of Health Planning and Management, 24*(Suppl. 1), S21-S29.

Oenga, I. & Ikumi, P. (1999). PAR outcomes Nyakerato in Kenya. *PLA Notes, 35*, 79-84.

Office for the Coordination of Humanitarian Affairs. (2012). OCHA on message: Inter-Agency Standing Committee. Retrieved from https://www.unocha.org/sites/dms/Documents/120229_OOM-IASC_eng.pdf

Olivera, O., in collaboration with Lewis, T. (2004). ¡*Cochabamba! Water war in Bolivia*. Cambridge, MA: South End Press.

Olu, O., Usman, A., Woldetsadik, S., Chamla, D., & Walker, O. (2015). Lessons learnt from coordinating emergency health response during humanitarian crises: A case study of implementation of the health cluster in northern Uganda. *Conflict and Health, 9*(1). doi: 10.1186/1752-1505-9-1. Retrieved from https://www.ncbi.nlm.nih.gov/pmc/articles/PMC4405854/

Ooms, G. (2006). Health development versus medical relief: The illusion versus the irrelevance of sustainability. *PLOS Medicine, 3*(8), 1202-1205.

Orr, B. & Annis, J. (2009). Participatory approaches and community management in engineering projects. In J. Mihelcic, L. Fry, E. Myre, L. Phillips, & B. Barkdoll (Eds.), *Field guide to environmental engineering for development workers: Water, sanitation, and indoor air* (pp. 31-56). Reston, VA: American Society of Civil Engineers Press.

Ortiz, F. G., Perén, C. S., Escobar, M., & Cifuentes, J. P. (1999). Aguacatán in Guatemala: How seven communities joined hands. *PLA Notes, 35*, 42-46.

Osborn, G. & Ohmans, P. (2005). *Finding work in global health: A practical guide for jobseekers or anyone who wants to make the world a better place*. Saint Paul, MN: Health Advocates Press.

O'Toole, T. P., Aaron, K. F., Chin, M., H., Horowitz, C., & Tyson, F. (2003). Community-based participatory research: Opportunities, challenges, and the need for a common language. *Journal of General Internal Medicine, 18*(7), 592-594.

Pal, R. K. (2016). Efficient use of biomass in improved cookstoves. *Journal of Engineering Science and Technology, 11*(12), 1808-1817.

Palmer, D. & Wolf, C. (2008). *Handbook of medicine in developing countries* (3rd ed.). Bristol, TN: Christian Medical & Dental Associations.

Pan American Health Organization. (1999). *Humanitarian assistance in disaster situations: A guide for effective aid*. Washington, D.C.: PAHO.

Pan American Health Organization. (2001). Health indicators: Building blocks for health situation analysis. *Epidemiological Bulletin, 22*(4), 1-5.

Pan American Health Organization. (2003). *WHO-PAHO guidelines for the use of foreign field hospitals in the aftermath of sudden-impact disasters*. Washington, D. C.: PAHO & WHO.

Patel, P. B., Hoyler, M., Maine, R., Hughes, C. D., Hagander, L., & Meara, J. G. (2012). An opportunity for diagonal development in global surgery: Cleft lip and palate care in resource-limited settings. *Plastic Surgery International*, 892437. doi:10.1155/2012/892437

Peabody, J. W., Taguiwalo, M. M., Robalino, D. A., & Frenk, J. (2006). Improving the quality of care in developing countries. In D. T. Jamison, J. G. Breman, A. R. Measham, G. Alleyne, M. Claeson, D. B. Evans, ... P. Musgrove (Eds.), *Disease Control Priorities in Developing Countries*. (2nd ed.). Washington, D. C.: The International Bank for Reconstruction and Development / The World Bank; New York: Oxford University Press.

Peleg, K. & Kellermann, A. L. (2012). Medical relief after earthquakes: It's time for a new paradigm. *Annals of Emergency Medicine, 59*(3), 188-190.

Perrin, P. (1996). *War and public health: Handbook on war and public Health*. Geneva: International Committee of the Red Cross Publications.

Peterson, S. (2002). Epidemic disease and national security. *Security Studies, 12*(2), 43-81. https://doi.org/10.1080/09636410212120009

Pfeiffer, J., Johnson, W., Fort, M., Shakow, A., Hagopian, A., Gloyd, S., & Gimbel-Sherr, K. (2008). Strengthening health systems in poor countries: A code of conduct for nongovernmental organizations. *American Journal of Public Health, 98*(12), 2134-2140.

Pickford, J. (1995). *Low-cost sanitation: A survey of practical experience*. London, UK: ITDG Publishing.

Powell, D. L., Gilliss, C. L., Hewitt, H. H., & Flint, E. P. (2010). Application of a partnership model for transformative and sustainable international development. *Public Health Nursing, 27*(1), 54-70.

Prasad, S., Aldrink, M., Compton, B., Lasker, J., Donkor, P., Weakliam, D., Balasubramaniam, R. (2022). Global health partnerships and the Brocher Declaration: Principles for ethical short-term engagements in global health. *Annals of Global Health, 88*(1): 31, 1-9. doi:http://doi.org/10.5334/aogh.3577

Redmond, A. D., Mardel, S., Taithe, B., Calvot, T., Gosney, J., Duttine, A., & Girois, S. (2011). A qualitative and quantitative study of the surgical and rehabilitation response to the earthquake in Haiti, January 2010. *Prehospital and Disaster Medicine, 26*, 449–56.

Redmond, A. D., O'Dempsey, T. J., & Taithe, B. (2011). Disasters and a register for foreign medical teams. *The Lancet, 377*, 1054–1055.

Redwood-Campbell, L., Hunt, M., Schwartz, L., Sinding, C., Elit, L., De Laat, S., & Ranford, J. (2011). Ethics in the delivery of humanitarian health response: Learning from the narratives of health care workers [Abstract]. *Prehospital and Disaster Medicine, 26*(Suppl. 1), S34.

Reisman, J., Arlington, L., Jensen, L., Louis, H., Suarez-Rebling, D., & Nelson, B. (2016). Newborn resuscitation training in resource-limited settings: A systematic literature review. *Pediatrics, 138*(2), e20154490. doi:10.1542/peds.2015-4490

Roberts, M. (2006). A piece of my mind. Duffle bag medicine. *JAMA, 295*(13), 1491-1492.

Roche, S. D., Ketheeswaran, P., & Wirtz, V. J. (2016). International short-term medical missions: A systematic review of recommended practices. *International Journal of Public Health, 62*, 31–42. https://doi.org/10.1007/s00038-016-0889-6

Rodney, W. (2011). *How Europe underdeveloped Africa*. Baltimore, MD: Black Classic Press. (Original work published 1972)

Rodriguez-Garcia, R., Macinko, J., & Waters, W. (2001). *Microenterprise development for better health outcomes*. Westport, CT: Greenwood Press.

Rollnick, S., Miller, W., & Butler, C. (2008). *Motivational interviewing in health care: Helping patients change behavior*. New York, NY: The Guilford Press.

Rozier, M. D., Lasker, J. N., & Compton, B. (2017). Short-term volunteer health trips: Aligning host community preferences and organizer practices. *Global Health Action, 10*(1), 1267957. https://doi.org/10.1080/16549716.2017.1267957

Ruiz-Razura, A., Cronin, E. D., & Navarro, C. E. (2000). Creating long-term benefits in cleft lip and palate volunteer missions. *Plastic and Reconstructive Surgery*, 105(1), 195–201.

Russel, C. & Smeaton, T. (2009). *From needs to assets: Charting a sustainable path towards development in Sub-Saharan African countries*. Rugby, UK: Practical Action Publishing.

Sachs, J. (2005). *The end of poverty: Economic possibilities of our time*. New York, NY: Penguin Books.

Sadana, R., & Blas, E. (2013). What can public health programs do to improve health equity? *Public Health Reports, 128 (Suppl.* 3), S12-S20.

Sahu, M. & Tirkey, R. (1992). A little experience of PRA exercise conducted at Mecluskigang. *RRA Notes, 16*, 57-59.

Savva, A. P., & Frenken, K. (2002). Irrigation manual – Planning, development monitoring and evaluation of irrigated agriculture with farmer participation. Retrieved from http://www.fao.org/publications/card/en/c/d6fdf228-f02d-51b4-9a37-a01c84112626

Schellenberg, J. A., Bryce, J., de Savigny, D., Lambrechts, T., Mbuya, C., Mgalula, L., & Wilcynska, K. (2004). The effect of Integrated Management of Childhood Illness on observed quality of care of under-fives in rural Tanzania. *Health Policy and Planning, 19*, 1–10.

Schilderman, T. (2010). Putting people at the centre of reconstruction. In M. Lyons & T. Schilderman with C. Boano (Eds), *Building back better: Delivering people-centered housing reconstruction at scale* (pp. 7-37). Warwickshire, UK: Practical Action Publishing.

Schlesinger, S. & Kinzer, S. (2005). *Bitter fruit: The story of the American coup in Guatemala* (2nd ed.). Boston, MA: Harvard University Press.

Schoepf, B. G., Schoepf, C. & Millen, J. V. (2000). Theoretical therapies, remote remedies: SAPs and the political ecology of poverty and health in Africa. In J. Y. Kim, J. V. Millen, A. Irwin, & J. Gershman (Eds.), *Dying for growth: Global inequality and the health of the poor* (pp. 91-126). Monroe, ME: Common Courage Press.

Schultz, A. (2010). Mission accomplished?: Measuring success on humanitarian trips. *ENT Today*. Retrieved from https://www.enttoday.org/article/mission-accomplished-measuring-success-on-humanitarian-trips/?singlepage=1

Seager, G. (2012). *When healthcare hurts: An evidence based guide for best practices in global health initiatives* [Kindle version]. Retrieved from https://www.amazon.com

Sellers, T. & Oloo A. J. (1995). Community mobilization against HIV infection in Kenya. *PLA Notes*, 23, 75-81.

Sen, A. (1999). *Development as freedom*. New York, NY: Random House, Inc.

Shah, S. (2011). The trouble with disaster relief. *Annals of Internal Medicine, 154*(8), 568-569. doi:10.7326/0003-4819-154-8-201104190-00011

Shepherd, A., Scott, L., Mariotti, C., Kessy, F., Gaiha, R., da Corta, L., … Wild, L. (2014). *The chronic poverty report 2014-2015: The road to zero extreme poverty*. Retrieved from http://www.chronicpovertynetwork.org/resources/2014/6/13/the-chronic-poverty-report-2014-15-the-road-to-zero-poverty

Shields, K. (1994). *In the tiger's mouth: An empowerment guide for social action*. Gabriola Island, BC: New Society Publishers.

Shiva, V. (2002). *Water wars: Privatization, pollution, and profit*. Cambridge, MA: South End Press.

Shrime, M., Sleemi, A., & Ravilla, T. (2015). Charitable platforms in global surgery: A systematic review of their effectiveness, cost-effectiveness, sustainability, and role training. *World Journal of Surgery, 39*(1), 10–20. doi:10.1007/s00268-014-2516-0

Sinclair, H. (2012). *Confessions of a microfinance heretic: How microlending lost its way and betrayed the poor*. San Francisco, CA: Berrett Koehler Publications, Inc.

Skinner, B. (2003). *Small-scale water supply: A review of technologies*. Warwickshire, UK: Practical Action Publishing.

Smith, K. R., Bruce, N., Balakrishnan, K., Adair-Rohani, H., Balmes, J., Chafe, Z., … Rehfuess, E. (2014). Millions dead: How do we know and what does it mean? Methods used in the comparative risk assessment of household air pollution. *Annual Review of Public Health, 35*, 185-206.

Snyder, J., Dharamsi, S., & Crooks, V. A. (2011). Fly-by medical care: Conceptualizing the global and local social responsibilities of medical tourists and physician voluntourists. *Globalization and Health, 7*(6). doi:10.1186/1744-8603-7-6

SODIS. (2011). SODIS method. Retrieved from https://www.sodis.ch/methode/index_EN.html

Southall, D., Cham, M., & Sey, O. (2010). Health workers lost to international bodies in poor countries. *The Lancet, 376*(9740), 498-499.

Sphere. (2018). *The Sphere handbook: Humanitarian charter and minimum standards in humanitarian response* (4th ed.). Retrieved from https://spherestandards.org/handbook-2018/

Ssembatya, J., Coghlan, A., Lumala, R., & Kituusibwa, D. (1995). Using Participatory Rural Appraisal to assess community HIV risk factors: Experiences from rural Uganda. *PLA Notes, 23*, 62-65.

St Clair, N. E., Pitt, M. B., Bakeera-Kitaka, S., Mccall, N., Lukolyo, H., Arnold, L. D., … Butteris, S. (2017). Global health: Preparation for working in resource-limited settings. *Pediatrics, 140*(5), e20163783. doi:10.1542/peds.2016-3783

Stevens, M. P., Elam, K., Stevens, L. F., Shodhan, S., Markley, D., Hemrajani, R., … Bearman, G. (2010). Medical needs assessment and infectious diseases concerns in rural Honduras – Implications for medical relief planning [Abstract]. *International Journal of Infectious Diseases, 14*, e427-e427.

Stockman, D. (1994). *Community assessment: Guidelines for developing countries*. Warwickshire, UK: Practical Action Publishing.

Styles, M. (2010). Nurseforce: Improvements in the healthcare systems of developing countries can only be achieved by training more nurses. *Nursing Standard, 25*(9), 22-22.

Suchdev, P., Ahrens, K., Click, E., Macklin, L., Evangelista, D., & Graham, E. (2007). A model for sustainable short-term international medical trips. *Ambulatory Pediatrics, 7*(4), 317-20.

Sykes, K. J. (2014). Short-term medical service trips: A systematic review of the evidence. *American Journal of Public Health, 104*(7), e38–e48. https://doi.org/10.2105/AJPH.2014.301983

Tankwanchi, A. B., Vermund, S. H., & Perkins, D. D. (2015). Monitoring Sub-Saharan African physician migration and recruitment post-adoption of the WHO code of practice: Temporal and geographic patterns in the United States. *PLoS One, 10*(4), e1-18.

Taylor, B. (1995). Bill Taylor: Interview. In D. Hunter, A. Bailey, & B. Taylor (Eds.), *The art of facilitation: How to create group synergy* (pp. 210-216). Tucson, AZ: Fisher Books.

Taylor-Ide, D. & Taylor, C. (2002). *Just and lasting change: When communities own their futures*. Baltimore, MA: The Johns Hopkins University Press.

Tayong, A. & Poubom, C. (1999). Convincing people to pay for water: Nkouondja in Cameroon. *PLA Notes, 35*, 52-55.

Tilman, D., Cassman, K., Matson, P., Naylor, R., & Polasky, S. (2002). Agricultural sustainability and intensive production practices. *Nature, 418*(6898), 671-677.

Tolley, E. & Bentley, M. E. (1992). Participatory methods for research on women's reproductive health. *RRA Notes, 16*, 63-68.

Tollman, S., Doherty, J., & Mulligan, J. (2006). General primary care. In D. T. Jamison, J. G. Breman, A. R. Measham, G. Alleyne, M. Claeson, D. B. Evans, … P. Musgrove (Eds.), *Disease Control Priorities in Developing Countries*. (2nd ed.). Washington, D. C.: The International Bank for Reconstruction and Development / The World Bank; New York: Oxford University Press.

Travis, P., Bennett, S., Haines, A., Pang, T., Bhutta, Z., Hyder, A. A., ... Evans, T. (2004). Overcoming health-systems constraints to achieve the Millennium Development Goals. *The Lancet, 364*(9437), 900-906.

Turnock, B. J. (2016). *Public health: What it is and how it works*. Burlington, MA: Jones & Bartlett Learning.

Unger, J. P., De Paepe, P., & Green, A. (2003). A code of best practice for disease control programmes to avoid damaging health care services in developing countries. *International Journal of Health Planning and Management, 18*(Suppl. 1), S27–S39.

United Nations Children's Fund. (2007). *The state of the world's children 2008: Child survival*. New York, NY: UNICEF.

United Nations Children's Fund. (2015). *Progress on sanitation and drinking water: 2015 update and MDG assessment*. Geneva, Switzerland: UNICEF and WHO.

United Nations High Commissioner for Refugees. (2007). *Handbook for emergencies*. Geneva: United Nations Press.

United States Agency for International Development. (2003). *Immunization essentials: A practical field guide*. Washington, D.C.: USAID.

United States Department of Health and Human Services. Office of the Assistant Secretary for Health. (2016). Public health 3.0: A call to action to create 21st century public health infrastructure. Retrieved from https://www.healthypeople.gov/sites/default/files/Public-Health-3.0-White-Paper.pdf

Van Hoving, D. J., Wallis, L. A., Docrat, F., & De Vries, S. (2010). Haiti disaster tourism – A medical shame. *Prehospital and Disaster Medicine, 25*(3), 201–2.

VanRooyen, M., Greenough, P.G., & Venugopal, R. (2005). International humanitarian assistance: Where do emergency physicians belong? *Emergency Medicine Clinics of North America*. 23(1). 115-131.

Varley, R. (1995). *Household credit for water and sanitation*. Retrieved from http://pdf.usaid.gov/pdf_docs/pnabu314.pdf

Versantvoort, J. M., Kleinhout, M. Y., Ockhuijsen, H. D., Bloemenkamp, K., de Vries, W. B., & van den Hoogen, A. (2019). Helping Babies Breathe and its effects on intrapartum-related stillbirths and neonatal mortality in low-resource settings: A systematic review [Abstract]. *Archives of Disease in Childhood* Published Online First: 05 July 2019. doi:0.1136/archdischild-2018-316319

Victora, C. G., Adam, T., Bryce, J., & Evans, D. B. (2006). Integrated management of the sick child. In D. T. Jamison, J. G. Breman, A. R. Measham, G. Alleyne, M. Claeson, D. B. Evans, ... P. Musgrove (Eds.), *Disease Control Priorities in Developing Countries*. (2nd ed.). Washington, D. C.: The International Bank for Reconstruction and Development / The World Bank; New York: Oxford University Press.

Victora, C. G., Hanson, K., Bryce, J., & Vaughan, J. P. (2004). Achieving universal coverage with health interventions. *The Lancet, 364*, 1541–1548.

Waddington, H., Snilstveit, B., White, H., & Fewtrell, L. (2009). *Water, sanitation and hygiene interventions to combat childhood diarrhea in developing countries*. International Initiative for Impact Evaluation. Retrieved from http://www.

ircwash.org/resources/water-sanitation-and-hygiene-interventions-combat-childhood-diarrhoea-developing-countries

Wall, L. L., Arrowsmith, S. D., Lassey, A. T., & Danso, K. (2006). Humanitarian ventures or 'fistula tourism'?: The ethical perils of pelvic surgery in the developing world. *International Urogynecology Journal and Pelvic Floor Dysfunction, 17*(6), 559–62.

WaterAid. (2011). Off-track, off-target: Why investment in water, sanitation and hygiene is not reaching those who need it most. Retrieved from https://www.issuelab.org/resource/off-track-off-target-why-investment-in-water-sanitation-and-hygiene-is-not-reaching-those-who-need-it-most.html

Wegelin-Schuringa, M. (2000). *On-site sanitation: Building on local practice.* Occasional Paper Series No. 16. IRC International Water and Sanitation Centre. The Hague: Netherlands: IRC.

Welbourn, A. (1992). A note on the use of disease problem ranking with relation to socio-economic well-being: An example from Sierra Leone. *RRA Notes, 16*, 86-87.

Werner, D. (1992). *Where there is no doctor: A village health care handbook.* Berkeley, CA: Hesperian Health Guides.

Werner, D., & Bower, B. (2012). *Helping health workers learn: A book of methods, aids, and ideas for instructors.* Berkeley, CA: Hesperian Health Guides.

Whitney, R., Stevens, M. P., & Bearman, G. M. (2011). Individual physician versus team-based medical encounters: Maximizing the efficiency of a medical relief service in rural Honduras. *International Journal of Family Medicine.* Epub 2011 Jul 5. doi:10.1155/2011/852963

Wijk-Sijbesma, C. (2001). *The best of two worlds?: Methodology for participatory assessment of community water services.* Delft, The Netherlands: IRC.

Wijk-Sijbesma, C. (2002). Planning and management. In J. Smet & C. Wijk-Sijbesma (Eds.), *Small community water supplies: Technology, people, and partnership* (pp. 26-45). Delft, The Netherlands: IRC International Water and Sanitation Centre.

Wilson, J. W., Merry, S. P., & Franz, W. B. (2012). Rules of engagement: The principles of underserved global health volunteerism. *American Journal of Medicine, 125*(6), 612-7.

Winblad, U. & Kilama, W. (1985). *Sanitation without water.* Houndmills, UK: Macmillan Publishers LTD.

Wise, J. (2011). Continuity and good management are key to better health outcomes in poor countries. *British Medical Journal, 343.* doi:10.1136/bmj.d6702

Wood, S., Sawyer, R., & Simpson-Hebert, M. (Eds.). (1998). *PHAST step-by-step guide: A participatory approach for the control of diarrhoeal disease.* Retrieved from https://apps.who.int/iris/handle/10665/63812

World Health Organization. (1993). *The new emergency health kit 98: Drugs and medical supplies for 10,000 people for approximately 3 months.* Geneva: WHO Press.

World Health Organization. (2000). *Guidelines for health care equipment donations.*

Retrieved from https://www.who.int/medical_devices/publications/en/Donation_Guidelines.pdf?ua=1

World Health Organization. (2005a). *IMCI handbook*. Geneva, Switzerland: WHO Press.

World Health Organization. (2005b). *World health report 2005: Make every mother and child count*. Geneva, Switzerland: WHO Press.

World Health Organization. (2007). *Everybody's business: Strengthening health systems to improve health outcomes. WHO's framework for action*. Retrieved from https://www.who.int/healthsystems/strategy/everybodys_business.pdf

World Health Organization. (2010). *WHO code of practice on the international recruitment of health personnel*. Retrieved from http://www.who.int/hrh/migration/code/code_en.pdf?ua=1

World Health Organization. (2011a). *Guidelines for medicine donations revised 2010*. (3rd ed.). Retrieved from https://www.who.int/publications/i/item/978924150198-9

World Health Organization. (2011b). *IMAI district clinician manual: Hospital care for adolescents and adults: Guidelines for the management of common illnesses with limited resources*. Geneva, Switzerland: WHO Press.

World Health Organization. (2013a). Classification and minimum standards for foreign medical teams in sudden onset disasters. Retrieved from https://www.who.int/hac/global_health_cluster/fmt_guidelines_september2013.pdf?ua=1

World Health Organization. (2013b). Global health workforce shortage to reach 12.9 million in coming decades. Retrieved from https://apps.who.int/mediacentre/news/releases/2013/health-workforce-shortage/en/index.html

World Health Organization. (2013c). *Hospital care for children: Guidelines for the management of common childhood illnesses*. Geneva, Switzerland: WHO Press.

World Health Organization. (2013d). *WHO model list of essential drugs: 18th List*. Retrieved from http://apps.who.int/iris/bitstream/10665/93142/1/EML_18_eng.pdf?ua=1

World Health Organization. (2016a). *Consolidated guidelines on the use of antiretroviral drugs for treating and preventing HIV infection: Recommendations for a public health approach*. Geneva, Switzerland: WHO Press.

World Health Organization. (2016b). *Global strategy on human resources for health: Workforce 2030*. Retrieved from http://apps.who.int/iris/bitstream/handle/10665/250368/9789241511131-eng.pdf?sequence=1

World Health Organization. (2017). Social determinants of health. Retrieved from http://www.who.int/social_determinants/thecommission/finalreport/key_concepts/en/

World Health Organization. (2018). Progress towards the SDGs: A selection of data from World Health Statistics 2018. Retrieved from https://www.who.int/gho/publications/world_health_statistics/2018/EN_WHS2018_SDGhighlights.pdf?ua=1

World Health Organization. (2021a). Adult mortality rate (probability of dying between 15 and 60 years per 1000 population). Retrieved from https://www.who.int/data/

gho/data/indicators/indicator-details/GHO/adult-mortality-rate-(probability-of-dying-between-15-and-60-years-per-1000-population)

World Health Organization. (2021b). Physicians density (per 1000 population). Retrieved from https://www.who.int/data/gho/data/indicators/indicator-details/GHO/physicians-density-(per-1000-population)

World Health Organization. (2021c). Life expectancy at birth (years). Retrieved from https://www.who.int/data/gho/data/indicators/indicator-details/GHO/life-expectancy-at-birth-(years)

Worldmapper. (2022a). Absolute poverty. Retrieved from https://worldmapper.org/maps/absolute-poverty-2016/

Worldmapper. (2022b). Infant deaths 2020. Retrieved from https://worldmapper.org/maps/infant-deaths-2020/

Worldmapper. (2022c). No water access. Retrieved from https://worldmapper.org/maps/housing-nowateraccess-2015/

Worldmapper. (2022d). Reference map. Retrieved from https://worldmapper.org/maps/worldmapper-basemap/

Wright, I. G., Walker, I. A., & Yacoub, M. H. (2007). Specialist surgery in the developing world: Luxury or necessity? *Anaesthesia, 62*(Suppl. 1), S84–S89.

Yunus, M. (1999). *Banker to the poor: Micro-lending and the battle against world poverty*. New York, New York: Public Affairs.

Zarocostas, J. (2010). WHO's head calls on donors to do more to protect poor countries' healthcare systems. *British Medical Journal, 340*(7756), 1104-1105.

Other books from Hesperian Health Guides

Where There Is No Doctor, by David Werner with Carol Thuman and Jane Maxwell. The most widely used health care manual in the world provides vital, easy to understand information on how to diagnose, treat and prevent common diseases. An emphasis is placed on prevention, including cleanliness, diet, vaccinations and the importance of community mobilization. 512 pages.

Where There Is No Dentist, by Murray Dickson, shows how to care for teeth and gums at home, and in community and school settings. Detailed and illustrated information on dental equipment, placing fillings and pulling teeth, teaching hygiene and nutrition, and HIV and oral health. 208 pages.

Helping Health Workers Learn, by David Werner and Bill Bower, is an indispensable resource that makes health education fun and effective. Includes activities, techniques, and ideas for low-cost teaching aids. A people-centered approach to health care, it presents strategies for community involvement through participatory education. 640 pages.

Disabled Village Children, by David Werner, covers most common disabilities of children. It gives suggestions for rehabilitation and explains how to make a variety of low-cost aids. Emphasis is placed on how to help disabled children find a role and be accepted in the community. 672 pages.

Helping Children Who Are Blind, by Sandy Niemann and Namita Jacob, aids parents and other caregivers in helping blind children from birth through age 5 develop all their capabilities. Topics include: assessing how much a child can see, preventing blindness, moving around safely, teaching common activities, and many others. 192 pages.

Helping Children Who Are Deaf, by Darlena David, Devorah Greenstein and Sandy Niemann, aids parents, teachers, and other caregivers in helping deaf children learn basic communication skills and a full language. It includes simple methods to assess hearing loss and develop listening skills, and explores how communities can work to help deaf children. 250 pages.

Helping Children Live with HIV, by Susan McCallister, Zoe Marinkovich, and Todd Jailer, is designed to empower families and others to support young children affected by HIV, Helping Children Live with HIV is full of clear information, activities and stories. It provides practical guidance to promote early childhood development through meeting the physical and psychosocial needs of children made vulnerable by HIV. 320 pages.

Workers' Guide to Health and Safety, by Todd Jailer, Miriam Lara-Meloy and Maggie Robbins, makes occupational safety and health accessible to those most affected by hazards — the workers themselves. An invaluable resource for training workers, supervisors, and safety committees, and in courses on labor relations. 576 pages.

Where Women Have No Doctor, by A.August Burns, Ronnie Lovich, Jane Maxwell and Katharine Shapiro, combines self-help medical information with an understanding of the social factors that limit women's health. Essential information on problems that affect only women or affect women differently from men. 584 pages.

A Health Handbook for Women with Disabilities, by Jane Maxwell, Julia Watts Belser and Darlena David provides women with disabilities and their caregivers suggestions on disability-friendly health care, caring for daily needs, having healthy and safe sexual relationships, family planning, pregnancy and childbirth, and defense against violence and abuse. The book also focuses on social stigma and discrimination. 406 pages.

Health Actions for Women, by Melissa Smith, Sarah Shannon and Kathleen Vickery, was field tested by 41 community-based groups in 23 countries and provides a wealth of clearly explained and engagingly illustrated activities, strategies and stories that address the social obstacles and practices that prevent women and girls from enjoying healthy lives. 352 pages.

Recruiting the Heart, Training the Brain, by America Bracho, Ginger Lee, Gloria P. Goraldo and Rosa María De Prado, tells the story of how Latino Health Access developed its groundbreaking model of peer-to-peer outreach and education in Santa Ana, California to address health problems exacerbated by poverty and discrimination. Their strategies and accomplishments will inspire change across an increasingly unhealthy America. 288 pages.

A Community Guide to Environmental Health, by Jeff Conant and Pam Fadem, will help urban and rural health promoters, activists and community leaders take charge of their environmental health. 23 chapters address topics from toilets to toxics, watershed management to waste management, and agriculture to air pollution. Includes activities, how-to instructions to make health technologies, and dozens of stories. 600 pages.

hesperian
health guides

2860 Telegraph Ave., Oakland, CA 94609
tel: (510) 845-4507
email: bookorders@hesperian.org
Visit our website for all books and resources: **www.hesperian.org**